EVOLUTIONARY THOUGHT IN AMERICA

Evolutionary Thought in America

EDITED BY

STOW PERSONS

ARCHON BOOKS
1968

Library of Congress Catalog Card Number: 68-21688
Printed in the United States of America

PREFACE

THE PRINCETON PROGRAM OF STUDY IN AMERICAN CIVILIZATION was organized for the purpose of enriching our understanding of American life and culture through cooperative teaching and writing. Each year the program conducts a seminar conference dealing with a broad aspect of our civilization. We have felt that some of these discussions deserved an audience beyond the students and scholars gathered in the conference room. A preceding volume dealt with a comprehensive selection of "foreign influences in American life." In a sense the present studies continue the same line of investigation. In its formal thought even more than in its social institutions the United States lies at the periphery of Western culture, and its major intellectual stimuli have at least until most recent times been derived from western Europe. This is as true of the theory of organic evolution as it is of the social ideas of the enlightenment or of the literary attitudes of romanticism, influences which preceded and conditioned the reception of evolution. The problem for the student of American culture is to lay bare the context in which the new ideas asserted themselves, and to examine the compromises and adjustments which necessarily resulted from the merging of the new with the old. The task has proved to be primarily historical, since it was chiefly upon the last generation of the nineteenth century that the burden of adjustment fell.

The chapters comprising the present volume were originally delivered as lectures before the undergraduate conference of the American Civilization Program during the academic year 1945-46. We were concerned in the first place to arrange the broadest possible intellectual context within which the diverse currents of thought influenced by the specific evolutionary concepts of the late nineteenth and twentieth centuries might be seen in proper perspective. This is the intention of the contributors to Part I, especially Professors Scoon and Northrop, whose respective historical and systematic analyses are designed to provide a background for the chapters in Part II, which deal with specific aspects of evolutionary thought in America.

The preparation of the lectures for publication was made possible by a grant from the Rockefeller Foundation. Collaborative ventures in scholarly inquiry have peculiar joys and sorrows of their own. One of the former is an editor's pleasant recollection of much kind assistance not only from the colleagues whose contributions are printed here but from many friends, students as well as teachers, whose comments and criticism have been of inestimable value to him.

STOW PERSONS

December 21, 1949

CONTENTS

ILLUSTRATIONS

Chapter III

Chapter IX

The illustrations for Chapter IX will be found in a separate section following page 396.

PART I

THE THEORY OF EVOLUTION

INTRODUCTION TO CHAPTER I

THE RISE AND IMPACT OF EVOLUTIONARY IDEAS

THE evolution of the concept of evolution has been a major enterprise of the Western mind. Professor Scoon traces it from the Christian faith in the millennium through the eighteenth-century belief in progress to the more generalized notions of natural and spiritual development in recent times. Out of these philosophic attitudes toward nature and experience, specific scientific concepts arose in the nineteenth century which attempted to describe and explain the evolution first of physical nature, then of organic forms.

The chief significance of evolutionary science for social and humanistic thought lay in its account of the factors or means by which organic evolution occurred. Apart from the fact of evolution itself, the quest for an understanding of the nature of the process has proceeded continuously since the time of Lamarck, more than a century ago, and has produced rationales of ever increasing complexity. Strengthened by the prestige of natural science and by their apparent capacity to explain the wondrous diversity of life forms, these rationales of evolution exerted powerful influence upon nonscientific thought at the end of the nineteenth century. Thus the general notion of development, applied to the problems of biological and paleontological science, received an elaborate set of effective agents which were now reintroduced with renewed vigor into nonscientific fields of thought—with what effect will appear in the following chapters.

S. P.

THE RISE AND IMPACT OF
EVOLUTIONARY IDEAS[1]

ROBERT SCOON

I

EVOLUTION has meant so many different things that I see no way to escape the task of stating at the outset of this chapter just what I propose to talk about. The following apparently arbitrary stipulations have gradually taken form during a long study of the subject; but unless I make them preliminary in this chapter, I shall have no standard of relevance, and such a standard, as we shall see, is necessary. At this stage they may be taken as assumptions, to be justified in the sequel; and there are three of them.

Evolution is almost inextricably associated with several other ideas, particularly development, growth, and progress; and one result of the critical thinking and research of the last century has been the gradual disentangling of these ideas. I shall not delay now to make this complicated discrimination. It seems to me sufficient at this point to say that I am interested in this whole cluster of ideas, but that evolution, so far as it can be isolated from the others, is central and predominant. My primary concern is thus the history of our present idea of evolution.

In the second place, although the history of this idea has been a long and varied one, stretching back to the ancient Greek scientists and philosophers, and owing much to some immediate predecessors of Darwin, I am sure we would all agree that something special and essential to it, as we now know it, took place with Charles Robert Darwin (1809–82). As Professor W. B. Scott remarked in 1916, "Frequently, the term [sc. Darwinism] is made a synonym of evolution, but it ought properly to be restricted to Darwin's explanation of evolution by natural selection." [2] This statement does not give the full story; but it puts us on the way to get it. In effect, Darwin gave the theory of evolution the status of a great scientific generalization, and from this position it has influenced every major field of our modern thinking, with the possible exception of physics and chemistry. Hence, while we cannot restrict our attention to Darwin and his successors, it is true that he fixed the fundamental features of the theory in a formulation that won wide acceptance and exercised very great influence.

Third, while this theory has had its most impressive successes in the field of biology and particularly in explaining the growth and change of organic species, it has never been limited to this subject matter. Even within the domain of natural science it is employed by geology to explain the process by which the earth's crust reached its present condition, and in astronomy to give a possible explanation of the series of changes which produce a planetary system out of a nebula. Furthermore, it is also used beyond the usual limits of natural science, so that it is more than a scientific term if we use "scientific" in the ordinary Anglo-Saxon sense; thus we have, for example, *The Evolution of Religion,*[3] *The Evolution of Modern Medicine,*[4] and *The Evolution of English Lexicography,*[5] all by responsible scholars who chose their words with discrimination.

Under the foregoing premises I am ready to propose that by evolution we mean strictly a continuous process of change in a temporal perspective long enough to produce a series of transformations. Thus evolution would be a kind of change, but not every change would be an evolution. A single change, for example, the killing of an animal, or the fall of a rock from a cliff, or an explosion, would not be considered evolutionary; and presumably a sudden mutation or sport among animate species would also be excluded unless it perpetuated its form in offspring and could be viewed as a stage in a series.

Again, neither mere locomotion nor a permanent rotation, revolution, or oscillation would fall within the proper extension of the concept. We are not so clear about cyclical processes other than locomotive, such as the recurring seasons of the year, and the birth, growth, and decay of human cultures according to certain philosophies of history; but perhaps most of us would be inclined to exclude them in so far as they are purely cyclical and repetitive, and admit them to the degree that they evince internal transformations. There is still less agreement on the relation between evolution and progress; but it seems to me the most careful thinkers now generally restrict progress to those cases where a value or standard of excellence is involved, as for instance in the growth of knowledge or the development of morality.

We must also at least raise a question about some biological concepts. The term "biology" was proposed independently by Lamarck and Treviranus in 1802, when evolutionary ideas were becoming prominent; and in the subsequent development of the science its various branches became thoroughly imbued with evolutionary interpretation. A professor of biology recently said: "We don't teach evolution any more, we simply presuppose it." But granting this interpenetration, there is still a question whether everything organic is as such evolutionary. The process of digestion, for instance, is an organic one, but is it necessarily an evolution? And if the organic relation is extrapolated to cover human societies and even a style of art, does evolution go with it? Again, if natural selection is understood simply as the operation of an environment in killing off the weakest specimens and preserving the fittest, is that process in and of itself evolution? We must be content here to ask these questions for the sake of accuracy, and at the same time to recognize that historically these two concepts of organism and natural selection have been so closely associated with evolution that it suggests them to us.[6]

II

Using this idea of evolution, we can say that it started where so many of our basic ideas were first formulated, in ancient Greece. The earliest scientist-philosophers, who became dissatisfied with their inherited mythology as an explanation of what they actually observed, tried to account for the world in its present multiplicity and interconnectedness by the hypothesis of a series of generations and transformations from one parent stuff, such as water, or a boundless reservoir of undifferentiated matter, or air. The significant feature of this theory for our present inquiry can be brought out by a comparison with the story of creation in the first chapter of Genesis; the Hebrew account uses the idea of repeated acts by the same agent (God), the products (heaven, earth, animals, man, etc.) being what we now see them to be, whereas the early Greek theory was that the original principle first separated off from itself a portion which had a new quality, then this portion produced still a different thing, and so on up to the present state of affairs. To put the matter in another way, the Hebrew story envisaged creation as the successive bringing into being by God of things that had not previously existed, with no such creative power passing into the creatures, while the Greek cosmologists thought of a progressive variation from an original, with each new member endowed with some capacity for future variation. This early Greek cosmology thus seems to me essentially evolutionary.

As inquiry into nature persisted and developed in Greek lands, two noteworthy extensions of the primitive evolutionary concept were made. First, it was applied specifically to what we now call the biological realm by Anaximander, and then more fully by Empedocles; and much later the Roman poet-philosopher Lucretius, who took over the system of the Athenian Epicurus, who in turn had borrowed without acknowledgment many ideas from many predecessors, advanced an evolutionary explanation of human societies. The other modification of the theory was its mechanization at the hand of the great atomist philosopher, Democritus, who was probably a contemporary of Plato. The extant fragments of his work are susceptible of different interpretations, but the main features of his theory seem to have been something like the following: the world started as an infinite number of atoms moving in an individualistic way in an infinite void; collisions of atoms naturally took place, and in these collisions some atoms became entangled and gradually built up large bodies like the earth and the stars; secondary processes then set in on each of these bodies, and on the earth, for example, all the water tended to get together in hollows while the land and other elements produced the phenomena of our present experience. We might call this theory mechanical (in contrast with organic) evolution, because it attempted to reduce all processes to laws of mechanics.

With these auspicious beginnings it might have been expected that Greek inquirers would develop the evolutionary idea in all sorts of interesting and fruitful ways; but it is quite clear why they did not do so, namely, because the idea ran counter to the common-sense belief in the fixity of species, which was given impressive philosophic support by Plato's doctrine of eternal forms. Plato thought of these forms in a mathematical and static fashion as changeless patterns, species, or definitions, which individuals more or less imperfectly embodied. Aristotle, who had strong biological prepossessions, adopted a dynamic theory of forms and softened the extreme rigidity of Platonism by his doctrine of potentiality and actuality, which could be used in a quasi-evolutionary sense, for example, to render the process by which living things were produced from germs. But in the end Aristotle thought of the world as a hierarchy of fixed species and levels of being from mere matter up to the Eternal Prime Mover, so that his philosophy, like that of Plato, emphasized the eternal order.

A further confirmation and consequent hardening of this doctrine occurred when the stream of Greco-Roman culture met and coalesced with the Hebrew-Christian. In the latter tradition no less than in the former, hard common sense pronounced: "The thing that hath been, it is that which shall be; and that which is done, is that which shall be done; and there is no new thing under the sun." [7] But a fresh element, and a very authoritative one, was added by the Christian church in the form of the ecclesiastical dogma of creation, according to which God originally created things in the species which we now see. Thus common sense or primary racial wisdom combined with a great philosophical interpretation and a magnificent theological myth to produce a belief in fixed, unchanging species that satisfied Western culture in the main for well over a thousand years. It was this same belief, in the form of the doctrine of special creation, that made the early modern formulations of evolution seem too implausible for serious consideration and that later constituted the basic opposition to Darwin's mass of evidence. Even Huxley, stout champion of evolution though he was, and antagonistic to the doctrine of special creation, had to admit three years after the publication of the *Origin of Species* that "Any admissible hypothesis of progressive modification must be compatible with persistence without progression, through indefinite periods." [8]

Under these circumstances men hardly thought of evolution and consequently did not look for it, so that the idea was practically dead from the time of the Roman Epicurean, Lucretius, to the eighteenth century. During this long period there were, to be sure, sporadic suggestions of it; but these suggestions were never followed up by investigation or put together into a systematic explanation weighty enough to break the common acceptance of special creation and eternal forms.

III

The necessary condition for a change in such a deeply entrenched position was of course a completely different attitude toward nature, a policy of patient investigation, willingness to see what had not been seen before, and correlation of results; and the inauguration of that policy distinguishes what we call the Modern Age from its predecessors. From the point of view of our present inquiry, one of the most significant expressions of this new spirit is found at the very beginning in Francis Bacon, who advocated a careful study of the deviating instances from a species. "For," he says, "with regard to these also, we must not desist from inquiry till we discern the cause of the deviation; the cause does not, however, in such cases rise to a regular form, but only in the latent process towards such a form . . ." [9] Clearly Bacon was not entirely satisfied with the traditional theory of types and in the truly modern spirit wanted to investigate the deviations or atypical instances. It is obvious how far this attitude could lead.

But such an attitude, though a precondition for amassing enough evidence to warrant a modification in the old belief in fixed species, was no more than a general habit of mind; and it was only gradually that actual data from first one field and then another began to accumulate to the point of establishing evolutionary processes in nature. These positive suggestions I would like to group under the three main headings of history, literature and philosophy, and natural science.

(a) *History*. There was one ambiguity in the classical-Christian view, namely, in regard to the status of human ideals. The classical stream of thought, although in the main it accepted the dualism of body and mind advocated by the great Athenian trio of Socrates, Plato, and Aristotle, still tended to a cyclical view of history without any real progress; and thus it also tended to consider the virtues as the eternal form of human nature. On the other hand, the Christians combined with their dualism of matter and spirit an eschatological belief that God was constantly at work in his church in a process of regeneration which would culminate in the millennium; and thus while nature, including the natural man, was subject to the fixed forms given it at creation, the supernatural or spiritual part of man, including the specifically religious virtues, was the arena in which God worked a gradual perfection.

Apparently there was no special difficulty about bringing knowledge into this system. Plato and Aristotle seemed to take it for granted that they knew all the essential features of the universe, so that the highest life for man was simply contemplation (not discovery), and this was the accepted attitude in the ancient and medieval cultures, though of course the Christian church added the doctrine that God had revealed once and for all in the Bible the supernatural knowledge that he wished his worshipers to have. But by the seventeenth century the modern investigation of nature had produced results that could only be described as new knowledge; and in the famous "quarrel between the Ancients and the Moderns," the latter side was led to take the position that knowledge is continually advancing toward perfection and that its advancement, though slow, is certain and endless.[10]

It might still have been possible to keep this progress of knowledge out of the realm of human nature simply by classing it as a phenomenon of the mind and adding it to the supernatural reason. But in the next (eighteenth) century a series of brilliant historians arose, who extended the idea of progress to many worldly features of human society, and thus introduced an essentially evolutionary interpretation into features of life which could not be considered supernatural.

The first of these historians seems to have been Giambattista Vico, who died in 1744 and who was so impressed by the success of the new physics and astronomy that he entitled his own work *Scienza Nuova.* This new science, however, was a science of man, and the basic principle on which it rested was the idea that the modern period of human culture, while dependent on previous eras, was in its essential features superior to them; thus Vico accepted both continuity and progress in cultural changes. Montesquieu (1689–1755) applied the same scientific attitude toward legal institutions, and attempted to show how the careers of states were influenced by their natural environments; while Turgot (1727–81) advocated historical continuity in opposition to the cyclical interpretation. At the same time Adam Smith (1723–90) in his *Wealth of Nations* studied the natural progress of opulence in a country and maintained that the best plan for bringing a people to greatness was to utilize the provisions of nature. Thus these historians of the eighteenth century, adopting a naturalistic attitude toward human culture, were led to an interpretation which emphasized historical continuity and progress.

(b) *Literature and philosophy*. The basic idea used by the historians was progress and it was applied to human life; but this idea easily passes into the vaguer notion of development, which can cover all kinds of continuous temporal processes. We can see this extension of meaning in the following passage from Diderot's *Pensées sur l'interprétation de la nature*, published in 1754:

Even if Revelation teaches us that species left the hands of the Creator as they are now, the philosopher who gives himself up to conjecture comes to the conclusion that life has always had its elements scattered in the mass of inorganic matter; that it finally came about that these elements united; that the embryo formed of this union has passed through an infinitude of organization and development; that it has acquired, in succession, movement, sensation, ideas, thought, reflection, conscience, emotions, signs, gestures, articulation, language, laws, and finally the sciences and arts; that millions of years have elapsed during each of these phases of development, and that there are still new developments to be taken which are as yet unknown to us.[11]

Thus human progress is seen as a late phase of a much more general process of development; and already there was the feeling of some kind of disparity between the doctrines of Revelation and the findings of the new sciences. From the middle of the eighteenth century, when Diderot wrote the passage I have quoted, to the middle of the nineteenth, when the first edition of the *Origin of Species* appeared, the idea of development with a strong naturalistic flavor occupied greater and greater attention, and the references to it are too numerous and varied to permit more than a selection of typical instances.

If we recall the work of the historians to whom I have previously alluded, we shall not be surprised to find that their ideas passed on into a philosophy of history based on the concept of development. Schelling (1775–1854) believed that history could be considered as a development with three main stages: the primitive, characterized by the predominance of fatalism; the active and voluntary stage, which was inaugurated by the Romans and still continues; and a future stage which will synthesize the principles of the two preceding stages. Moreover this human history, he held, was parallel to the processes of development in nature and in mind, so that he finally envisaged a general scheme of cosmic development, although vaguely defined and full of fanciful rationalistic extravagances. Hegel (1770–1831) adopted much the same kind of interpretation; but for him the three main stages of historical development were oriental despotism, classical slavery, and modern freedom, the last of which was realized most completely in the Prussian state. Again he held that this human history was in its entirety a kind of epitome of a vast cosmic process of development which was at bottom rational. But the mere temporal succession of stages explained nothing; and Hegel attempted to give it a rational explanation by interpreting it as a dialectical process from a positive position (thesis) through its negation (antithesis) to a synthesis, which then became a new thesis. Auguste Comte (1798–1857) also took an evolutionary view of human culture and assumed three stages, which he called the theological, the metaphysical, and the scientific, on the basis of the types of explanation offered for events. Since these stages were abstractly conceived as kinds of interpretation, it was easy for Comte to extend them to the various branches of learning and to hold that each branch must individually go through all three stages. Marx (1818–83), who in 1848 brought out the *Communist Manifesto* in cooperation with Engels and in 1859, several months before the appearance of Darwin's *Origin of Species,* published his *Critique of Political Economy,* which contained his fundamental ideas, based his main position on a general theory of history, in which he attempted to turn Hegel right side up. Whereas Hegel had regarded history as the march of reason through the world, Marx held that it was really only the effects of "the material conditions of life." As a general thesis, he says in the *Critique,* vi, "one can consider the Asiatic, ancient, feudal, and bourgeois modes of production as the progressive steps of the economic formation of society." Thus these thinkers applied the notion of development to the course of human life and also to the natural world.

During the same hundred years which we are considering evolutionary ideas found their way from various sources into literature. I have already referred to Diderot, who wrote at the beginning of the period. Only a little later the idea of development began to be used by zoologists, notably Buffon and Lamarck, whom we shall consider more fully subsequently, and in 1830 there was a debate in the French Academy on the fixity of species between Cuvier and Geoffroy St. Hilaire, the latter of whom had been impressed with Lamarck's theory. After this debate the idea of development was public property, and we have a record of how it excited Goethe in Germany, who had himself already been led by researches of his own to a theory which he called the metamorphosis of plants.[12] In England at the same time Tennyson was struggling to reconcile naturalistic evolutionary ideas with his belief in immortality, which he records in *In Memoriam,* published in 1850. Perhaps the best indication of what was going on is given by the parody of it in Disraeli's novel, *Tancred* (published in 1847), through the character of a charming lady of high society, called Lady Constance, in the following excerpt. "You know, all is development—the principle is perpetually going on. First there was nothing; then there was something; then—I forget the next—I think there were shells; then fishes; then we came—let me see—did we come next? Never mind that; we came at last, and the next change will be something very superior to us, something with wings." [13]

(c) *Natural Science.* Meanwhile the idea of development in a long, temporal perspective had been utilized in much more technical and systematic treatments by the sciences of astronomy, geology, and biology. In the first of these fields, the German philosopher Immanuel Kant (1724–1804), as well as the French astronomer Laplace (1749–1827), proposed the nebular hypothesis, according to which the different classes of stars represent stages in an evolution from nebulae to blue, yellow, and red stars. Geology, which ever since the time of Leonardo da Vinci (1452–1519) had been explaining such phenomena as the presence of fossil shells in bedrock far from the sea and at high elevations in terms of past events, like upheavals of the floor of the sea, and in the persons of Descartes (1596–1650) and Leibnitz (1646–1716) had got as far as the theory that the earth had passed through a molten stage, still tended to think of these past events as more or less isolated and disconnected cataclysms. But in the period we have under review two English geologists, Hutton (1726–97) and Lyell (1797–1875) systematized these ancient catastrophes in terms of present known processes. Lyell, whose book was published in 1830 and went through twelve editions, says:

I did not lay it down as an axiom that there cannot have been a succession of paroxysms and crises . . . but . . . I complained that in attempting to explain geological phenomena, the bias has always been on the wrong side; there has always been a disposition to reason *a priori* on the extraordinary violence and suddenness of changes, both in the inorganic crust of the earth, and in organic types, instead of attempting strenuously to frame theories in accordance with the ordinary operations of nature.[14]

This theory, called uniformitarianism, was a true evolutionary idea, in that it explained the present geological condition by the continuous action throughout past ages of the natural forces we observe today; and it had a direct influence on Darwin.[15]

But it was in biology that the evolutionary concept made its greatest headway during this period. Buffon (1707–88), director of a large zoological garden, questioned the reality of specific differences, such as those between a pig and an ass, and suggested that animal species might almost be arranged in a temporal series stemming from a common ancestor, if we did not know from Revelation that this was not the case. Lamarck (1744–1829) was not so fearful of the French court and the church, and came out definitely in favor of the evolution of species. He believed that these changes took place by the inheritance of characters acquired in use; for example, the giraffe continually stretched its neck in order to get the feed it wanted on the limbs of trees, and this stretching produced an actual elongation, which was inherited by its offspring. Lamarck's opinions were based on rather slim scientific evidence and at the same time ran contrary to the prevailing current of thought, so that they received little attention, until Darwinism produced an interest in its antecedents; then it was seen that Lamarck's theory of use inheritance formed a genuine alternative to Darwin's natural selection, and he took his place posthumously as one of the founders of biological evolution. Meanwhile Darwin's grandfather, Erasmus Darwin (1731–1802), who was a botanist, independently got the idea that species evolve, and he emphasized the factors of sexual selection, struggle for survival, and reproduction of the strongest; in fact, so many of his ideas read like clear anticipations of his grandson's that his biographer has claimed that "for every work by the grandson there was a corresponding chapter by the grandfather."[16]

(d) We may perhaps best conclude this section on the hundred years preceding the publication of the *Origin of Species,* with a notice of Herbert Spencer (1820–1902). His works appeared both before and after the publication of the *Origin of Species,* so that he does not belong completely to the period we are now studying. But in this period he had published his *Social Statics* (1850), *Psychology* (1855), and *Progress: Its Law and Cause* (1857), including an article on "The Development Hypothesis"; and encouraged by some of his friends, he had just completed and circularized a prospectus for a philosophical system based on evolution as a universal process, which was not brought out till later under the title of *Synthetic Philosophy*. Although this work was undoubtedly influenced by Darwin, we may confidently infer that his main ideas had taken shape antecedently and legitimately belong to the present section. Those ideas are given in his own later words as follows:

Whether it be in the development of the Earth, in the development of Life upon its surface, in the development of Society, of Government, of Manufactures, of Commerce, of Language, Literature, Science, Art, this same evolution of the simple into the complex, through successive differentiations, holds throughout. From the earliest traceable cosmical changes, down to the latest results of civilization, we shall find that the transformation of the homogeneous into the heterogeneous, is that in which Progress essentially consists.[17]

Thus Spencer held not only that there was evolution and that it was the fundamental principle throughout all nature, but also that it was inevitably toward perfection, "towards a complete development and a more unmixed good."

IV

Then came Charles Darwin (1809–82) and the publication of the *Origin of Species* (1859). The book may be considered the result of two main factors: first, the thorough and meticulous first-hand investigation, in the best tradition of modern science, of the flora and fauna of the Galapagos Islands, made as the naturalist for the five-year surveying expedition of the government brig *Beagle;* and second, over twenty years of theorizing about the mass of data he had accumulated, during which the data themselves were increased by studies of the variation of animals under domestication. About eleven months before the book was published, Darwin received a letter from his friend Alfred Russell Wallace (1823–1913), in which the latter outlined a theory substantially similar to that reached by Darwin.[18] After some correspondence it was agreed that both Darwin and Wallace should present their ideas at the next meeting of the Linnaean Society in 1858. In the following year Darwin's book appeared.

The full title read *On the Origin of Species by Means of Natural Selection, or the Preservation of Favoured Races in the Struggle for Life*. The word evolution did not occur in the first edition; but it is perfectly clear that by the phrase, origin of species, Darwin meant an evolutionary process of continual small variations which ultimately amounted to a species recognizably different from any which had before existed. The main emphasis was not on hidden similarities between species that look different, nor a series of sporadic changes, nor an arrangement of species in a systematic classification, nor even on mere descent from a common ancestor; the emphasis was rather on a process of minute variations, conceived as a regular natural law. By this concept Darwin not only brought to a head his own investigations, but also, although he did not acknowledge, and perhaps was not fully conscious of, his debt to previous evolutionary thinkers, gave a clear focus to their multifarious researches. By this same concept, moreover, Darwin broke radically with the traditional doctrine of eternal forms and special creation. Francis Bacon (above p. 9) at the beginning of the modern period had been impressed with deviating instances in a species, but was so much under the influence of the traditional doctrine that he specifically denied that they sprang from a "regular form" and regarded them on the contrary as "errors of Nature"; now in Darwin's thought deviation is replaced with variation, and instead of regular forms with errors we have continuous variation from parents. Likewise, the particular version of the old doctrine in Christian theology, according to which species are (not eternal forms, but) permanent arrangements made by God at creation, must also be discarded or revised if Darwin's view was accepted, for there was nothing permanent except variation; and the opposition between the two interpretations was only sharpened and broadened by the publication of Darwin's later works, particularly *The Descent of Man* (1871), and *The Expression of the Emotions in Man and Animals* (1872).

The first five chapters of the *Origin* state the fundamentals of the theory, and the verifiable applications of it. The next four chapters are devoted to a consideration of the objections that could be raised to it. Chapters X to XIII give a masterly presentation of the evidence for it, from three different fields: first, the geological record of fossil forms interpreted in temporal perspective; second, the geographical distribution of plants and animals with their variations under local environments; and third, the morphological and embryological data that suggest a common stock and variations from it in offspring. The final chapter is a recapitulation of the whole argument.

The book thus contained a massive accumulation of data, simplified by a single natural law; but it also attempted a causal explanation of the process involved, by means of the idea of natural selection. Briefly, this idea meant that the natural environment tended to preserve certain variants and to kill off the others, so that in the full account of the evolutionary process the species of any particular time and place would have to be understood as those variants from a parent stock which were sustained by the environment. This idea had come to Darwin (and also to Wallace) from a study of Malthus' *Essay on Population,* where the author maintained that a people tends to increase faster than its supplies of food, so that there is a competition for these supplies, in the course of which a certain number of persons lose their means of subsistence and perish. This competition for limited supplies easily passed over into the notion of a struggle for existence, in which nature was blamed not only for the scanty sustenance but also for the animal warfare; hence Tennyson's conception of "nature red in tooth and claw." Although Darwin's idea of natural selection included such instances, it was much broader and embraced cases where a variant could not survive the climate or geological conditions, without any reference to competition with other individuals or species. Furthermore, the idea of natural selection was also based on an analogy with domestic breeding, in which new strains of animals are developed, and struggle for survival is completely absent; according to this analogy nature simply acts like a human breeder, preserving and developing certain strains and allowing others to die without reproducing. Nevertheless, as Darwin's full title and the last page of the Conclusion show, the struggle for existence in its various forms weighed so heavily in his thought that it was practically a counterpart of natural selection; and these two phrases, used to describe summarily the factors at work in the evolutionary process, became the distinguishing mark of Darwinism, both in its technical biological meaning and its wider social applications.

Darwin was a great empirical investigator, and it is perhaps not surprising that he lacked both historical knowledge of his subject and theoretical precision in his generalizations. But the very success of his own work stimulated scholarly interest along each of these lines, so that for the third edition he himself prepared a "Historical Sketch," in which he noted, though quite inadequately, the views of some of his immediate predecessors, including his grandfather (in a footnote), Buffon, and Lamarck. Moreover, although in this sketch he speaks of "the views and erroneous grounds of opinion of Lamarck," yet in the body of his work he employs Lamarck's idea of use inheritance, and in the last (sixth) edition he admits that he formerly underrated "the frequency and value" of use inheritance, direct environmental effects, and "variations which seem to us in our ignorance to arise spontaneously" (p. 657). These phrases reveal not merely a historical ignorance with regard to the contributions of earlier investigators but also a lack of precision in his own thinking. Besides admitting three or four uncorrelated factors without even recognizing their inconsistency, he advanced a theory of his own which brings together in an apparently impressive formulation two operations which are, separately, mysteries, namely, organic variation and the selectivity of an environment.

Variation in inheritance is not explained, it is simply taken for granted; and to make matters worse, the language is sometimes framed in such a way as to suggest that the environment may cause the variation, or that chance is a cause, and even that "Variation will cause the slight alterations . . ."[19] There can be small doubt that none of these absurdities represents Darwin's real position—he specifically says so with regard to chance; but they do reveal the fact that he has no explanation of variation. Again, the other concept, natural selection, is a glib expression whose fatal vagueness appeared the moment it was analyzed. Nature is a big word; can Darwin specify just what feature or features of a particular environment operated to preserve a particular variation, so that it becomes possible to predict which variant will survive and which will not? He used the term "favoured races," and it was Herbert Spencer who coined the phrase, "survival of the fittest"; but whether it be favored or fittest or something else like stronger or viable, it amounts to little more than the survival of those that survive, and Darwin himself later admitted: "I suppose natural selection was a bad term; but to change it now, I think, would make confusion worse confounded, nor can I think of a better."[20] The truth thus seems to be that Darwin's formula, "the natural selection of numerous successive, slight, favourable variations,"[21] is not a causal explanation in any strict sense, and its scientific usefulness lay rather in its succinct description of a certain total effect, which served both to establish the fact and to set off a long train of significant researches.

It is clear that this theory is naturalistic in the sense that it attempts to describe organic (not to speak of geological and cosmological) processes in terms of their natural conditions, and thus it belongs not only in the evolutionary tradition which went back for a hundred years, but also in the main stream of modern science; so that to call it naturalistic is scarcely more than to call it scientific. But this is by no means the whole story. Until Darwin made this evolutionary naturalism plausible to scientists and a large following of generally intelligent persons, modern science had extended its sway over the material world, including the physiological processes of man's body, but had left untouched the distinctively human activities of the mind; these were still regarded as the region of purpose, will, mind, spirit, and the clear evidence of a divine Creator. Now Darwin, particularly in his later works, the *Descent of Man* and the *Expression of the Emotions in Man and Animals,* showed that in his fully developed theory man could not be said to have any more distinctive a position than any other terrestrial species and that even his most cherished sentiments were but the product of an evolutionary process which linked him with the other animals. This was naturalism at a spot where it really hurt; and as if that were not enough, the theory also maintained that species had altered since they left the hands of their Creator, so that it seemed to derogate from the omnipotence of God and contradict the biblical account of creation, then almost universally interpreted in terms of the doctrine of special creation and eternal forms.

Thus Darwin's work was not only a great scientific generalization from a mass of hitherto uncorrelated or unknown data but also a violation of established religious doctrines; and on both accounts it had to meet criticism. Not all scientists were convinced; while some religious people accepted it as another instance, like that of the Copernican cosmology, where new knowledge develops our understanding of God's way with the world.

V

Both in defending and elaborating his theory, Darwin was greatly aided by a group of friends and protagonists, of whom perhaps the most generally influential were Spencer and Huxley; and although, as I have previously said, Darwin did not even use the term evolution in the first edition of the *Origin,* that was the name under which his theory as a whole was put forward and which he himself adopted. Thus, as Professor Allan Nevins says: "Until the doctrine was fully introduced to the world by Darwin,

Spencer, and others, historians had talked of development rather than evolution. . . . Now it was demonstrated by careful investigation that species or types did change into others. In short, development had become evolution." [22] Speaking very roughly we may therefore say that the evolutionary idea in the modern period started in the form of progress, first applied to human institutions by the early eighteenth-century historians, then shifted to the more general notion of development for about a hundred years, and finally became evolution under the influence of Darwin and his group.

The subsequent developments of this theory may be conveniently treated under three heads: first, the biological; second, the social and moral; and third, the religious and philosophical.

Writing under the heading of Geology in *The Development of the Sciences*,[23] Professor C. R. Longwell remarks:

It is difficult for us to understand that during more than half a century paleontologists saw clearly the evidence of successive faunas leading continuously to higher organization, and yet did not sense or admit the obvious implication. . . . Charles Darwin in 1859 furnished the key that arranged all the facts of paleontology in sensible order. The doctrine of evolution acted like a blood transfusion; it changed paleontology from a rule-of-thumb technique into a science with a firm philosophic foundation.

Much the same could be said of biology as a whole; the idea of evolution transformed it from a mainly classificatory discipline, thoroughly elaborated by Linnaeus (1707–78) and Agassiz (1807–73) on the basis of constancy and continuity of species, to an experimental causal investigation, and from a loose conglomeration of subjects such as taxonomy, anatomy, and physiology, to a more integrated and independent science on its own philosophical foundation.[24]

Of the specialized problems which Darwinism posed, probably the most important was that concerning the causal factors of heritable variations. Samuel Butler (1835–1902), the severest critic of Darwin as well as the first historian of evolution, traced the idea of use inheritance, which Darwin frankly accepted, to Lamarck, and brought out the fundamental incompatibility of this explanation with natural selection. Butler himself adopted the Lamarckian viewpoint and roundly attacked Darwin's assumption that living organisms could be explained as purposeless machines; so that Darwinism now became an alternative to Lamarckism, and the issue was not merely the inheritance of acquired modifications, but also the role played by the efforts and desires of the organism as against a mechanistic interpretation of life. Though Butler was not widely influential during his lifetime, other voices to much the same effect were raised, and in the 1890's they became known as Neo-Lamarckians, so that the situation of evolutionary theory took on the aspect of a controversy between the Neo-Lamarckian and the Neo-Darwinian parties. This controversy had at least one beneficial result; the criticisms directed by each side against the other revealed such weaknesses in both that it became apparent that the dispute needed to be broken up into subsidiary problems susceptible of further scientific investigation.

On the whole, the weight of the evidence that has accumulated since then is against Lamarck's contention that characters developed by individual usage can be inherited. On the other hand, the influence of the environment on the organism is undoubted, and the only question is whether it can be reduced to the physical concept of cause and effect. Much progress has been made in discovering correlations stated in physicochemical terms, particularly in the subscience of biochemistry; but as yet these cover hardly more than the lower reaches of the subject, and above them there stretches a graded series of types of functional interrelations up to the apparently teleological preadaptation of organs, revealed by physiology, and finally those cases when the organism purposely modifies its environment. The current concept of adaptation may be interpreted as a sensible straddle designed to minimize polemics and let biologists get on with their investigations until we have more evidence.

Meanwhile the exclusion from inheritance of both organic usage and environmental influences on organic usage suggested that species-forming variations should be looked for in the mechanism of reproduction. And here three very significant lines of inquiry have been developed: first, an investigation of the details of reproduction; second, an inquiry into the question whether new species do not after all, contrary to the views of Darwin and Lyell, arise from sudden sports; and third, the question how one can determine a species.

The first of these problems was taken up by the German Neo-Darwinian, August Weismann (1834–1914), received a tremendous impetus from the researches of the Austrian monk, Gregor Mendel (1822–84), and in the present century gave rise to the sub-science of genetics. Weismann, through a very careful study of the germ plasm, was led to make a distinction between germ cells, whose function, he held, is purely the reproduction of new individuals and their own germ cells, and, on the other hand, somatic cells, whose function is the building up of the new body. Mendel's researches on the crossing of breeds in certain plants brought out the difference between dominant and recessive characters and the law of their combination. Subsequent investigations with more refined chemical techniques have suggested the existence of genes, submicroscopic carriers of hereditary characters; so that from this new point of view the inheritance of an individual results from the chance union of certain genes in the germ plasm of his parents. Here the random element is back in the picture, and the environment now includes the host organism in which the genes reside, with a fresh question whether it influences the genes or not.

A second line of inquiry induced by dissatisfaction with the evolutionary theory about the turn of the century was suggested by the Dutch botanist, Hugo de Vries (1848–1935). Darwin had assumed that evolution took place by the piling up of very small variations over long periods of time and many generations, and it was in these terms that the theory won recognition. But as the concept of natural selection showed one weakness after another under careful analysis, de Vries was led to the idea that evolution might occur by means of sudden great changes, which he called mutations. Of course biological sports are a well-known phenomenon, so that the theory was a priori plausible; but since they occurred irregularly and infrequently, it was difficult to investigate them until researches in genetics showed that they could be induced by subjection of genes to heat, X rays, ultraviolet light, and other treatments. By these means investigators were enabled to discover large numbers of minor mutations, occurring much more commonly than the instances investigated by de Vries. But the existence of these micro-mutations, as they are sometimes called, raises the question how to distinguish them from the small variations which Darwin postulated, and more generally how to differentiate mutation and variation.

Perhaps the best current usage could be summarized as follows. Variation is the wide term for any difference from parents or from a loosely conceived norm, and it would include individual nonheritable adaptations to environment as well as the reappearance of recessive Mendelian characters from remote ancestors. Mutation is that class of variations which are unpredictable, and yet inheritable, produced by changes either in genes and chromosomes, or in the chromosome content of cells; and it is in turn subdivided into the systemic (profound morphological modifications, such as de Vries had in mind), and micro-mutations involving common small alterations. This usage suggests the development of the science since Darwin—we can say with a good deal of confidence that variation is a fundamental character of animate organisms, in approximately the same sense as that motion is a fundamental character of inanimate matter; and also that inherited variations, both Mendelian and mutational, are, as Darwin maintained, always traceable primarily to organic, rather than environmental processes. On the other hand, this same usage reveals the ignorance that continues with regard to "the cause." Many correlations of high frequency have been established, but biologists are still forced to invoke chance to a degree which has sometimes given the erroneous impression that they are satisfied with it as an explanation.

The third set of investigations that has recently sprung from evolutionary theory is concerned with the basic concept of species. Darwin showed that species are not immutable, and Wallace went so far as to maintain that there is no limit of variability to a species. Furthermore, recent investigations have brought to light instances where "a species" varies almost continuously from one location to the next through a long series. But with these temporal and geographical variations what *is* a species? Does not the whole idea of species reduce to a pragmatic convenience for classification? Can it be given a scientific meaning?

A pointed significance has been recently given to the problem by its extension into anthropology, and the attempt to distinguish different human races. It has been shown[25] that the population of modern civilized countries represents a mixture of many older racial strains, and thus it is now next to impossible to discover a pure human race. From this point of view, the concept of a human species becomes a highly theoretical computation of sets of inherited characters common to a group which normally interbreeds. Thus "the population of the U.S.A.," though a very useful and significant concept for anthropological, demographic, and political purposes, would be biologically uninteresting to the degree in which immigration introduces foreign strains and also to the degree in which there are elements in the population of this country, such as some local or Indian groups, which do not normally intermarry with the others. From the genetic standpoint these considerations suggest the existence of specific sets of genes which continue to reproduce until disturbed by alien admixtures; and the development of this line of inquiry should give greater precision to the definition of species.

The evolution of *Homo sapiens* is much more complex and confusing than any other in the whole biological field, in much of which the essential characters of species are sufficiently clear to permit progress in fruitful investigation; but the theoretical problems concerned with the concept of species are scientifically and philosophically crucial. They form the subject matter of the sub-science of systematics.[26] This subject is the modern development of Linnaeus' Scala Naturae, and of the various systems that began with Aristotle.

If we project all these considerations speculatively into the future, it seems extremely difficult to interpret our present evolutionary biology as merely an infant science, still in the swaddling clothes of classification, which physics outgrew long ago. If variation and evolution are real and continuous, there will never be a point at which the classification of living forms is complete—classification will be as permanent a part of the science as variation is of its objects. From this position the further speculation naturally arises that biology deals with a sector of reality so much more complicated than the physical sector that it will have to be understood ultimately in its own terms. Meanwhile probably most of us want biology to go ahead with its concepts and find out what it can, without prejudging it as a kind of unachieved physics.

VI

In Darwin's mind there was apparently no clear line of demarcation either between biology and other closely allied sciences, or between science and morality; and his theory of evolution easily ranged into psychology and ethics. In the sixth edition of the *Origin of Species* (p. 669), he wrote: "We may look with some confidence to a secure future of great length. And as natural selection works solely by and for the good of each being, all corporeal and mental endowments will tend to progress towards perfection." Thus from the beginning the scientific theory was impregnated with connotations of human progress, goodness, and perfection; and this line of thought was continued not only in Darwin's own later works but also in the writings of his chief protagonists, Spencer and Huxley. From these primary sources it passed into the main stream of our cultural tradition, where it has qualified almost every minor current.

Thus the first and perhaps the most important fact about the theory of evolution in the social and moral field was the tremendous fertility of the fundamental idea. It had the capacity to stimulate new and significant explanations in one department after another; and even though many of these suggestions have not stood the test of criticism, still our thinking has been immensely enriched by the process.

Naturally such a condition was bound to produce incompatible suggestions and to give later generations, such as ours, an impression of confusion. Spencer maintained that the ideal for human life is merely a kind of elongation of the evolutionary operation into an evolved society, where individual and social needs would be perfectly adjusted; while Huxley contended that "the ethical progress of society depends, not on imitating the cosmic process, still less in running away from it, but in combatting it." [27] The attitude known as Social Darwinism expanded the idea of struggle for survival into a social doctrine of ruthless economic competition and class conflict; but Kropotkin in his *Mutual Aid: A Factor in Evolution* (1917) and other writers have clearly shown that cooperation is effective and important not only among men but also in the lower animals. Again, some optimistic writers believed that they could use evolution to unify all knowledge of man in society and even to formulate a scientific ethics; and yet, on the other hand, studies in the evolution of morality have led to moral relativism and skepticism. These instances are sufficient to indicate both the profusion and the confusion of evolutionary thinking with regard to human life.

But a large body of careful research and critical appraisal has gradually been built up, and on this basis it seems possible to discern certain widely accepted conclusions. In the first place, there is good reason to believe that the studies of the history of social institutions, including morality and religion, have firmly established the fact of evolution in this field. The ground had been prepared by the work of the historians and philosophers of the

eighteenth and early nineteenth centuries, to whom I have previously alluded (above p. 10); but the post-Darwinian investigations were undertaken not only in the light of the scientific
theory of evolution, but also with a more scholarly and objective
attitude toward history. Among the more significant early efforts
were Sir Henry Maine's *Ancient Law* (1861), which disclosed
a movement "from status to contract" in the societies studied,
W. E. H. Lecky's *History of European Morals from Augustus to
Charlemagne* (1869), and E. B. Tylor's *Primitive Culture* (1871),
in which many religious beliefs of highly developed societies were
traced back to early animism. Herbert Spencer's numerous works
on sociology and ethics appeared in the 1880's and '90's; while
Huxley's famous Romanes lecture entitled *Evolution and Ethics,*
in which he rejected the attempt to use evolution as a standard
for morality, was delivered and published in 1893. Three years
previously J. G. Frazer had brought out his *Golden Bough,* in
which he meticulously studied the evolution of a particular early
religious rite from antecedent sympathetic magic. The subsequent
literature is too voluminous to catalogue; but we should at least
notice L. T. Hobhouse's *Morals in Evolution,* Edward Westermarck's *Origin and Development of Moral Ideas,* and the writings
of the French sociologists, Lévy-Bruhl and Émile Durkheim.

Through this massive accumulation of evidence for the evolution of all kinds of social institutions there runs one insistent
problem: Is the evolutionary process continuously uniform in the
sense that the same factors operate at the end as at the beginning?
The uniformitarian hypothesis had started in geology, first
broached by James Hutton (1726–97), and firmly established by
Sir Charles Lyell's *Principles of Geology* (1830–33); then through
paleontology it naturally passed into evolutionary biology and was
implicit in the theory of natural selection, whence it was taken
into the social and mental field. In its full form, perhaps best seen
in Spencer and Haeckel, it means not only that there has actually
been a monistic process of evolution from matter through life to
mind, but also that the subsequent phases of this process can be
explained in terms of the earlier and simpler, the mental and
moral in terms of the organic, and in general the higher by the
lower; and furthermore, the process as a whole is determined and
automatic and predictable. The forms in which this problem appeared in certain important lines of investigation are worth a brief
consideration.

A relatively simple form occurs in popular judgments of the type: man is "nothing but" an animal; or Dewey's incautious statement: "For practical purposes morals mean customs, folkways, established collective habits." [28] This kind of identification has become known as the evolutionary fallacy because there is so obviously more in the final product than in the prototype.

An almost equally naïve interpretation, but in the opposite direction, as it were, occurs in the assumption that evolution implies perfecting, as Darwin suggested in the passage quoted at the beginning of this section. Subsequent historical studies have made it clear that mental and moral evolution may be the reverse of perfection, namely, retrogression or degeneration. And this evidence is important as it necessitates divorcing the concept of progress from that of evolution, and shows that progress must be measured in terms of values which do not appear at all in purely organic evolution.

A more subtle form of this same problem appeared in the attempt to discover a single line of evolution from a primitive condition to its present-day descendant—just as the forefoot of the horse has been evolved by successive losses of a toe from a four-toed ancestor of the Eocene period, so, it was supposed, our monotheism has developed through polytheism from animism in a set pattern for all cultures. But more thorough anthropological investigations have failed to reveal any such unitary pattern; instead there are many different lines of development, and the reason seems to be that any religious or social institution is at least partly invented by human intelligence to meet particular conditions. In the highly developed cultures rational selection plays a far more influential role than natural selection. Here then the uniformitarian interpretation begins to crack badly, for if we hold that the evolutionary process is determinate and natural in any definite sense, then the intelligence which interferes with it, for example, by keeping biologically unfit individuals alive, can hardly be natural in the same sense; and if we try to escape from this reasoning by simply asserting that the intelligence, as a product of the evolutionary process, *must* be natural, then we are forced into the position that whatever the intelligence does is natural, and in so so far as morality is the work of intelligence we have lost all ground for a distinction between good and bad.

It was thus in ethics that the ultimate test of this evolutionary uniformitarianism came. The doctrine was couched in several plausible formulations, but the central theme amounted to the contention that our morality, including conscience, duty, and the distinction between right and wrong, is a social product, which has developed from the struggle for existence in groups, and that any particular moral principle is to be scientifically validated in terms of basic human needs and group survival value. There were so many questionable assumptions involved in this position that a long debate was required to bring them all into the open and assess their cogency; but they have been exhaustively discussed by James Ward, *Naturalism and Agnosticism* (1899), W. R. Sorley, *Ethics of Naturalism* (1904), and many others, including the recent writers of textbooks in ethics. The weight of the evidence is now so heavily against the doctrine that it has been called the naturalistic fallacy, because it attempts to identify goodness with the natural conditions under which it appears.

At this point naturalism split and the term became ambiguous. One part of it stubbornly repudiated the accusation of fallacious reasoning, maintained the reduction of the mental and moral to the organic, and became the modern edition of materialism. But the larger and far more influential part, perhaps best represented by John Dewey, insists on the reality of moral ideals and is content to show their natural conditioning. This latter school has utilized the evolutionary studies of social institutions to demonstrate with convincing thoroughness that every concrete ideal arises out of a particular environment and in turn affects it; and through this two-way connection the ideal becomes empirically knowable. The polemical side of the doctrine is directed particularly against dualisms in which the transcendental term is held to be unconditioned or absolute.

Thus the failure of evolutionary ethics to establish natural selection and organic activity as a sufficient basis for morality and a moral science is balanced by the success with which moral institutions and ideals have been correlated with natural conditions and results. These correlations have inevitably led into the allied fields of anthropology, sociology, economics, politics, psychology, and medicine, and the sum of them all has been envisaged as the goal for institutes of human relations. Not only has ethics taken its place in the general field which we call the social studies, but also it has had to extend its own scope so as to include consideration of such topics as family life, leisure and art, professional codes, economic justice, and international morality. The meaning of human life and of the good life has been greatly enriched through this new understanding of its natural setting, and thus it may fairly be claimed that the ideas which sprang from the central theme of evolution, though some have been discarded, have in effect written another chapter in ethics.

VII

We come finally to the impact of evolutionary ideas on the ultimate considerations of religion and philosophy. And here we shall have to bear in mind the complexity of the data that suddenly were thrust into the forefront of the minds of thinkers and that, especially in the quarter century after Darwin, operated to mask the real issues before adequate critiques, analyses, and lines of experimentation could be built up. Evolution in the strict sense, development, progress, species constant or constantly changing, new knowledge versus the eternal verities, science versus religion, creation theological and biological, inheritance and environment, naturalism and supernaturalism, mechanism and organism—all these and other considerations formed a welter of ideas that somehow were coherent enough to conflict and yet incoherent enough to permit a fresh systematization in religion and philosophy.

A. *Religion.* It is surely one of the ironies of history that the same western European culture which had committed itself so wholeheartedly to a religion that maintained a doctrine of final revelation should have gone on to produce natural science with its tremendous modern innovations. For the purpose of this chapter we must restrict our interest as narrowly as possible to the part played by evolution in this situation; but it would be a great mistake to overlook the fact that the part played by evolution was an act in a far larger drama. The condemnation of Galileo for his adoption of the Copernican cosmology by the Cardinal Inquisitors in 1633 and his forced recantation provided only the most specious of victories for the church. "Then began the long fight between science and dogma, in which traditionalists fought a losing battle against new knowledge." [29]

After Newton put the Copernican hypothesis on a firm and convincing mathematical foundation, the battle initiated by the church was so obviously a losing one that it gradually ceased to be a battle at all. The philosophies that took their main inspiration from empirical science and the mechanistic principles of Newton were of course very distasteful to the churches; but by that time the Reformation had come and gone, there was no longer a single church with a unified weight of influence, and the opposition to the new science was more latent and scattered than open and effectual. But the theory of evolution in the nineteenth century, and particularly Darwin's theory, seemed to galvanize this religious opposition into action again. In England, for example,

There arose, in fact, that long Victorian conflict, discreditable on the whole to both parties concerned, called the conflict between science and religion. It is better, though more cumbersome, to call it a conflict between some scientists and some religionists. . . . The more combative men of science joined battle, very properly, with the improper claims made by religionists on behalf of religion, and the more combative men of religion joined battle, very properly, with the improper claims made by scientists on behalf of science, and in the result there was the delusive appearance of conflict between "religion" and "science" all along the line.[30]

Mutatis mutandis, much the same account would hold for the other countries of western Europe and America.

Other factors besides evolution became implicated in this conflict, for example, mechanism, materialism, and determinism; and we must try not to be led off our track by these extraneous issues. Also, while, as Professor Somervell maintains, there was a "delusive" aspect of this conflict, there was also a real one that centered about the problem how devout Christians were going to deal with advances in knowledge, of which evolution was only the latest and most provocative instance. It so happened that at this juncture the difficulty over evolution combined with two other difficulties, namely, the "higher criticism," which disclosed the natural conditions under which the various books of the Bible, including the Gospels, had been produced; and, second, the studies in comparative religion, which showed that several other faiths besides Christianity, but not easily classifiable as primitive superstitions, also claimed supernatural inspiration. Thus the theory of evolution took on added significance by association with these other considerations and became a primary factor in forcing the issue of a Christian policy toward new knowledge.

As a matter of fact, three distinguishable policies were developed, the first of which was what we may call the naïve Protestant reaction. This was essentially the recrudescence of the primitive attitude of outright condemnation manifested in the case of Galileo; but there was this new feature—the Protestant tradition commonly involved a literalistic interpretation of the Bible, and from this standpoint Darwin's theory seemed in flat contradiction to biblical doctrine. For example, the statement that God created man in His own image appeared quite irreconcilable with the view that man had descended from apelike ancestors; and the biblical account of creation had been so completely identified with the scientific acceptance of permanent species[31] that the whole Christian doctrine of creation, and with it the whole Christian doctrine of God's relation to the world, seemed imperiled by Darwin's evidence for the "origin of species" after creation.

And so some earnest champions of Protestantism went into action to kill Darwinism. Only a year after the publication of the *Origin of Species,* the Anglican Bishop Wilberforce, in a debate with Huxley at Oxford, attempted to laugh the theory out of court by asking Huxley if he claimed descent from a monkey on his father's or his mother's side. In 1925 at the Scopes trial in Tennessee, the Baptist William Jennings Bryan took the position that the theory of evolution ran counter to the views of the majority of taxpayers, and implied that "the spiritual doctrine that all men will stand at last equal before the throne of God meant . . . that all men are equally good biologists before the ballot box of Tennessee." [32] And again, it was predominantly Protestant states of the American union that attempted to legislate evolution out of existence by forbidding the teaching of it in their institutions of public education.

A second policy, much more carefully thought out, was adopted by Roman Catholic thinkers. Although they were not hampered by literalistic interpretations of biblical phrases, still Darwin's general picture of the evolutionary process, as well as his particular theory of natural selection, seemed to extend the concept of a godless and purposeless mechanism to the sphere of life and mind, where it endangered the fundamental doctrines of theism and the immortal soul. The position that they finally elaborated, as summarized in the article on evolution in the *Catholic Encyclopedia,* is based on the following distinctions: "(1) between the theory of evolution as a scientific hypothesis and as a philosophical speculation; (2) between the theory of evolution as based on theistic principles and as based on a materialistic and atheistic foundation; (3) between the theory of evolution and Darwinism; (4) between the theory of evolution as applied to the vegetable and animal kingdoms and as applied to man." By the use of these distinctions, the author accepts the "scientific" account of the evolution of animate species, but pronounces the Darwinian theory of selection "scientifically inadequate," and concludes that "the human soul could not have been derived from that of the brute, since it is of a spiritual nature; for which reason we must refer its origin to a creative act on the part of God." The essence of this position seems to be that science, if properly interpreted, does not conflict with sacred dogma.

The third policy was a reformulation of Christian doctrine in the light of the new evidence. Such a reformulation, it was claimed, was in the spirit of St. Augustine, who successfully combined early Christian religious fervor with Greek learning, and of St. Thomas Aquinas, who, in spite of the interdict of the Archbishop of Paris, transferred theology from a Platonic to an Aristotelian basis. The movement became known as Modernism, and originally it was adopted by many Catholics as well as Protestants. But in 1907 Pope Pius X exterminated it in the Roman Church by the Encyclicals *Lamentabile* and *Pascendi Gregis,* implemented by the excommunication of a French and an English leader of the movement (Abbé Loisy, Father Tyrrell); and since then it has been confined to Protestant circles. The basic position of the Roman Church is given by the Vatican Council of 1870 in these words: "that meaning of the sacred dogmas is perpetually to be retained which our holy Mother the Church has once declared; nor is that meaning to be departed from under the pretence or pretext of a deeper comprehension of them." In contrast to this position, the Modernists not only accepted the full scientific theory of evolution, but also applied the idea of evolution to religion itself. Thus, as Sir William Dampier puts it,

In place of the theory of a rigid and complete body of doctrine, delivered once for all to the Saints, a theory constantly liable to dislocation through the shocks of historical discovery, religious men gained the vision of an evolution of religious ideas, of continuous revelation marked at certain times by supreme outpourings, but never ceasing to interpret the Will of God to mankind.[33]

Thus the Modernists took the position that the new knowledge could be used to gain "a deeper comprehension" of God's ways in the world than was given by the old dogmas.

B. *Philosophy*. I have taken pains to bring out the significance of evolution in fields other than biology; but still there would be general agreement, I believe, that its pre-eminent success was in the field of living things—here its addition to knowledge was most profound and far-reaching. Previous to 1800, knowledge of living things was embodied in a number of scattered disciplines, such as physiology, botany, natural history; and the integration of these subjects which took place in the nineteenth century was accomplished not on the basis of evolution as the central concept, but on that of biology, that is, the science of living things. On the other hand, this statement is merely the description of a result, and it leaves unexplained the reason why these various disciplines should unite at this time, and also why they should succeed in forming a coalition strong enough to warrant our present distinction between them and the long-established physical sciences. I believe that it was the understanding of the evolutionary process which in large measure mediated the formation of an autonomous science of living things, and which has enabled this science to take a position by the side of physical science.

The idea of evolution formed a kind of focus which drew to it a cluster of other ideas, such as organism, heredity, species, social organization, individual adaptation, environment, variation, each of which, when surcharged with evolutionary meaning, seems to fall outside the fundamental physical categories of length, mass, electric charge, etc.; and all together, they suggested line after line of fruitful researches, recognizably different from those of physics and chemistry and yet yielding information that commanded respect.

The world of science is identified by Kant [sc. roughly 1800] with the sphere of applied mathematics, the Newtonian scheme of acting and reacting particles; and the world of science is conterminous with the realm of the knowable. . . . The great biological advance belongs to the century between us and Kant, and we should expect accordingly to find in the science and philosophy of to-day [sc. 1916] a more adequate interpretation of the characteristic attributes of life than is offered in the Kantian theory. On the whole, this expectation is not disappointed.[34]

The same contrast between the philosophy at the beginning and at the end of the century may be brought out in another way. Although, as I have pointed out (above, p. 11), Hegel gave a primary significance to the concept of development, and held that history showed successive stages in a temporal process, his main contention was that these stages are logically necessitated, and this position made him disdainful of attempts at evolutionary theory. In his *Encyclopedia,* published in 1817, he writes:

Nature is to be regarded as a *System of Grades,* of which the one necessarily arises out of the other, and is the proximate truth of the one from which it results,—but not so that the one were *naturally* generated out of the other. . . . It has been an inept conception of earlier and later "Naturphilosophie" to regard the progression and transition of one natural form and sphere into a higher as an outwardly actual production. . . . Thinking consideration must deny itself such nebulous, at bottom sensuous, conceptions, as in especial the so-called *origin,* for example, of plants and animals from water, and then the *origin* of the more highly developed animal organisations from the lower.[35]

It was just this "inept," "nebulous," "sensuous" concept that Darwin made into a theory precise enough to rank as scientific, and that Herbert Spencer, Haeckel, Bergson, Samuel Alexander, Lloyd Morgan, and Whitehead took over into a characteristic evolutionary philosophy.

In reviewing this philosophy it may be helpful to distinguish two main attitudes within it. The first of these attitudes was based on the idea of evolution as a cosmic process, found in all parts of nature, so that the phenomena of life are merely a specific application of the general principle. The second attitude envisaged evolution more narrowly and specifically as an organic process characteristic of life and therefore marking off the animate from the inanimate realm.

The former of these attitudes was adopted by Herbert Spencer even before Darwin published the *Origin of Species.* Spencer utilized the idea of evolution to unify the whole world of experience on a naturalistic foundation, and the result was a theoretical assimilation of man and society to physical nature. The evidences for this unitary principle he found

in the evolution of the sidereal universe out of the primitive nebula, in the history and development of the earth; in the origin of life and of new and more complex species of organism; in the formation of complex ideas out of the primitive manifold of sensory "shocks;" in the building of an integrated will out of elementary reflexes; and in the progressive complication and organization of society.[36]

Putting all these evidences together, Spencer formulated the general principle in a now famous piece of lexicography, as follows: "Evolution is an integration of matter and concomitant dissipation of motion; during which the matter passes from an indefinite incoherent homogeneity to a definite coherent heterogeneity; and during which the retained motion undergoes a parallel transformation." [37]

Ernst Haeckel (1834–1919), professor of zoology in the University of Jena, continued the same tradition, but brought to it the added authority of the mantel of science; and his best-known work, *Die Welträtsel,* published in 1899,[38] enjoyed an extraordinary vogue. He held that all the riddles of the universe could be resolved by two ultimate laws: first, "the fundamental law of the constancy of matter and force"; and second, "the universal law of evolution." These two principles together establish "the monism of the cosmos" on a naturalistic basis, and are sufficient to disprove the three great dogmas of the personality of God, the immortality of the soul, and the freedom of the will, on which Christian dualisms rest.

The two foregoing thinkers were noteworthy chiefly for their thoroughness in elaborating a philosophical generalization of the concept of evolution within a naturalistic framework. Professor Alfred North Whitehead (1861–1947) of Harvard started with this same framework but passed on to complete metaphysics, conceived as a mathematical system of postulates and deductions, in which, however, the main features of evolution are given a central role. Utilizing the insights of the new physics, Whitehead abandons the Newtonian scheme of rigid material particles with definite locations in an inflexible three-dimensional geometry for an interpretation of nature in which entities are conceived as organisms with internal relations of interpenetration and mutual adaptation, and which he calls the doctrine of organism.[39] On this basis he proceeds in *Process and Reality* to elaborate a set of categories for the interpretation of the world, in which " 'Creativity' is the universal of universals characterizing ultimate matter of fact," and is defined as "the principle of novelty" (p. 31). This concept of creativity as the principle of novelty in the actual world may be interpreted as a rendering of Darwin's discovery of new animate species, and also of the ancient religious intuition of a God who proclaims: "Behold, I make all things new";[40] and if it is taken as a highly generalized description of the actual state of affairs, it would seem to rank logically as a hypothesis comparable to Darwin's natural selection and subject to the same canons of judgment. On this basis, Whitehead remains within the tradition we are at present considering because he does not attempt to bifurcate the world between life and matter; but on the other hand, he is distinguishable from Spencer and Haeckel, who belong to the same tradition, in that he tends to assimilate the physical to the biological, while they did the reverse. He is perhaps most significant, however, for the thoroughness with which he has attempted to think through the idea of a process, in this case evolution or creativity, as more than an adjective of ultimate reality, an idea suggested by the recent physical equation for matter and energy; from this point of view, even God is envisaged as both an actual entity and also as an evolutionary process with a primordial and a subsequent nature.

The other evolutionary tradition in philosophy stems from the contrasts that emerge between physics and biology in their modern developments. By and large, evolution has proved uninteresting to physics and chemistry, in spite of the fact that many biologists have taken pains to accept the ideals of mathematical physics and have encouraged the development of such hybrid sciences as biochemistry and biophysics. This broad divergence, in turn, rests upon more specific differences: such basic biological categories as heredity and adaptation seem to find no analogues in physics and chemistry; the pure mechanisms of inanimate nature seem to become recognizably vaguer in living matter; and the fineness of adjustment, the complexity, and the subordination of present to future dispositions in organisms inevitably suggest something nearer a planned economy than a chance collocation of elements that blindly run. In general, life seems to stand "above" the rest of nature instead of cuddling up in an inconspicuous corner of it.

The first important expression of this point of view occurred in the works of the French philosopher, Henri Bergson (1859–1941). He wrote at a time of marked dissatisfaction with evolutionary theory,[41] which seemed unable to get beyond a perpetual dispute between Neo-Darwinians and Neo-Lamarckians. Bergson tends to identify these two positions with two different types of explanation, which he calls respectively the mechanistic and the teleological; and he rejects both of them as inadequate because vital processes are neither purposive nor mechanical. He proposes an intermediate position, which he calls creative evolution and which centers on a vital force (*élan vital*), whose characteristics in the main purport to be just those features of biological evolution which have actually appeared. But in the development of his theory the contrast between the biological and the mental (purposive) yields to a more fundamental contrast between both of them and the physical realm. Bergson's writing has a Gallic richness of expression that makes theoretical simplification seem like bad taste; but, taking the necessary risk, I would say that the net result of his thought is to emphasize the distinction of life from matter, and the main feature of life as a kind of organic inventiveness in meeting changed environments, so that sense of direction and predictability are at a minimum.

Bergson's assumption of a vital force, distinct from physico-chemical energies, coincided with a recrudescence of vitalistic theories among zoologists and botanists, the most striking of which was perhaps that of the German Hans Driesch (1867–1941). He instances cases of regeneration after mutilation; for example, if the head of a certain kind of sea anemone (*Tubularia*) is cut off at any chosen level of the stem, a corresponding length of stem with a new head will be grown. Such phenomena inevitably suggest the presence in individual organisms of some central director, which Driesch calls entelechy or psychoid; this is not a kind of energy and even lacks the characteristics of quantity, but yet it is constantly spoken of as an agent.[42] The same conception seems to underlie Bergson's assumption of a vital force that is yet not physical energy; and the difficulty inherent in all such schemes is that, after separating and contrasting life and physical matter, they invoke a vital principle to interfere with the natural course of physical processes.

But the distinction between the biological and the physical realms is too fundamental and empirical to be discarded simply because one particular explanation of it turns out to be a failure; and there have been two further significant developments in the attempt to meet the problem philosophically. The first is the theory known as emergent evolution; and it may be said to have stemmed from one side of Driesch's thought,[43] and to have been elaborated by the British philosopher Samuel Alexander (1859–1938)[44] and the British biologist C. Lloyd Morgan.[45] Driesch in one passage[46] suggests that what he has in mind is "order of relation and nothing else." Professor Alexander has picked up this idea, discarding the assumption of superior (sc. nonphysical) causes as well as all implications of vitalism, and attempted to conceive of the world as a naturalistic order of levels of relatedness, of which the main ones are spatio-temporal point-instants, then composite matter, life, consciousness or mind, and finally deity understood as that level which presses onward toward higher levels. In so far as this theory unifies the world under the single concept of a nisus toward higher levels (evolutionary progress), it belongs with those of Spencer, Haeckel, and Whitehead in the first tradition I described above; but I am putting it in the second tradition because its main significance seems to me to lie in its resolute attempt to formulate a descriptive theory of levels of reality, in which life is distinguished from physical and spatio-temporal events. It is this aspect of Alexander's thought that Lloyd Morgan in turn takes over and develops into the full-blown theory of emergent evolution.

The most important points of this theory seem to me to be the following: (a) it is consciously naturalistic, in the sense that it attempts to formulate empirically known present conditions; (b) these conditions include higher and lower levels of existence, and more specifically the fact that life is "higher" than matter, and mind "higher" than life; (c) the levels are not causally related in the ordinary physical sense in which the higher could cause the lower, or vice versa, but in a special dual way called involvement and dependence such that, for example, mental events always involve physiological events while the latter sometimes depend upon mental correlates. The chief difficulty of the theory lies in its use of such concepts as "emerge," "supervene," "higher," and "level," for which there are no satisfactory scientific meanings; but on the other hand it seems to be working in the right direction in so far as it seeks to establish correlations or uniformities of any kind, e.g., involvement and dependence, without limitation to the current condition of physical science.

This brings us to the second significant development I referred to above, which is a shift in the meaning of mechanism. At the beginning of the nineteenth century Laplace, working on a generalization of Newtonian mechanics, maintained that a sufficiently informed scientist could calculate the whole past and future history of the universe from a knowledge of the configuration and velocities of the masses composing it at any particular moment; but the evolutionary theory and the more recent revolution in physical theory have made Laplace's suggestion seem like an "over-estimation of the possibilities of mechanism." [47] Moreover the concept of mechanism itself, upon analysis, reveals an ambiguity between the notion of machine (which includes some human purpose) and the laws of mechanics (which are independent of human purpose); the new physics is forced to face correlations, such as indeterminacy, which are not mechanical in Laplace's sense; and most of modern biology and modern psychology is based on "Mechanisms" of a higher level of interpretation,[48] e.g., adaptation, neurosis, which cannot be at present expressed in terms of masses and velocities. But it may be questioned whether, if we have to take mechanism up on to these higher levels, it is worth preserving, since the main virtue of the term seemed to be derived from the fact that it could only be used on the lowest possible level. Thus the old conflict between mechanism and vitalism is stale; vitalism in the strictest sense lost, but only when mechanism broadened out into the general idea of any naturalistic, empirically verifiable correlation. And coincidentally, the prerogative position of physics as the beau ideal of science has shown signs of yielding to a more pluralistic philosophy in which biology and psychology are given places alongside of physics, even if their correlations cannot be reduced without remainder to matter-energy equations and deductively systematized.

Here we seem to be at the heart of the philosophical problem for our generation. When the scientific theory of evolution won acceptance in the last century, its significance, as I have tried to show, was manifold; but certainly one fundamental significance was its suggestion of a process of upbuilding and creativity in the universe, quite the reverse of the repetitiousness of mechanism, the gradual disintegration implied in the Second Law of Thermodynamics, and even the tight logical determinism of rationalistic monisms such as those of Spinoza and Hegel. Against all these interpretations of nature as essentially a dead hand of law squeezing every activity into some pre-existent groove, evolution pointed to new species of living things, a continuous process of organic invention (adaptation), and a cosmological organization loose enough to permit a real freedom to human endeavor. The classic expression of this point of view is given in William James's (1842 –1910) protest against the "block-universe eternal and without a history." [49]

Just here, however, lies the trouble—is evolution a scientific law, or the denial of such law? On the one hand, in spite of the naturalism that disturbed so many thinkers, the theory of evolution has always contained a feature of variation and novelty, which, when strictly analyzed, looks like unpredictability and freedom to invent new organic arrangements, where "new" is to be understood simply as what did not before exist; and this attitude, when carried out rigorously, seems to imply either actual indeterminism or at best selection among limited possibilities at present unknown. On the other hand, if we assume that these limited possibilities will be brought to light and formulated in laws as the biological sciences advance, then presumably we will be back in something like the point of view of special creation and eternal forms, and all the hullabaloo about evolution would have to be considered premature; for physical science is perfectly competent to deal with the concept of orderly change, and in so far as that is all evolution is, there would be no need to make a special point about it.

Each of these alternatives is so unsatisfactory that we are impelled to search for some more adequate theoretical interpretation; but from here on is mostly ignorance. There does, however, seem to be enough positive evidence, already unearthed, in regard to variation, adaptation, heredity, and organic composition, to suggest that we are on the track of some new kinds of correlation, which cannot be subsumed under any present laws of physico-chemical science, and yet are not conscious, purposive, or mental in any strict sense. This in turn suggests that the animate world may be somehow intermediate between inanimate matter and thought, and that perhaps the best rendering of our contemporary information consists in continuing the policy of letting investigations of matter, life, and mind proceed along independent lines, with a constant pressure for philosophical integration.

NOTES

1. In writing this chapter I have benefited to an extent that would be difficult to specify from the prolonged criticisms, constructive suggestions, and enthusiastic encouragement of Professors G. L. Jepsen and F. B. Van Houten of the Department of Geology, Princeton University. I also want to acknowledge my great indebtedness to my colleague

in philosophy, Professor Ledger Wood, and to Professor Stow Persons of the History Department for putting at my disposal their unusually wide, rich, and accurate understanding of the history of ideas.

2. W. B. Scott, *The Theory of Evolution* (New York, Macmillan, 1919), preface, p. v.

3. Edward Caird, *The Evolution of Religion* (New York, Macmillan, 1893).

4. Sir William Osler, *The Evolution of Modern Medicine* (New Haven, Yale University Press, 1922).

5. Sir James Murray, *The Evolution of English Lexicography* (Oxford, Clarendon Press, 1900).

6. It is perhaps worth noting that a good deal of the material introduced by Professor H. F. Osborn, *From the Greeks to Darwin* (New York and London, Macmillan, 1894), shows only a biological interest without any suggestion of evolution.

7. Eccles. 1:9.

8. Thomas H. Huxley, "Geological Contemporaneity," *Selected Works* (New York, Appleton, n.d.), VIII, "Discourses Biological and Geological," 306.

9. Francis Bacon, *Novum Organum* (Oxford, Clarendon Press, 1889), II, sec. 29.

10. J. B. Bury, *Idea of Progress* (London, Macmillan, 1920), pp. 104–105, 109, 112, 126, 171.

11. Quoted by Osborn, *op. cit.,* p. 116.

12. *Conversations of Goethe with Eckermann and Soret,* trans. by J. Oxenford (London, Bell, 1883), under Aug. 2, 1830; quoted from J. Barzun, *Darwin, Marx, Wagner* (Boston, Little, Brown, 1841), p. 50.

13. Benjamin Disraeli, *Tancred* (London and New York, John Lane, 1905), p. 149.

14. Charles Lyell, *Life, Letters, and Journals of Sir Charles Lyell* (2 vols., London, Murray, 1881), II, 3.

15. *The Life and Letters of Charles Darwin,* ed. by Francis Darwin (London, John Murray, 1888), II, 196: "I never forget that almost everything I have done in science I owe to the study of his great works."

16. E. L. Krause, *Erasmus Darwin* (London, Murray, 1879), p. 132; quotation from Brazun, *op. cit.,* p. 51.

17. Herbert Spencer, *Illustrations of Universal Progress* (New York, Appleton, 1865), chap. i.

18. Cf. the summary given by Donald Culross Peattie, "The Evolution of Charles Darwin," *Reader's Digest* (Sept.; 1945), p. 54.

19. Charles Darwin, *Origin of Species* (6th ed. New York, Appleton, 1889), p. 146; quoted by Barzun, *op. cit.,* p. 81.

20. Darwin, *Life and Letters,* II, 318.

21. Darwin, *Origin of Species* (6th ed. London, John Murray, 1906), p. 657.

22. Allan Nevins, *Gateway to History* (Boston, Heath, 1938), p. 263.

23. C. R. Longwell, "Geology," in *The Development of the Sciences,* Second Series (New Haven, Yale University Press, 1941), p. 170.

24. Cf. L. L. Woodruff, "Biology," in *ibid.,* p. 216. And on the term "biology," cf. this chapter, p. 6.

25. Cf. Carleton S. Coon, *The Races of Europe* (New York, Macmillan, 1939).

26. Cf. Ernst Mayr, *Systematics and the Origin of Species from the Viewpoint of a Zoologist* (New York, Columbia University Press, 1943); and the discussion by Glenn L. Jepsen, in the *Amer. Jour. of Science, 241* (1943), 521–528.

27. Thomas H. Huxley, *Evolution and Ethics* (London, Macmillan, 1893), p. 34.

28. John Dewey, *Human Nature and Conduct* (New York, Holt, 1922), p. 75.

29. B. Russell, *History of Western Philosophy* (New York, Simon & Schuster, 1945), p. 492.

30. D. C. Somervell, *English Thought in the Nineteenth Century* (5th ed. London, Methuen, 1947), pp. 129, 130.

31. Cf. Linnaeus: "We reckon as many species as issued in pairs from the hands of the Creator." Quoted from Somervell, *op. cit.,* p. 126.

32. Walter Lippmann, *Men of Destiny* (New York, Macmillan, 1927), p. 55.

33. Sir William Dampier, *History of Science* (New York, Macmillan, 1936), p. 336.

34. A. Seth Pringle-Pattison, *The Idea of God* (Oxford, Clarendon Press, 1917), p. 69.

35. Art. 249, trans. by James Hutchison Stirling, *Secret of Hegel* (2 vols., London, Longmans, Green, 1865), II, 615.

36. Alfred Weber and Ralph B. Perry, *History of Philosophy* (revised ed. New York, Scribner, 1925), p. 485.

37. Herbert Spencer, *First Principles* (New York, Appleton, 1877), p. 396.

38. English trans., *The Riddle of the Universe* (New York and London, Harper, 1901).

39. Alfred North Whitehead, *Science and the Modern World* (New York, Macmillan, 1926), pp. 55, 115.

40. Rev. 21:5.

41. Cf. above, p. 21.

42. Hans Driesch, *Science and Philosophy of the Organism* (2 vols., London, Black, 1908), II, 82, 169, 238.

43. An interesting anticipation of this theory appeared in the work of the American geologist Joseph Le Conte, *Evolution. Its Nature, Its Evidences, and Its Relation to Religious Thought* (2d ed. New York, Appleton, 1891).

44. Samuel Alexander, *Space, Time, and Deity* (2 vols., London, Macmillan, 1920).

45. C. Lloyd Morgan, *Emergent Evolution* (London, Williams & Norgate, 1923), *The Emergence of Novelty* (London, Williams & Norgate, 1933).

46. Driesch, *op. cit.,* II, 169.

47. Dampier, *op. cit.,* p. 340.

48. Cf. H. N. Russell, *Fate and Freedom* (New Haven, Yale University Press, 1927), chap. i.

49. William James, *A Pluralistic Universe* (New York, Longmans, Green, 1909), p. 310.

INTRODUCTION TO CHAPTER II

EVOLUTION IN ITS RELATION TO THE PHILOSOPHY OF NATURE AND THE PHILOSOPHY OF CULTURE

PROFESSOR NORTHROP is a persuasive advocate of the view that an authoritative philosophy for the social and cultural life must be derived from the laws of nature as understood by the best informed minds of the age. Only thus can the conflicting values of contemporary nationalities and intellectual traditions be merged in the common philosophy of life which is such a vital prerequisite for a world community.

The three major traditions of evolutionary thought distinguished by Professor Northrop—the Aristotelian, the Hegelian, and the Darwinian—have entailed social philosophies consistent with their respective first principles. Against the broad perspective provided by his discussion it becomes apparent that the chapters in Part II deal primarily with problems arising from the impact of Darwinism, which is the dominant evolutionary tradition of the English-speaking world. It will also appear, as Professor Northrop insists, that the assumption of the similar character of natural and social evolution proved to be a crucial point in the whole discussion, and that the formulation of independent theories of cultural evolution was essential to the assimilation of the idea.

S. P.

II

EVOLUTION IN ITS RELATION TO THE PHILOSOPHY OF NATURE AND THE PHILOSOPHY OF CULTURE[1]

F. S. C. NORTHROP

THE thought of the nineteenth century was dominated by the concept of evolution. One of the major tasks of our own century is to carry through a critique of this concept. This critique must apply to culture as well as nature, since the concept of evolution has been applied to both domains of human knowledge.

The term evolution is used in a large number of different senses. In its broadest sense it expresses the notion that time is of the essence of things. In this broad sense the Aristotelian philosophy of nature and culture of the Middle Ages was evolutionary. It will be recalled that Aristotle's physics and metaphysics conceived of reality as the informing of otherwise formless matter by form, a process which because of the stubbornness of matter took time. But Aristotelian biology was evolutionary in another sense. In his *Historia Animalium* Aristotle classified living creatures in terms of genera and species arranged in a serial order from the simple to the complex. Aristotle was quite well aware also that his scientific method of classification was not neat and perfect. Certain specific individual living creatures fell into one species with respect to certain of their characteristics and into another species with respect to other characteristics. Thus Aristotelian biology, at least in the hands of Aristotle, never had quite the cast-iron fixity of types which many of its modern critics attribute to it. Considerations such as these indicate that a proper critique must distinguish the Aristotelian medieval from the modern concept of evolution.

But even within the modern world there are differing concepts of evolution. This fact is often overlooked by members of the culture of Great Britain and the United States, since evolution with such people tends to be associated initially at least with the name of Darwin. In the cultures of Germany and Russia, however, evolution is connected with the name of Hegel and his successor Marx. The Darwinian Anglo-American and the Hegelian Germanic-Russian concepts of evolution are radically different. Moreover, the Hegelian theory of evolution arose many decades earlier than the Darwinian Anglo-American theory. Hegel died in 1831. Darwin's *Origin of Species* was published twenty-eight years later, and even his famous letter to Asa Gray, in which for the first time he stated his positive theory, was not written until 1857.

The appreciation of the radical differences between these two modern theories of evolution is of great importance. It involves much more than a matter of intellectual curiosity. The ideological conflicts between the communistic Russians and the Anglo-American democracies at the present moment cannot be fully appreciated unless the contrast between the Darwinian and the Hegelian conceptions of evolutionary change are fully understood. Similarly, within the history of the Russian Revolution, the issue between the Mensheviks and the Bolsheviks turned around the question whether the socialistic state is to be brought in by the essentially Darwinian evolutionary change called "gradualism" or the more abrupt revolutionary change prescribed by the dialectic of Hegel.

Once these different modern conceptions of evolution are noted, the important question arises—what is the source of these differences? The pursuit of this question in the case of the Russian and German revolutionary theory of evolution leads back behind both nature and culture to the philosophy of Hegel. When we ask in turn how Hegel came to this philosophy we are guided still farther back to the philosophy of Fichte, which arose in order to solve the problem of the relation between moral philosophy and natural philosophy left by Kant. It is to be noted also that Hegel's philosophy was most obviously and primarily a philosophy of mind and of culture. It was, however, a philosophy of culture which was also applied to the natural sciences and to nature. Consequently, for both the contemporary Russian Communists who follow Marx and the German idealists who followed Hegel, the processes of nature as well as of culture obeyed the law of negation, opposition, and subsequent synthesis prescribed by the logic of dialectic. These considerations make it evident also that an effective critique of the concept of evolution must concern itself with the philosophy of both nature and culture.

In the case of the Anglo-American Darwinian or post-Darwinian theories of evolution, the philosophical foundation for the conception of evolutionary change which is affirmed is not so obvious. Anglo-Americans are inclined to think of evolution as a purely scientific theory. It is to be noted, however, that Marx and his followers conceive of their quite different concept of evolution in similarly empirical scientific terms. It is true, however, that the Anglo-American concept was formulated by scientists such as Charles Darwin quite apart from the issues and problems of modern philosophy, whereas the Marxist and Hegelian theory is a direct and explicit consequence of the work of professional philosophers who wrestled with the inescapable problems of modern philosophy. But this difference as we shall see is somewhat more apparent than real. For it was the clarification and explicit formulation of the assumptions of modern science, in mathematical physics to be sure rather than in biology, which produced and rendered inescapable the issues of modern philosophy. This must soon concern us in greater detail.

But even the formulation of the Anglo-American concept of evolution at the hands of Wallace and Darwin and their successors is by no means devoid of its philosophical assumptions and consequences. This becomes especially clear when one contrasts it with the Aristotelian conception of evolution. In fact, we can grasp the full force of either the Hegelian or the Darwinian conceptions of evolution only if we conceive them as the expressions of two different modern philosophies of science which stand over against the Aristotelian philosophy.

Our analysis of the different senses in which the word evolution is used in the Western world has guided us therefore to the recognition of the need for considering each meaning in its relation to the particular philosophy of natural science and of culture which it entails. Two of these philosophies have now become evident: (1) the Aristotelian philosophy of science and the humanities underlying the medieval conception of temporal change; and (2) the post-Kantian Fichtean and Hegelian philosophy underlying the dialectical revolutionary conception of evolutionary change. The philosophy at the basis of the Darwinian conception of evolution by means of gradual minute steps is not so obvious. Nonetheless, it is to be found in the previous scientific and philosophical foundations of the modern world, especially as they work themselves out in British empirical philosophy and in the French philosophy of Descartes. Viewed from this standpoint, Darwinism turns out to be little more than the carrying through for biological creatures including man of a philosophy of science established for nature generally by Descartes, Newton, and Locke.

To the exposition of the three philosophies underlying the three major Western conceptions of evolution we must now turn. As we do this certain other complexities must be kept in mind. We shall find that all three conceptions of evolution assume that the character of evolutionary change is the same in nature as it is in culture. There is no a priori reason why this should be the case. In fact, we shall find that empirical evidence indicates unequivocally that it is not the case. Thus a proper critique of evolution must refuse to take it for granted that evolution in the philosophy of culture is identical with evolution in the philosophy of nature.

Another complexity must be kept in mind. Even within the modern non-Hegelian theory of biological evolution there are differences of conception centering on differing emphases given to the role of internal and environmental influences in the evolution of new species. The work on genetics by Mendel has tended to emphasize abruptness rather than gradual minute changes, in this respect being somewhat analogous to the Hegelian theory. This similarity, however, is far from identity, since there is no evidence from genetics or from the study of mutations which indicates that these abrupt changes obey the Hegelian dialectical law of thesis, antithesis, and synthesis. Thus the theory of mutations falls within the general framework of the modern Anglo-American philosophy of science rather than within that of the post-Kantian, Hegelian, and Marxian philosophy.

Nevertheless pre-Kantian French and Anglo-American social science has not always restricted itself to the gradualistic or the mutation theory of biological evolution. Spencer, to be sure, generalized the law of evolution for biology so that he could extend it to social institutions also. With the Frenchman Comte, however, social evolution tended to follow a law of its own having nothing to do with principles governing evolution in natural science. His law of societal evolution was defined purely culturally in terms of the distinction between the theological, the metaphysical, and the scientific attitudes toward experience. Thus it will be recalled that, according to Comte, every society proceeds through three stages from an initial theological epoch by way of an intermediary metaphysical period to culminate in the final scientific stage. This cultural definition of the law of social evolution gave Comte's positivistic sociology much more in common with Hegel and Marx than with Spencer or Darwin. Nevertheless, there was a difference. For Comte the culturally defined stages of social evolution were not governed by the Hegelian dialectic.

THE ARISTOTELIAN CONCEPTION OF EVOLUTION

The Aristotelian conception of the reality of temporal changes in nature cannot be understood apart from the metaphysics of Aristotle, which rests in turn upon his physics. This physics was the final conception of science to which the ancient Greeks came as the result of investigations in empirical and formal geometry, stereometrical chemistry, and mathematical astronomy. The later Greek scientists and the majority of medieval scientists took Aristotle's physics for granted and supposed it to have been established empirically, with precisely the same confidence as characterized traditional modern physicists with respect to the mechanics of Galilei and Newton.

According to Aristotelian physics the universe was conceived as finite in its macroscopic magnitude. It was also conceived as material. For reasons having to do with the assumptions necessary to validate the mathematical method of exhaustion, Aristotle and his contemporaries were led to reject the atomic theory of matter held by both Democritus and Plato. This in turn removed all grounds for the Democritean and Platonic epistemological distinction between nature as sensed and nature as conceived in one's scientific theory. Thus the Aristotelian thesis arose that the sense world is the real world and that there are no scientific or philosophical concepts given to the intellect which are not first presented through the senses. Matter consequently became identified with sensed matter; hence, the inescapably qualitative character of the Aristotelian physics. Moreover, since atomicity of substances was rejected and since nature as given through the senses is a continuum, this sensuous matter was in turn regarded as continuous, except as sensuously differentiated by different sensed qualities.

Since nature as sensed is undergoing continuous change, generation was regarded as real, the principle of becoming was made metaphysically basic, and time was regarded as of the essence of actual existent things. This entailed that the entities of nature did not have fixed properties throughout time, as was the case with the atoms of Democritus. Instead, Aristotelian substances could only realize their full nature by means of a process in time. Growth and generation are real metaphysical elements in the nature of living things. Strictly speaking, a living organism with Aristotle is a life history. It requires time for its full nature to unfold. Thus not merely within the life history of an individual organism but between one generation and another generation of organisms in a given species time is involved.

This conception, it is to be noted, was in direct opposition to the previous Democritean theory of living creatures. According to the latter theory all change which exhibited itself as an alteration of property rather than an alteration of position was mere appearance. The supposedly scientific objects in nature were material atoms in motion in the void. These atoms had fixed properties unalterable with time. Thus all apparent change due to generation was conceived by the Democritean philosophy of science and by Empedocles, as at bottom nothing but change due to the motion of material atoms whose properties did not change with time. The Aristotelian thesis that the real natural object is the sensed natural object gave change due to generation as real a status in scientific knowledge as change due to motion.

If temporal development is of the essence of natural objects, how then does the Aristotelian conception of evolution differ from the modern one? The first step toward an answer to this question involves an understanding of the Aristotelian conception of form.

According to the Aristotelian physics and metaphysics, natural objects were not merely material. They were also composed of another component which Aristotle termed form. Thus any natural object was conceived as made up of matter and form. This matter and form in its unity Aristotle called a substance.

Since the Aristotelian epistemology required that all scientific concepts be derived through the senses, form had to be identified with the sensed qualities which differentiate one part of continuous sensed matter from another part. At bottom there were in the Aristotelian physics but four elementary sensuous forms: hot, cold, wet, and dry. In terms of these four sensuous forms, Aristotle defined the four basic chemical materials of Greek science: earth, air, fire, and water. All other substances in nature were combinations of these four chemical materials. Thus, fire, for example, was any material given to the senses which is sensed as both hot and dry. Any such quality as actually sensed in a material substance Aristotle termed the positive form.

Were this the full account of the Aristotelian physics and metaphysics, his theory of evolution might have been identical with that of any Anglo-American modern such as Locke or Hume. What made the Aristotelian concept of evolution unique was Aristotle's doctrine of form by privation. No concept in the whole of Aristotle's philosophy is more important. It measures the difference between his theory of temporal change in nature and that of any other Western thinker.

The key to the discovery of the form by privation centers in a common-sense experience. If one places one's hand upon a cold windowpane, thereby sensing matter as cold, one knows the form "cold" in the status of positive form. This is an experience which everyone would admit. One other somewhat surprising fact, however, is also made possible by such an experience. One is able to assert as true not merely the proposition "the material windowpane is cold," but also the proposition "the material windowpane is not hot." The peculiar fact is that the senses give us only the sensation of coldness; they do not in this instance convey the sensation of warmth. Nonetheless, from this experience we are able to get a proposition which is true that contains the form "hot."

How is this possible? Aristotle asks. His answer comes in terms of his logical doctrine of opposites, the essence of which is the form by privation.

According to the doctrine of opposites, sensations do not come to us as bare atomic data. Certain sensuous qualities preclude the sensing of others at the same time and place. Sensuous qualities related in this fashion Aristotle terms opposites. Thus hot is the opposite of cold, and wet is the opposite of dry. It is because hot is thus logically related to cold by the logical relation of opposition that in sensing the material windowpane as cold we are enabled to assert that the windowpane is not hot. A form or sensuous quality which is thus logically present in experience as the logical opposite of the positive form which is sensed, Aristotle terms a form by privation.[2] Thus when one senses the windowpane as cold, cold is present as positive form and hot is logically implicit in the situation in the status of form by privation.

With Aristotle the notion of form by privation serves other

functions than that of accounting for the truth of negative propositions. It also provides a meaningful definition of the potentiality of substances. A substance has only those potentialities which are already implicit in it in the status of form by privation. Thus a form by privation defines the potentiality of a substance to become other than what it is as positive form now. In this manner, Aristotle avoids the Parmenidean difficulty facing any philosophy of becoming, of explaining how genuine novelty in time avoids the absurdity of creating something out of nothing. What happens in temporal creativity, according to Aristotle, is that the potentiality of a substance becomes actualized. But until one has defined potentiality, such a statement is meaningless verbiage. And it is precisely this definition of potentiality which the Aristotelian doctrine of form by privation provided. Real change is possible because form by privation, which defines the potentiality of a substance, can replace its opposite, thereby shifting to the status of positive form. Thus, when after holding my hand upon the material windowpane for a considerable time a real process of change of quality occurs in which the sensation of cold is replaced by that of hot, what has happened according to Aristotle is that hot which was initially in the status of form by privation has shifted to the status of positive form, cold in turn reversing the direction of this shift. Such is the ultimate nature of all temporal change which is real according to Aristotle.

This has the consequence of making it impossible for any creature in nature to realize as actual in fact any qualities which were not in it initially potentially in the status of form by privation. It is precisely in this requirement that the Aristotelian doctrine of the final formal cause has its metaphysical basis. This is what Aristotle means when he says that the final cause is last empirically but first logically. The point is that no form can be exemplified actually in time in a given substance as positive form if that form was not in that substance logically and initially in the status of form by privation. Consequently every individual creature in nature moves toward an actual temporally embodied goal as guided by the previously existing form of that goal in the status of form by privation.

We are now in a position to give a partial definition of the Aristotelian conception of evolution. The Aristotelian conception of evolution is teleological evolution in which there is but one final cause or goal for any given creature, and this goal is determined by the presence in the creature from its very beginning of the form in the status of form by privation which defines that goal.

The form by privation is the key to the Aristotelian philosophy of science and to the medieval concept of temporal change in an additional respect. If we knew sensuous forms such as hot and cold and wet and dry merely in the status of positive form, there would be no alternative whatever for us but to suppose, after the manner of the modern empiricists, Locke, Berkeley, and Hume, that they are merely temporary transitory particulars. For all that we sense is a particular blue or a particular sensation of hotness at a given place at a given time. Moreover, every particular form given through the senses vanishes with time. It is the form in the status of the form by privation which convinces Aristotle that the ideas given through the senses are nonetheless logical universals with a persistent logical immortality.

Consider what we know when upon sensing the windowpane as cold we are able to know the true proposition, "The windowpane is not hot." In the true knowledge expressed in the latter proposition, the idea of hotness is not present as a particular here and now; it is present instead merely as a meaning which may take on particularity in some other instance of hereness and nowness when it shifts to the status of positive form. Thus in the status of form by privation "hot" is not a sensuous particular, it is a logical universal. Moreover, it is an immortally persisting logical universal because otherwise reality would not have the potentiality to become what now as positive form it is not.

This means that the appearance of any form in the status of positive form in a living creature or in the origin of a given species in time must always be conceived as the temporal embodiment of an immortal eternal nontemporal form previously subsistent in the temporal process in the status of form by privation.

At last we have arrived at the heart of the Aristotelian conception of evolution. Evolution is the teleological process in time directed toward one and only one absolutely predetermined goal. This goal may be actualized in matter at a given instant in time, but the form which defines that goal and which directs the creature or creatures toward that goal is not temporal or transitory but eternal and immortal, causally efficient always, in the status of form by privation. Thus, whereas the forms of new species can for Aristotelians originate in the status of positive form at a particular instant in time, exactly as Darwin maintained, there is no creation of the form of that species in its status as form by privation at a given instant of time. For Aristotelians the final cause of organic evolution may originate as positive form in matter at a given instant of time, but in itself in its status of efficient cause guiding the temporal process toward its actualized goal and in its status of form by privation defining the potentialities of the process from the infinite past, it is nontemporal in origin and immortal.

But one additional factor is required to complete the Aristotelian conception of evolution. Because all knowledge is given through the senses, Aristotelian science proceeds by the inductive methods of observation, description, and classification. These methods result in the ordering of all natural creatures, inorganic and organic, in a hierarchical system of classification composed of genera and species. Any given species is defined by specifying its nearest genus in the system of classification and the differentiating quality which distinguishes it from other species in that genus. This means that any creature in nature is in its very essence, or in other words as designated by its scientific definition, a part of a hierarchical order. Thus there is not merely the organization or formal cause of a given organism, but also there is an organic relationship between the final causes of all natural objects. In fact, the temporal process is the result of the embodiment of the hierarchical order of the organic relations of all species in otherwise formless matter.

This Aristotelian conception of biological evolution had many merits. The doctrine of irreducible formal causes accounted for biological organization. The Aristotelian thesis that the sense world is the real world enabled biologists to take the growth, generation, and reproduction of living things at their face value as real. Finally, the adaptation of organisms to their environment was accounted for, since the form of the environment and the form of the creature were both defined in terms of their status in the hierarchical order of all creatures in nature, and the specific forms of this order were organically related, and hence adapted the one to the other.[3]

It is to be noted in conclusion that once this Aristotelian philosophy of science is accepted all the traditional medieval arguments for the existence of God become valid. It is only when these arguments have content read into them in terms of the assumptions of modern science and philosophy that they become untenable. It is to be noted also that the Aristotelians conceived of cultural institutions and the good church and the good state in terms of this hierarchical teleological order as defined by the final cause of this Aristotelian philosophy of science. In short, for Aristotle and for the Thomistic Roman Catholic culture which has followed him, the philosophy of culture is identical with the philosophy of nature, and the final cause of nature, the Unmoved Mover, is also the final cause of the good society.[4]

THE MODERN FRENCH AND ANGLO-AMERICAN CONCEPTION OF EVOLUTION

The traditional modern conception of evolution in cultures west of the Rhine is connected with the names of Darwin, Spencer, and Comte. All three differ most fundamentally from Aristotle.

Darwin tells us that the more he reflected upon the empirical evidence the more the fact of adaptation presented the fundamental problem for him. This fact would hardly have given rise to a problem had he come to the empirical evidence from the standpoint of the Aristotelian philosophy of science. Obviously evidence must have appeared previous to Darwin's reflections which forced him to approach the natural history data of biology with scientific assumptions which made the fact of adaptation an enigma. This evidence is not difficult to discover. It appeared in the science of physics with Galilei's analysis of the motion of the projectile[5] and with the new science of mechanics deductively formulated by Newton which was required as a generalization of the new concept of force necessitated by Galilei's analysis.

This new physics entailed a thoroughgoing repudiation of the Aristotelian physics and philosophy of science. So far as nature is concerned, all final causes were repudiated. Once the positions and momenta of the masses of a given system were known, the final state of the system was determined necessarily according to the principle of mechanical causation. Thus with one stroke the Aristotelian doctrine of potentiality and of forms by privation was repudiated and with it the entire Aristotelian theory of irreducible formal causes.

Descartes noted that since biological organisms, including the bodies of men, are made of material substances therefore biological causation must be mechanistic also. Consequently, the Aristotelian account of biological organization and adaptation could no longer be regarded as the correct scientific analysis of these facts. Hence Darwin's problem.

Galilei indicated one other consequence of the new physics which was devastating with respect to the Aristotelian philosophy of science. Foreseeing the kinetic theory of heat and gases, he noted that the sensation of hotness is not an intrinsic predicate or property of the objects of scientific knowledge. These objects as conceived by modern physics possess only shape, extension, inertia, and so forth. The sensuous qualities, such as warmth, color, fragrance, etc., as Galilei emphasized, do not belong to the object of knowledge and would completely vanish were the observer removed.[6] Newton went a step further, emphasizing that not merely sensed qualities but even the sensed spatial and temporal relations between them are appearances also and not to be confused with the objective real and mathematical space in which the masses of physics are located.[7]

This had the effect of returning Western science to the Democritean and Platonic philosophy of science with its epistemological distinction between nature as sensed and nature as conceived in one's experimentally verified, deductively formulated, and mathematically expressed scientific theory. As a consequence, the sensed processes of nature are no longer taken at their face value, since sensed temporal becoming is regarded as appearance rather than reality. In fact the tendency is to regard all observed instances of temporal change as the mere effects upon the observer of the motion of chemical and physical entities, the intrinsic properties of which do not change. Thus in modern science there is a sense in which temporal changes in nature are regarded as less ultimate scientifically than was the case with them in the science and philosophy of Aristotle.

Furthermore, because of the mechanistic character of Newton's physics, the observed organization of living things and the apparently organic adaptation of living creatures to their environment tended to be regarded as the mere effects of underlying kinetic physical-chemical processes, rather than to be treated as irreducible formal causal principles after the manner of Aristotle. Need one wonder therefore that Darwin, immersed as he was in the assumptions of modern science, should find the fact of adaptation between the living organism and its natural environment presenting him with a problem?

Even so, his approach to its solution was quite independent of the modern theory of physics and chemistry. His conclusions rested solely upon biology proper and the approach of the natural historian to its subject matter by means of the Aristotelian scientific methods of observation, description, and classification. It was Darwin's use of the scientific methods of the Aristotelians in their own natural history type of biology and science which made the departure of modern biology from the Aristotelian conception of evolution so decisive.

Nothing could be more neutral theoretically than the report of Darwin's first investigations as recorded in his *Voyage of the Beagle.* There is scarcely a hint from one end of the volume to the other of the new theoretical conclusions which Darwin is later to draw from the facts which it contains. In the introduction to his *Origin of Species,* Darwin tells us that, although on his return home from the voyage of the Beagle in 1837 reflection upon the facts gathered suggested that these facts "seemed to throw some light on the origin of species," it was only after five years of further work that he allowed himself to "speculate on the subject." He tells us also that it was not until 1844 that he sketched out his conclusions. Among these conclusions reached in 1844 was the proposition "Species are not immutable." The Aristotelian conception of immortal organic forms had been rejected. Furthermore, a different positive conception of evolution had been put in its place.

This positive theory can be best understood by pursuing the steps which led Darwin to it. Even before the voyage of the Beagle, Darwin had read Sir Charles Lyell's *Principles of Geology.* From this work he obtained the conception, basic to all his future thinking, of how vast changes are brought about by gradual natural processes. The voyage of the Beagle made him aware, through the fossil remains which he observed, of the need of classifying living creatures with respect to the geological period in time at which they lived on the surface of the earth. This voyage also acquainted him with many species in neighboring areas with slight differences between them. These were the facts which "seemed to throw some light on the origin of species." In 1838 he read Malthus who underlined the point that "many more individuals of each species are born than can possibly survive." By putting this fact together with the previously noted fact of closely related species and the additional well-known fact of the varieties within a given species, Darwin had at hand a suggestion of the mechanism of the origin of species. As he expressed it, he had a hypothesis upon which to work. The succeeding years up to the publication of the *Origin of Species* in 1859 were concerned with the establishment of this hypothesis.

The hypothesis in its most general form involved what Darwin termed a "new view" of the classification of living organisms. The essential point in the novelty consisted in the introduction of time within the relatedness of the biological forms themselves. In the Aristotelian classification temporal relatedness was not intrinsic to the formal cause itself. As we have previously noted, the hierarchical order joining species to genera in the Aristotelian biology was in itself timeless and immortal, subsisting with the logical immortality characteristic of logical universals. Time for Aristotle referred only to the actualization of the formal order in otherwise unformed matter. For Darwin, on the other hand, the relation between the form of one species and that of another was a temporal relation. As he put at the end of the *Origin of Species,* "a natural arrangement must be genealogical." Thus not merely the actualization of the form in matter but also the origin of the form as form was a temporal event.

This entailed that the forms or properties defining a given species and the adaptation of that form to its environment is effect rather than cause. The question then arose concerning the mechanism by which this effect is produced.

The concept which provided the basis for the understanding of this mechanism was the concept of descent. All previous investigators including Aristotle had recognized the role of this concept with respect to the relation between individuals of different generations in the same family or species. The joining of different species by a temporal relation was tantamount to a generalization of the concept of descent so that it applied to the relation between species as well as to the relations between generations of individuals within a given species. Conversely, this generalization of the notion of descent leads to the doctrine of "the common parentage of allied forms."

It remained to specify how within this conception new species arise. Darwin finds his first basic clue in the notion of slight variations. That any given species has many varieties is well known. Darwin assumes that varieties can be "incipient species." Conversely, he holds that "each species first existed as a variety." Beside this fact of variability he sets what he terms often the powerful "force of inheritance." All this being accepted, it remains merely to find a factor which selects from the possible varieties one which the powerful force of heredity will perpetuate.

Domestic breeding shows Darwin how varieties are turned into species by man. The "principle of natural selection" provides the mechanism by means of which this is accomplished by nature, especially when it is noted, following Malthus, that more organisms are produced than can actually survive in the face of the available food supply. The latter fact insures an inescapable "struggle for existence." In this struggle any organism possessing a variation which permits it to take advantage of resources in the environment of which other organisms in the same species cannot take advantage is automatically selected. Thus very slight differences initially may produce very marked distinctions later between the resultant species. In this manner Darwin arrives at the "theory of descent [of all species from a common parentage] with modification through variation and natural selection." [8]

Note the philosophical consequences. Upon the basis of biological data of the natural history type alone, Darwin is led to the same rejection of irreducible formal and final causes and to the same conception of natural design and adaptation having its basis in purely mechanical causes to which the physicists Galilei and Newton were guided in their studies of the inorganic world. Evolution is to be sure a primary concept. Time exhibits not merely the actualization of form in new material bodies, but also the origin of new forms themselves. In the latter sense time introduces more novelty for the modern biologist than it did for his medieval predecessors. But in another sense time is less significant for the modern than it was for the Aristotelian. This is the case because the product of evolution for Darwin and his successors is the origin of a biological species and the biological adaptation to the environment is a relation which is an effect rather than an ultimate and irreducible formal cause. Moreover, nature in evolution achieves its apparent adaptations and design not positively, guided by a purposeful timeless final cause in the status of form by privation as was the case with Aristotle, but negatively and by indirection and trial and error, wasting countless variations before it finds one which gives its possessor an advantage over its competitors.

Viewed in the light of the entire history of Western science, what Darwin (like his predecessors Galilei and Newton) did was to take the philosophy of Western science back from that of Aristotle or his predecessor Plato to that of the mechanist Democritus. In Greek times the Democritean philosophy of science was worked out for biology by Empedocles. It is not an accident that Empedocles formulated the same two principles of struggle for existence and survival of the fittest by a process of mechanical natural selection which Darwin revived in the nineteenth century.[9] Such considerations indicate that the scientific theories of a given age, for all their differences, are of a piece, and that when certain basic premises in the philosophy of science are accepted the logical consequences of those premises are likely to make their appearance also.

Only in one respect is the philosophy of science of Darwin's biology different from that of Democritus and Empedocles or that of Galilei's and Newton's modern mechanics. Nowhere does Darwin draw the distinction insisted upon by Democritus, Galilei, and Newton between nature as sensed and nature as conceived in one's scientific theory. This distinction is, however, implicit in the Darwinian theory that the observed order or design and adaptation in nature cannot be taken at their face value as Aristotelian formal causes or primary irreducible facts. Since the time of Darwin, however, this epistemological distinction between natural processes as observed and these same processes as scientifically understood has become more explicit even for biology. This has occurred with the atomistic and physical-chemical analyses of living creatures[10] and with the clearer conception of the source of the variations upon which Darwin's powerful "force of heredity" operates. Now it is generally accepted that any variations which are significant in heredity must arise in transformations or mutations of the genes of the cells. This amendment or complement of the Darwinian theory, however, in no way changes the general Darwinian philosophy. It merely makes more explicit than was the case with Darwin, the details of the mechanism by means of which nature achieves its ends without recourse to irreducible formal or final causes.[11]

Such is the contrast between the French and Anglo-American modern theory of evolution and the premodern Aristotelian theory. It remains to note the characteristic of this modern conception, continuously emphasized by Darwin, which puts it in contrast with the theory of evolution of the German Hegelians and their successors, the Russian Marxists. This factor the Russian Bolshevik Marxists have termed "gradualism."

More perhaps than any other element in his entire doctrine, this notion dominated Darwin's thought. This was the key idea which he acquired from the reading of Lyell's *Principles of Geology.* It appeared in his *Voyage of the Beagle* in connection with his notation of slight differences between varieties and between species. It appears again at the beginning of the *Origin of Species,* with its emphasis upon slight variations, and in the summary at the end of the volume, where he refers to "the principle of successive slight variations." Again and again, in the final chapter of this work, Darwin speaks of "the accumulation of innumerable slight variations" and of "gradations." He writes,

Nothing at first can appear more difficult to believe than that the more complex organs and instincts have been perfected, not by means superior to, though analogous with, human reason, but by the accumulation of innumerable slight variations, . . . It is, no doubt, extremely difficult even to conjecture by what gradations many structures have been perfected . . . ; but we see so many strange gradations in nature, that we ought to be extremely cautious in saying that any organ or instinct, or any whole structure, could not have arrived at its present state by many graduated steps.

Again, a few pages later, "According to the theory of natural selection an interminable number of intermediate forms must have existed, linking together all the species in each group by gradations as fine as our existing varieties." Again: "If we allowed long enough intervals of time, geology plainly declares that species have all changed; and they have changed in the manner required by the theory, for they have changed slowly and in a graduated manner." Darwin ends his classic volume by noting that Mr. Herbert Spencer has securely based psychology, and thereby indirectly sociology, on similar gradual evolutionary changes. Thus the way is prepared by Spencer for the extension of the French and Anglo-American modern concept of evolution from nature to culture. It is to be noted, therefore, that with Darwin and Spencer as with Aristotle the character of evolutionary change in cultural institutions is identical with its character in the systems of nature.

THE MODERN GERMAN AND RUSSIAN
CONCEPT OF EVOLUTION

It is the emphasis upon gradual variations which places the modern French and Anglo-American conception of evolution in sharp contrast with that of the modern Germans and the contemporary Russians. The source of this difference must now concern us.

The primary thing to keep in mind about the cultural institutions of the French and Anglo-American modern world is that so far as they have been modern they have had their roots in political, religious, and economic theories which found their unity in pre-Kantian modern philosophy, and more particularly in that branch of pre-Kantian modern philosophy known as British empiricism. German and Russian cultural institutions on the other hand so far as they have been modern have found the philosophical foundations of their economic, political, and social ideologies in post-Kantian philosophy.[12]

The Germanic and Russian conception of evolution is no exception to this rule. Its connection with the post-Kantian philosophy of Hegel is even more obvious and explicit than is the connection of the Darwinian theory of evolution with the philosophy of science of Galilei and Newton and Locke. Consequently, it is in post-Kantian philosophy and the considerations which led informed modern minds to accept it that we must look for the meaning and the grounds of the Hegelian and Marxist theory of evolution.

The grounds were made evident by the British empirical philosophers themselves when they pursued the philosophy of science designated by Galilei and Newton to its complete logical consequences. The specific steps in this pursuit are too technical and numerous to be repeated here.[13] Suffice it to say that the theory of the relation between Newton's physical objects in public mathematical space and time and his sense qualities in sensed space and time, as specified by Galilei and Newton, entailed the theory of ideas of John Locke, and this theory in turn entailed the philosophy of Hume. But the latter philosophy, as Hume made evident and as Kant realized upon his reading of Hume, was quite incapable of providing the concepts actually present in mathematics and in Newton's mathematical physics, in both of which Kant was most proficient.[14]

Hume made it evident that Locke's theory of ideas has the consequence of making it necessary to define every concept in every branch of science and every department of human experience in terms of nothing but sense data and their sensed associations. Upon this basis Newton's public mathematical space and time should not exist since, as Newton pointed out at the beginning of his *Principia,* this space and time are quite different from, and are not to be confused with, sensed space and time. Physics furthermore uses a concept of causality with respect to which a specification of the positions and momenta of the masses of a system enables one with the assumption of the laws of Newton's physics to deduce logically or mathematically the future state of that system. Locke's theory of ideas, on the other hand, as Hume made evident, restricts the notion of causality to nothing more than a theoretically unjustified hope that successive contiguous sense qualities which have been sensed together in the past will occur together in the future. Mathematicians saw also that the technical concepts of the differential calculus cannot be defined in terms of blues, greens, reds, flavors, and other sense qualities as Locke's theory of ideas would entail. It was considerations such as these from the sciences of mathematics and mathematical physics which made evident the inadequacy of the modern British empirical philosophy, and which led Kant to the formulation of a different philosophy which would provide within itself the ideas or meanings sufficient to give the concepts of mathematics, mathematical space and time, and causality as required by Newton's mathematical physics.[15]

This new modern philosophy of science appeared in Kant's *Critique of Pure Reason.* The positive content of this critique need not concern us here, since it throws no light upon the concept of evolution with which our inquiry is concerned. It is only in what the philosophy of Kant's *Critique of Pure Reason* cannot provide, that is, in its negative consequences, that it is relevant to our purposes.

These negative consequences were noted by Kant. Newton's mechanics had exhibited nature as thoroughly mechanistic and deterministic in character. This followed, as Laplace emphasized, because of the concept of causality in Newtonian physics which we have just noted. With Kant's philosophy of science and his *Critique of Pure Reason* this absolute determinism and necessity was extended from the object of scientific knowledge to the scientist himself as the knower of that knowledge. This happened in Kant's philosophy of science because in order to account for Newton's mathematical space and time and the type of causality in Newtonian physics, none of which is given through the senses, Kant had located the source of these nonempirical factors in scientific knowledge in the character of the knower himself. Thus, according to Kant's philosophy of science, man as knower brought to the data of sense the forms of sensibility of mathematical space and time and the categories of the understanding, among which causality in the sense in which it is used in Newton's physics was one. Those forms and categories had, according to Kant, the attributes of universality and necessity. This meant that man had no choice with respect to the use of them. Thus, in Kant's philosophy of science, man as knower became as absolutely determined and dominated by necessity as was nature, the object of knowledge.

This entailed that man himself and anything else which he knows by empirical scientific and theoretical a priori methods is dominated completely by necessity. Thus within the philosophy of science as it bears either on the scientist as knower or the subject matter known there was for Kant no meaning whatever in human freedom. Furthermore, as Kant made evident, there was also no meaning nor valid argument for any of the concepts of religion.

Consequently, after Kant had completed his philosophy of science, a major question remained—what is the philosophical basis of morality and religion? One might have supposed at this point that, since Kant found certain factors in human experience such as morality and religion for which his philosophy of the *Critique of Pure Reason* could not account, he would conclude that therefore there must be something wrong with this philosophy. This, however, was not Kant's procedure. He took the correctness of his philosophy of science for granted with respect both to the nature of the knowing self and the nature of the known object. No alternative therefore remained but for Kant, for the first time in Western history, to ground morality, religion, and the humanities including the social sciences on a philosophy quite other than the philosophy of natural science. Thus a gulf between one's philosophy of moral, religious, and other cultural values and one's philosophy of scientific knowledge was introduced into the modern world to create a conflict and a demoralization from which it is yet to recover.

But our purpose is to find the meaning and the grounds of the post-Kantian conception of evolution. To this end we must take Kant's conception of the philosophy of science and his different philosophy of the humanities for granted.

His philosophy of the humanities started with the concept of freedom, a concept which his philosophy of natural science did not provide. The moral life, with its experiences of choice and especially of remorse, is meaningless if everything is absolutely determined. Remorse is an illusion unless the act which produced it was such that one was free initially to have chosen a different act. Since freedom has no basis in Kant's philosophy of mathematical natural science, its source must be allowed for in a moral philosophy *sui generis*. This autonomous moral philosophy Kant outlined in his *Critique of Practical Reason*. The essence of its thesis is expressed by saying that it is not the empirically tested hypotheses of scientific reason but the immediate demands of practical action which provide the grounds for moral conduct. Religion and the social sciences, termed Geisteswissenschaften, have the same practical basis. Why these practical demands can be separated from the nature of man and his universe as designated by the empirically verified hypotheses of the philosophy of natural science, Kant never made clear.

But this absolute dichotomy between moral philosophy and natural philosophy presented a difficulty. If the modern man's scientific philosophy tells him that he is governed by complete necessity, whereas his moral philosophy tells him that he is rooted in freedom, which is he to believe? In other words, what is the relation between the moral philosophy of Kant's *Critique of Practical Reason* and the natural philosophy of his *Critique of Pure Reason*? To leave them both on the same level is to leave the modern man in conflict with himself with respect to the diverse claims and attractions of the scientific and moral components of his nature. Clearly, once both are accepted, this conflict can be resolved only by reducing the one to the other.

This reduction was achieved by Fichte in terms of the primacy of the practical reason. With him it became not merely the philosophical ground of morality, religion, and cultural institutions but also of scientific knowledge. Even nature itself and the natural scientists' theories of nature are consequences of the logical demands of the morally free ego. Thus it happened with Fichte that the philosophy underlying cultural institutions and their evolution became prior to and the criterion of the philosophy of nature and of evolution in nature. This was the case even though the concept of evolution was merely suggested in his later works and not made articulate by Fichte. It remained for Hegel to develop this latent element in the Fichtean philosophy.

Fichte did, however, first make articulate the law which must govern a theory of evolution which is grounded in such post-Kantian philosophical premises. The manner in which this came about must now concern us.

Fichte began with the concept of freedom at the basis of Kant's moral philosophy. Freedom, Kant emphasized, implies the existence of the free moral individual. Fichte noted, however, following Hume, that this notion of a substantial moral ego is not given empirically. It can be known only by hypothesis. This means that it must be posited. What justifies this positing, according to Fichte, is not empirical scientific knowledge but the demands of the moral life grounded in freedom. But morality, Fichte said, is meaningless without opposition. A morality which could achieve itself by merely being chosen by the free moral ego would be too easy to be real. Thus the moral life presupposes not merely the self but also the negating of that self to provide the opposition sufficient to make the actual moral life of man meaningful. This negate of the self, or nonego, Fichte identified with nature. Thus the presuppositions of the moral life guarantee not merely moral philosophy but also natural philosophy. In this manner, the gulf between scientific knowledge and moral philosophy is removed. The former is a mere consequence of the demands of the latter.

The result is that reality is conceived as made up of two components, the one the moral agent, the other nature. These two components, furthermore, are related by the relation of negation. Nature is the negating of man, the moral ego. Thus in the heart of reality there is an opposition between two basic components, the ego and the nonego. Since everything else in reality is an expression of these two components, this relationship can be generalized into a law which must hold for all things. When thus generalized it is called the relation between a thesis and its antithesis.

But if one stopped at this point one would be left with another dualism. Furthermore, Fichte remembers that both the moral ego and nature are not given but are posited. The source of this positing cannot be the individual man since man is the end product of the positing, not its origin. Hence there must be a superpositor other than man the moral ego and the latter's negate nature. This superpositor Fichte calls the Absolute. Thus Fichte affirms that the moral life presupposes not merely the moral ego and its antithesis nature, but also the Absolute positor or will. He emphasizes, because of the fact that the moral ego is an end product of the positing rather than its author, that he would be guilty of a contradiction if he located the source of the antithesis between the moral ego and nature in the free will of the moral ego rather than in the free will of the Absolute ego.[16]

But in the Absolute ego reality exhibits itself as having a more basic and underlying unity from which the antithesis between the ego and nature is derived, which for this very reason próvides a synthesis by means of which the dualism between the human moral ego and nature can be removed.

It appears, therefore, that reality is to be conceived to be grounded in freedom, but in the freedom of the will of the Absolute rather than in the freedom of the will of the moral human individual. This point is very important because it shows how the post-Kantian moral philosophy which began with the notion of the freedom of the human individual ended with his enslavement in the will of the Absolute.

It follows also from this Fichtean analysis that reality is governed by an explicit logic of development: the logic of thesis negated by antithesis and then because of the all-embracing unity of the Absolute reconciled in a higher synthesis. This law is termed the logic of dialectic. Since this dialectic governs the coming of the Absolute consciousness to self-consciousness, and since according to the philosophy of Kant and his successors all the content of human knowledge whether in nature or culture has to conform to the forms which the knowing consciousness brings to the empirical data of consciousness, it follows that everything known, whether in culture or nature, must evolve according to the dialectical law of thesis, antithesis, and synthesis, the latter synthesis in turn becoming a new thesis which gives rise to its antithesis, thereby leading on to a higher synthesis.

It remained merely for Hegel to work out this dialectical theory of evolution governed, not by gradualism and slight variations, but by sharp negations and antitheses, in terms of the content of the scientific knowledge of nature and the content of the historian's empirical knowledge of culture. Since everything in both realms must conform to this dialectical law, and since the law by its very nature requires time for its operation, evolution becomes the very essence of reality in both fields. Furthermore, since this law is ultimate and everything is governed by it, human cultural institutions and personal knowledge being but the consequences of the consciousness of the Absolute will coming to self-consciousness as governed by this law, the human freedom with which the Kantian and Fichtean moral philosophy began turns out in the end to be the mere consequence of the divine determinism and no alternative remains but to identify the ideal in culture with the historical dialectical evolution of the actual.[17] Hence Hegel's epistemological doctrine of the concrete universal and his ontological dictum that the ideal is the real and the real is the ideal.

The Hegelian philosophy has of course many further ramifications. However, for the purposes of this inquiry these further subtleties need not concern us. Nor need we spend time upon the marked differences between the Marxian materialistic content and the Hegelian idealistic content of the dialectical historical process. The important point is that for both the traditional modern Hegelian Germans and the contemporary Russian Communists, reality is basically historical and evolutionary in character and the evolutionary process is governed by the Hegelian dialectical law of thesis, antithesis, and synthesis. Moreover, for both, the law governing the evolution of cultural institutions is identical with the law determining the natural processes in organic and inorganic nature.

The importance of the distinction between the Hegelian and Marxian dialectical evolution and the Darwinian evolution by gradual slight variations can hardly be overemphasized. Once the Hegelian and Marxian identification of the ideal for culture with the historically actual is admitted, the consequence immediately follows that the good for society can be achieved only by the abrupt and sharp negation of traditional ideas of the good and by the repudiation of the cultural institutions constructed in terms of the traditional ideals. In short, revolution rather than gradual evolution is necessary for the achieving of the good state.

Nowhere does this fact exhibit itself more dramatically than in the Russian Revolution with its issue between the Mensheviks and the Bolsheviks. Both the Mensheviks and the Bolsheviks were Communists. Their aim was to achieve a socialistic state. The Mensheviks were, however, for the achievement of socialism by gradual means and by compromises and associations with the middle-class democrats. The Bolsheviks, on the other hand, insisted upon the necessity of revolution and forbade all compromise with the middle-class democrats on the ground that the good state could be achieved only by completely negating the thesis for which the middle-class democracy, grounded in the pre-Kantian British empirical philosophy, stands.

According to the Bolsheviks, the Mensheviks were in error because their conception of the way in which the good state is to be achieved was grounded in a false theory of evolution. Lenin, in *The Teachings of Karl Marx,* put the matter as follows:

In our times, the idea of development, of evolution, has almost fully penetrated social consciousness, but it has done so in other ways, not through Hegel's philosophy. Still, the same idea, as formulated by Marx and Engels on the basis of Hegel's philosophy, is much more comprehensive, much more abundant in content, than the current theory [i.e., Darwin's] of evolution. A development that repeats, as it were, in spirals, not in a straight line; a development in leaps and bounds, catastrophes, revolutions; . . . ; inner impulses for development, imparted by the contradiction, the conflict of different forces and tendencies reacting on a given body or inside a given phenomenon or within a given society; . . . —such are some of the features of dialectics as a doctrine of evolution more full of meaning than the current one.

This makes it clear why the Hegelian dialectical philosophy of history is basic to the entire Bolshevik Communist theory.

For both Marx and Engels, were a choice necessary, it was more important that one should accept the Hegelian dialectical theory of evolution than that one should accept the Feuerbachian and Marxian materialistic theory of the content of this evolutionary process. That this is so is shown by Marx and Engels' attack upon the Bauer brothers who followed Feuerbach in the latter's materialism but who were ignoring Hegel's dialectical theory of evolution in their argument for the achievement of the socialistic state by gradual nonrevolutionary means.

CONCLUSIONS

What conclusions are to be drawn from the three major conceptions of evolution of the Western world which have been analyzed?

One point of agreement is to be noted. Each affirms that the law governing the evolution of cultural institutions is identical with the law governing the evolution of nature's systems. An examination of the respective merits of each of the three theories of evolution shows that this common assumption of the identity of social and natural evolution must be repudiated. These respective merits must now concern us.

The key idea in the Aristotelian conception of evolution was its concept of purpose as embodied in its notion of the final cause. The point at which this Aristotelian theory is sound appears in connection with the control of the political, economic, and religious ideologies of men over their conduct.

The Declaration of Independence is an example of such an ideology. The Constitution of the United States is another example. The Marxian philosophy is a third. The democratic ideology introduced into Mexico through the teachings of Voltaire and the French Encyclopedists at the end of the eighteenth century is a fourth. Each one of these ideologies became accepted by a majority of the people in certain communities and forthwith proceeded to function as the final cause which directed their subsequent behavior in founding their respective political and economic institutions. In all these instances we find social processes arriving at a preaffirmed end, not indirectly and mechanically by a wasteful process of trial and error working upon slight variations and governed by a mechanical principle of natural selection, but directly as guided by the specific end which the ideology in question defines.

For example, the democratic ideology of Voltaire and the French Encyclopedists entered Mexico in the eighteenth century and became accepted as a working ideal in the first Mexican Revolution of 1810. The next sixty-five years were occupied in actualizing this ideal in the social institutions of the country and in the customs of its inhabitants. The same is true of the Bolshevik Communist ideology in twentieth-century Russia. The full revolution of the proletariat was completed in 1918. None of the leaders of the Communist state believe, however, that the Communist theory of the sound economic order and the good political order was fully actualized in fact at that time. The revolution insured merely that the Bolshevik Communist theory of the good society was to become the final cause at which the leaders of the state would aim. The actual embodiment of this economic and political order in *de facto* institutions would require several five-year plans. Thus, in connection with the evolution of cultural institutions, the Aristotelian conception of evolution contains an empirically verifiable truth.

It is to be noted however that even for cultural evolution the Aristotelian conception holds only for that portion of the cultural process in which a given people in a given geographical area are governed by a constant social ideology. It will be recalled that it was of the essence of the Aristotelian conception of evolution that there is but one final cause and that this final cause is timeless. Hence it follows on the Aristotelian theory, as the Roman Catholic Church actually maintains, that there should be but one social ideology at all times for all men.

That this is not the case the history of social institutions in the same geographical part of the world, as well as the differences in social ideologies in different parts of the world at the same instant of time, clearly show. The culture of Mexico, for example, has been dominated since 1500 by at least six different and for the most part mutually contradictory cultural ideals.[18] In 1500 the social ideology was purely Indian in origin. It involved a very remarkable internally related system of scientific, religious, social, and aesthetic values. With the triumph of the Spaniards under Cortez in 1521 the hierarchical, monarchical, aristocratic, theocentric ideology of Roman Catholic Spain became the final cause determining the specific character of the cultural institutions of Mexico for the next 289 years. This was succeeded in the revolution of 1810 by the previously mentioned democratic idea of the good society derived from Voltaire and the French Encyclopedists. The latter ideology in turn was replaced by the scientific positivism of Comte in the Diaz dictatorship which came to power around 1870.[19] This was succeeded by a return to the democratic conception of the final cause governing good social behavior in the second democratic revolution of 1910. This in turn was superseded by the combination of political democracy and economic communism expressed in the former Rockefeller Center fresco of Diego Rivera. Apart from this conception the behavior of the Cárdenas government in Mexico in the third decade of this century and the negotiations between the foreign ministers of Mexico and the secretaries of state of the United States concerning foreign oil concessions in Mexico cannot be understood. This historical sequence of different and conflicting political ideologies in Mexico shows conclusively that social and cultural evolution is not governed, as the Aristotelian conception of evolution affirms, by a single timeless final cause.

The differences in political ideologies in the United States, Russia, India, Spain, and Great Britain at the present moment show conclusively also that at a given instant of the historical process the final causes of peoples and cultures in different parts of the world, as expressed in their economic, political, and religious ideologies, are not identical.

It appears, therefore, that two conclusions can be drawn with respect to the Aristotelian conception of evolution. First, its emphasis upon purposeful final causation is correct for the development of cultural institutions within any historical period which for a given people is dominated by one constant cultural ideology. Second, the Aristotelian conception of one timeless final cause is, however, incorrect for the evolution of social institutions in its entirety.

When we come to the latter evolution it is the Hegelian rather than either the Aristotelian or the Darwinian theory of evolution which is the most illuminating. Our listing of the six major different, and often conflicting, ideologies of Mexico since 1500 makes this clear. Not only has there been the sequence of ideologies which the dialectical theory of evolution in either its Hegelian or its Marxian form affirms, but each one of these ideologies is brought in not by slow gradual minute changes but by abrupt revolution. Each transformation in Mexico from one ideology to another was accompanied by a revolution. But this phenomenon is not peculiar to Mexico. The ideology which has dominated the culture of the United States was confirmed by the Revolution of 1776. The Menshevik socialistic-democratic ideology replaced the old tsarist medieval conception of the good state in the Russian Revolution of 1917. And similarly the Bolshevik Revolution of the proletariat pushed aside the Menshevik socialistic-democratic ideology in the Russian Revolution of 1918. Likewise the British House of Commons began the wresting of political sovereignty from the king in the Puritan revolution of 1640. It appears, therefore, that when we consider the evolution of social and cultural institutions through lengthy periods of time, it is neither the Aristotelian nor the French and Anglo-American Darwinian but the Hegelian revolutionary conception governed by the logic of negation which is the correct one in occidental culture.

When we turn to nature, Darwin, rather than either Aristotle or Hegel, comes into his own. All the evidence of modern physics, together with both Darwinian and Mendelian biology, combine to negate the validity of the Aristotelian doctrine of nature's processes governed by a single timeless final cause. But the Hegelian and Marxian dialectical theory is equally untenable with respect to nature. In none of the scientifically verified theories of nature of the modern world is nature itself designated as obeying the dialectical law of thesis, antithesis, and synthesis.

One factor, however, in natural science does obey such a law. This factor exhibits itself in the successive theories of nature to which the scientist is led. Any one of these theories does negate its predecessor. For example, Einstein's special theory of relativity negates the principle of the addition and subtraction of velocities referring to different Galilean frames of reference which was valid in Newton's physics. Newton's physics negated the definition of force in Aristotle's physics. Aristotle's physics in turn negated the principle of indivisibles with magnitude which was affirmed by the previous science of both Democritus and Plato. The invariant Riemannian space-time metric of Einstein's general theory of relativity likewise involves postulates which negate the basic assumptions of the classical Euclidean geometry of space. Thus, whereas nature itself does not construct itself first on Aristotelian principles and then negate these principles in a revolution to construct itself on Newtonian principles, after the manner of evolution in culture, the evolution of the natural scientists' *theories* of nature do pass through these abrupt revolutions governed by the logic of negation. Thus Hegel and Marx are erroneous with respect to the application of the dialectical logic of negation to the evolution of nature itself, but correct, as Émile Meyerson[20] has pointed out, with respect to the physicists' theories about nature.

It appears, therefore, that each of the three major Western conceptions of evolution—Aristotle's, Darwin's, and Hegel's—has something to say for itself. Aristotle's conception is incorrect for nature but correct for culture within a given brief period of cultural history when the evolution of the cultural institutions of a given people is dominated by a constant ideology. The development of the cultural institutions of the United States since 1776 under the guidance of the ideology defined by its Declaration of Independence and its Constitution is an example. The Darwinian conception of evolution, even as amended by the Mendelian theory, is correct for nature but incorrect for culture, whether culture be considered over the whole expanse of history or over the shorter periods when it is dominated by a constant ideology. The Hegelian and Marxian revolutionary dialectical theory of evolution is incorrect for nature and for those briefer periods of a specific culture when it is dominated by a constant ideology, but correct (a) for Western culture over the whole range of its history and (b) for Western scientific theories about nature. These considerations enable us to understand in a positive way why the traditional assumption, held in common by Aristotle, Darwin, and Hegel, to the effect that the law of the evolution of nature is identical with the law for the evolution of culture, must be rejected.

The problem immediately arises: what is the relation between the revolutionary dialectical evolution of culture dominated by the logic of negation and the more gradual continuous Darwinian evolution of nature grounded in the logic of identity? The clue to the answer to this question is already present in the two factors previously noted with respect to which the Hegelian dialectical type of evolution is valid. These two factors are the evolution of Western cultural institutions when considered over the full range of their history, and the evolution of the natural scientists' *theories* about nature.

It happens that the validity of the Hegelian theory of evolution in these two apparently different places is not an accident. For in point of fact the shift from one cultural ideology to another in the history of Western civilization is essentially connected with the similar shift from one philosophy of science to another in the successive Western scientific theories concerning nature.

This essential connection between Western ideas of the good for culture and Western scientific theories of the true for nature, is tremendously important. It provides the desperately needed solution for the major problem of the contemporary world divided by its conflicting ideologies. Some method [21] must be found for determining, in a manner valid for all, the particular existing or new ideology to succeed the many present conflicting doctrines.

The reason for this essential connection between the good ideology for culture and the true scientific theory or philosophy of science for nature will reveal itself if we ask the question to which our evidence has led us—why does the Hegelian type of evolution with its logic of negation apply both to the evolution of Western cultural institutions over the long range and also to the evolution of the scientists' theories about nature? An examination of the relation between the specific cultural ideology which has dominated the Western world at a given period of its history and the scientists' theory of nature which has dominated scientific thought at that same period or at a slightly earlier period, provides an answer to this question.

Consider the dominant ideology of the premodern Western world. It is well known that in educational policy, political theory, and religious doctrine it was defined by St. Thomas Aquinas. It is equally well known that St. Thomas identifies the human soul and God the Father in Roman Catholic religious doctrine with the form of the living body and the final cause of nature, or Unmoved Mover, in Aristotle's metaphysics. But there is not a concept in Aristotle's metaphysics which does not appear in his earlier work, the *Physics.* Thus St. Thomas' philosophy of the good for culture was identical with the medieval scientists' philosophy of the true for nature. In similar fashion, Lucretius' philosophy of the good for the humanities was identified with the Democritean philosophy of science for nature. Likewise, the Augustinian and Platonic philosophy of the divine and the good for the humanities, which was so different from that of Aristotle and the later St. Thomas as to give rise to the sharp and bitter debates between William of Champeaux and Abelard, was identical with the philosophy of natural science of Plato's Academy with its sharp non-Aristotelian distinction between the sense world and the real world and its threefold distinction between "sensibles," "mathematicals," and "ideas."

In fact, it was Socrates and Plato, in the middle books of the *Republic,* who first specified this identity of the philosophy of the good for culture with the empirically verified philosophy of science for nature, as the correct method of escaping the sophistry and relativism of philosophies of the humanities which are grounded autonomously in the humanities. Humanistically grounded philosophies of the good, as Plato and Socrates saw, beg the point at issue. The philosophy of the humanities cannot be based on the humanities because one's inspected, humanistic values and one's cultural institutions are, in considerable part at least, reflections of one's philosophy. Thus, instead of philosophy being grounded in the humanities, the humanities, when their criterion of the good is nonsophistic and noncircular in its basis, are grounded in a philosophy which has its justification in a subject matter other than that of the humanities.

This subject matter, as both Socrates and Plato saw, is to be found in nature when nature is approached by the methods of observation, hypothesis, and the deductively formulated theory of Western science, and when these scientifically verified hypotheses are analyzed by the philosopher's method of dialectic (which incidentally is nothing but logical analysis) to bring out the primitive ontological and the implicit epistemological assumptions. As Socrates put it in the Seventh Book of the *Republic* (533): "The power of dialectic alone can reveal this [cultural idea of the good], and only to one who is a disciple of the previous sciences." If one turns back a few pages to the place where these "previous sciences" are specified, one discovers that each of these sciences was a mathematical natural science, namely, arithmetic, plane geometry, stereometry, and astronomy. To these sciences and to these alone the philosopher applies dialectic and arrives at the idea of the good, according to Socrates and to Plato.

Socrates and Plato have been as prophetic with respect to what has actually happened in Western civilization as they were correct in their designation of the method for determining the correct idea of the good for culture in a civilization of the Western type. The following considerations make this clear: the first major systematic scientific theory and attendant philosophy of science in the Western world was formulated by Democritus and Leucippus. The idea of the good for the humanities which this philosophy defines appears in the poem *De rerum natura* of the Roman poet Lucretius. This theory of natural science broke down soon after Democritus because of its incapacity to give anything more than an artificial account of the existence of arithmetically incommensurable, geometric magnitudes such as those present in the ratio of the side of a square to its diagonal. As a consequence the Democritean scientific theory and attendant philosophy of science of nature was replaced by that of Plato's Academy.[22] The philosophy of culture and the humanities which this philosophy of nature entails was developed by Socrates and Plato. This philosophy of natural science in turn broke down, even before Plato's death, because of its incapacity to provide the scientific assumptions necessary to validate the mathematical method of exhaustion. Then the postulate of indivisibles with magnitude upon which the Platonic theory of science rested was negated and replaced with the assumptions of the scientific theory of Aristotle.[23] The different idea of the good for the humanities and conception of the divine for religion which this entailed came out in the debates between Abelard and William of Champeaux and in the theology of St. Thomas Aquinas.

So long as scientifically informed men had confidence, as they did up to the time of Galilei, in the Aristotelian theory of nature, the Aristotelian grounded ideology of the good for culture held sway over the minds of Western mankind. With the investigations of Galilei, however, it became evident to the majority of Western scientists, as we have previously noted, that the Aristotelian physics must be negated and that the physics of Galilei and Newton must be accepted in its stead. Immediately it became evident to Galilei, Descartes, and Locke among others that this entailed a repudiation not merely of the Aristotelian and Thomistic theory of the true for nature, but also of the Aristotelian and Thomistic ideology of the good and the divine for culture. It is upon Locke's particular articulation of the philosophy of both man and nature entailed by Newton's physics that in major part the traditional idea of the good in the culture of the United States rests.[24]

Certain developments in the modern world have, however, obscured this essential connection between the good philosophy of culture and one's philosophy of science for nature. There are important reasons for believing that this unfortunate obscurity is the source of the ideological confusions and conflicts and the demoralization of the contemporary Western world with respect to its values and their relation to natural science.

This obscurity was not without its causes. When modern philosophers such as Locke and Leibnitz proceeded to apply the method of dialectic of Socrates and Plato to the hypothesis of Newton's physics to make articulate the cultural idea of the good for the modern world, something novel in the history of Western civilization occurred. Certain elements in the Newtonian physics as formulated by Galilei and Newton led to one philosophy. Other elements led to a different and often contradictory philosophy. This appears in the case of Locke and Leibnitz. Thus the modern man found himself with conflicting ideas of the good for modern culture rather than with a single idea of the good specified by the philosophy of Newtonian physics.

It has been shown elsewhere[25] that what this really meant was that Newtonian physics as formulated by Galilei and Newton was self-contradictory. For certainly a consistent scientific theory cannot give rise to contradictory consequences when its ontological and epistemological assumptions are developed logically. Unfortunately, however, modern philosophers did not interpret the situation in this way. Instead the opinion arose that the differing modern philosophies and their respective different ideas of the good for culture were independent of the philosophy of science.

Furthermore, even within the Lockean philosophical articulation of Newtonian physics contradiction arose. This articulation led to the conception of nature as an aggregate of material substances located in public mathematical space and acting upon an aggregate of mental substances or persons to cause the latter to project back the immediately sensed continuum of colors, sounds, and odors in sensed space and time as mere appearances. This theory however entailed Locke's theory of ideas to the effect that all meanings in the mind refer to nothing but sense data or their sensed associations. Berkeley and Hume had no difficulty in showing that this theory of ideas renders Locke's mental and material substances meaningless and hence nonexistent. Thus the modern man found himself left with the philosophy of Hume, according to which reality is nothing but sense data, their sensed associations, and their sequence. This entailed a quite different idea of the good for politics, religion, and economics than the one derived from the philosophy of Locke.

But Hume's philosophy in turn exhibited itself to informed scientists as wholly inadequate to provide the concepts sufficient to define the technical ideas of mathematics or to meet the theoretical requirements of the mathematical portion of Newton's physics. When Kant made articulate the philosophy which seemed to be required by Newton's physics to take care of its systematic theoretical deductive mathematical character, modern man found himself with another philosophy with its quite different idea of the good for culture. In fact, Kant's philosophy brought in an independent reason for supposing that the philosophy of culture has no connection with the philosophy of nature.

This reason has been indicated above in our consideration of the philosophical origin of the dialectical theory of evolution. When Kant's philosophy of science became formulated it had a character such that it provided no meaning for human freedom and the assumptions necessary to make the moral life meaningful. Thus Kant had no alternative once his philosophy of science was taken for granted but to affirm that moral philosophy and the philosophy of nature are autonomous subjects having no connection the one with the other.

We need hardly wonder, therefore, that the contemporary Western world is dominated by a large number of differing ideas of the good for culture. Unless this situation is corrected, democracy will very soon find itself in Great Britain and the United States as well as in Germany and France without any majority opinion. When this happens, government will fail to function, and Western cultural institutions will crumble because of lack of agreement among the majority of men with respect to the philosophy of culture in terms of which political, economic, and religious organizations are to be constructed and maintained. It is a very serious thing to find oneself living in a Western type of civilization at a time when there are a tremendous number of different and contradictory ideas of the good for culture. This is a far more threatening and dangerous situation than even that created by the discovery of the atomic bomb. It is not merely our technological instruments but also our conflicting humanistic ideals which place us in a desperately precarious situation.

It is exceedingly important, therefore, that we seek out as quickly as possible the error occurring at the very beginning of the modern world which led us, in our passage from its philosophy of science to the attendant philosophy of culture, into the relativistic ideological impasse in which we now find ourselves. Elsewhere this error and its eradication have been indicated.[26] The result seems to be a philosophy of science, verified by the methods of science in a manner which makes it valid for everyone, which at the same time provides a unique and apparently globally adequate philosophy of culture. Thus the classical identification of the philosophy of the good for culture with the philosophy of nature as derived by formal analysis (i.e., dialectic) from the publicly verifiable hypotheses of science, as specified first by Socrates and Plato, is restored.

In any event, this identification of the philosophical criterion of the good for culture with the scientifically verified philosophy of the true for nature enables us to understand why not merely the evolution of cultural institutions but also the evolution of the natural scientists' experimentally verified theories concerning nature undergo the abrupt revolutionary changes in time as specified by the Hegelian dialectic of negation. If one's correct ideology of the good for culture is in part at least defined in terms of one's scientific theory of the experimentally verified for nature, it follows that when in time new scientific evidence forces scientists to negate the postulates of their traditional theory and put at least one postulate which is the antithesis of a traditional one in the new theory, then one's idea of the good for culture must undergo a similar revolution. Hu Shih, the former Chinese Ambassador to the United States, writes in his *Chinese Renaissance* of the unique contributions of Western civilization to the world as follows: "The highly developed scientific method in all its phases of operation and the historic or revolutionary view of humanity . . . I consider the most important contributions of modern philosophy in the Western world." It appears that these two contributions are essentially related.

Dr. Hu's observation implies that Oriental civilization never developed or pursued scientific method and never went through the revolutionary type of evolution characterizing the civilization of the West. Dr. Hu's classic work, *Scientific Methods of Ancient China,* confirms the first point. A comparison of Oriental civilization with Western civilization confirms the second.

Dr. Hu's study shows that the ancient Chinese philosopher Mo Ti had a formulation of the empirical portion of Western scientific methodology. It is quite clear, however, that even Mo Ti never grasped the deductively formulated type of theories of Western scientific procedure.

A consideration of the role of deductively formulated theory in Western scientific method is most relevant to our purpose. It is by this procedure with its attendant scientific method of hypothesis that Western science has been able to establish trustworthy and pragmatically effective knowledge of factors in nature which cannot be directly observed. Because of such procedure the Western scientist has been able to conceive of nature as having a character quite different from what nature exhibits to our senses in observation. Thus Democritus, Plato, Galilei, and Newton, as we have previously noted, drew a sharp distinction between nature as sensed and nature as conceived in our deductively formulated and experimentally verified scientific theories.

But all such theories by their very nature have to be verified indirectly through their deductive consequences. Since this indirect method of verification always commits the logical fallacy of affirming the consequent, any one of these experimentally verified Western scientific theories is never absolutely certain. It is subject to rejection and replacement by a basically antithetical hypothesis with the discovery of new empirical information. Thus it becomes evident that it is in the character of Western scientific methodology and in the hypothetical nature of the type of theory which this methodology confirms that the dialectical evolutionary character of Western scientific theories and the similarly dialectical evolutionary character of Western cultural institutions over the long range have their basis.

These considerations make one other point clear. Although the Hegelians and the Marxists are correct in their theory that cultural evolution is governed by the logic of negation rather than the logic of identity and gradualism, they are quite erroneous in their additional contention that this dialectical evolution is absolutely determined. For the dialectical type of evolution is an effect, as the analysis in the above paragraph indicates, rather than a primary causal principle. *There is nothing in one scientific theory which determines what its successor will be. Furthermore, the logic of negation when applied to a given thesis does not designate a unique antithesis.* For any given cultural ideology involves several basic postulates. This makes it possible to negate a given traditional theory in a large number of different ways, depending upon which particular postulate one chooses to reject. But once this failure of the logic of negation to generate a specific unique antithesis of a given traditional thesis is admitted, then the notion of dialectic *determinism* collapses. The evolution of cultural institutions is not now determined to proceed toward any now ascertainable preordained final synthesis such as the one historically present in Hegel's nineteenth-century Germany or the Marxists' supposedly inevitable classless society. Where culture goes in the future, what its future ideology will be, is a function, in considerable part, of one's philosophy of nature, and this depends upon the unpredictable theories to which scientists are led by hypothesis in order to account for all the empirical data now before them and the new empirical data which later observation and experimentation bring forth.

So much for the character of Western scientific method in its bearing on the evolution of Western cultural institutions. It remains to examine the culture of the Orient with respect to the questions suggested above—whether it exhibits a comparative lack of this sequence of ideological revolutions so characteristic of the historical civilization of the West.

The answer must be, comparatively speaking, in the affirmative. Before the revolution of 1912 the ideology of the culture of China at, say, the end of the nineteenth century A.D. was for the most part identical with its ideology in 660 B.C. To be sure, Chinese historians draw distinctions seemingly analogous with those in the West between the Chinese medieval and the modern world. But these distinctions turn around the difference between Confucianism and Neo-Confucianism. They express differences no more deep going or radical than the difference between the Thomism of St. Thomas Aquinas and the contemporary Neo-Thomism of Professor Maritain. Chinese Neo-Confucianism came no nearer to producing even the suggestion of a revolution in the ideological foundations of Chinese civilization than has Professor Maritain's Neo-Scholasticism to creating an explosion beneath the doctrinal foundations of the Roman Catholic Church.

It will be worth our while to consider briefly the methodological reason why this is the case. It is not unconnected with our previous observation that Oriental civilization never developed nor seriously pursued the theoretical hypothetical type of inquiry of the scientific methods of the West. Instead, as the leaders of Oriental thought continuously inform us, the Oriental mind has grounded its philosophical knowledge and its cultural values in the empirical methods of immediate apprehension or intuition and contemplation. What we apprehend with immediacy is what it is; it is not a postulated hypothesis indirectly verified and subject to change with further information. Thus a culture whose values were grounded in such a methodology of philosophical knowledge would be expected to be devoid of the revolutionary reconstructions in philosophical theory and cultural ideals which characterize the West.

The Oriental emphasis upon intuition calls to mind a more recent theory of evolution in the West, the theory associated with the French philosopher Bergson. The unique methodology in part underlying this Bergsonian theory is that of intuition. Thus in Bergson we have an appearance in the West of the philosophical method underlying the culture of the Orient.

Along with Bergson's theory of evolution there is an accompanying theory termed emergent evolution. The essential thesis underlying this theory affirms that each new product of evolution introduces at least one new primitive assumption. Thus present apparent novelties cannot be deduced from previous constant factors. It is to be pointed out that the portion of experience which lends weight to this doctrine is that portion given with intuition. Sensed water obviously has different properties from sensed hydrogen and oxygen. Thus Lloyd Morgan's and Alexander's doctrine of emergent evolution has an implicit intuitive element in common with Bergson's evolution which is grounded explicitly in intuition.

It is to be pointed out, however, that the sensed eclipse which one inspects today has intuitively given novelties in it which are quite different from the sensed state of nature ten years ago. Yet the eclipse today can be mechanistically deduced from that previous state of astronomical nature. Thus the fact that sensed water is different from sensed hydrogen and oxygen is by no means decisive with respect to the establishment of the theory of emergent evolution.

Nonetheless, there is an element in the Bergsonian and the emergent theories of evolution which is unique and cannot be denied. This is the intuitive element. It will be recalled that the Aristotelian, Darwinian, and Hegelian theories are alike in being exceedingly formal and theoretic in character. Thus they represent the approach to experience with the more theoretical method of Western science, whereas Bergson and the emergent evolutionists represent in part the equally valid and essential approach by pure nontheoretical empiricism and intuition.

Unfortunately, however, both the Bergsonian and the more recent theories of emergent evolution attribute to intuition inferred theoretically known factors which intuition cannot give, thereby completely muddling intuitively known with theoretically designated factors in human and scientific knowledge. The result is neither a correct account of the deliverances of intuition nor an adequate conception of the inferred theoretically known and indirectly verified factors in biological evolution.

Consequently, the problem of clarifying the relation between the more recent theories of evolution of Bergson and Lloyd Morgan and the classical theories of Aristotle, Hegel, and Darwin is that at bottom of exhibiting the relationship of the immediately apprehended or intuitive component in scientific knowledge to the indirectly verified, theoretically designated component. But this is to clarify also the relation between Western civilization which, as the above analysis has shown, has been dominated largely by revolutionary cultural evolution, and traditional Oriental civilization which, being grounded primarily in the immediacy of intuition not subject to rejection with further information, has remained comparatively static in time without evolution.[27] An adequate conception of evolution and the philosophy of nature and culture must combine both components.

NOTES

1. The author is indebted to the Viking Fund for a grant which has made possible research in this field and the final completion of this paper.

2. *Physics,* Book I, "Works of Aristotle," ed. by W. D. Ross (London, Oxford University Press, 1930), Vol. II.

3. For a further account of Aristotelian biology in its relation to organization and adaptation see the writer's *Science and First Principles* (New York, Macmillan, 1931), chap. i; also L. J. Henderson, *The Order of Nature* (Harvard University Press, 1917), chap. ii.

4. See also the writer's *The Meeting of East and West* (New York, Macmillan, 1946), chap. vii.

5. See Ernst Mach, *The Science of Mechanics* (Chicago, Open Court, 1919), chap. ii.

6. See E. A. Burtt, *Metaphysical Foundations of Modern Physical Science* (New York, Harcourt, Brace, 1925), chap. iii.

7. See Newton's *Principia* (Cajori ed. Berkeley, University of California Press, 1934), p. 6.

8 Charles Darwin, *Origin of Species,* chap. xv.

9. *The Fragments of Empedocles,* trans. into English verse by W. E. Leonard (Chicago, Open Court, 1908).

10. See David Burns, *An Introduction to Biophysics* (London, J. and A. Churchill, 1921).

11. See C. C. Hurst, *The Mechanism of Creative Evolution* (Cambridge University Press, 1932). Two pictures appear opposite the title page of this volume; they are of Darwin and of Mendel.

12. See *The Meeting of East and West,* chaps. v and vi.

13. *Ibid.,* chap. iii.

14. For evidence of Einstein's agreement with Kant upon this point, see my chapter, "Einstein's Conception of Science," in *Albert Einstein: Philosopher-scientist* (Evanston, Ill., Library of Living Philosophers, Inc., 1949), pp. 385–408.

15. See the writer's "Natural Science and the Critical Philosophy of Kant," in *The Heritage of Kant,* ed. by G. T. Whitney and D. F. Bowers (Princeton University Press, 1932).

16. *The Vocation of Man,* trans. by William Smith (LaSalle, Ill., Open Court, 1940). See also Fichte, *Grundlage der gesamten Wissenschaften Lehre,* especially the "Dritter Teil, Vierter Lehrsatz."

17. See Hegel, *Lectures on the Philosophy of History,* trans. by J. Sibree (London, Bonn, 1857); and *Lectures on the History of Philosophy,* trans. from the German by E. S. Haldane (Keegan Paul, 1892).

18. See *The Meeting of East and West,* chap. ii.

19. See Leopoldo Zea's two volumes: *El Positivismo en Mexico* (1943) and *Apogeo y Decadencia del Positivismo en Mexico* (1944). Both published in Mexico, D. F., by El Colegio de Mexico.

20. "L'Evolution de la raison," in *La Deduction relativiste* (Paris, Payot, 1925).

21. For a specification of this method, see chaps. xvii and xxi in the writer's *Logic of the Sciences and the Humanities* (New York, Macmillan, 1947); also *Jour. of Legal Education*, I, No. 4 (1949), 482–494.

22. See the writer's "Mathematical Background and Basis of Greek Philosophy," in *Philosophical Essays for Alfred North Whitehead*, ed. by Otis Lee (New York, Longmans, Green, 1936).

23. See Aristotle, *De Caelo 271b12, 303a21, 306a27*, and *De Gen. et Cor. 325b25*.

24. See *The Meeting of East and West*, chap. iii.

25. *Ibid.*

26. *Ibid.*, chap. xii.

27. *Ibid.* See also Alfred North Whitehead, *Concept of Nature* (Cambridge University Press, 1920), and his *Nature and Life* (University of Chicago Press, 1934); also Ralph S. Lillie, *General Biology and Philosophy of Organism* (University of Chicago Press, 1945).

INTRODUCTION TO CHAPTER III

GENETIC NATURE OF DIFFERENCES AMONG MEN

ONE of the major effects of the science of evolution upon the popular mind has been to sharpen the modern consciousness of race differences. An emerging science of race has thrust before it a pseudo science of race prejudice. The early years of the present century saw the culmination of this pseudo science in the movement which attempted to account for cultural achievement and material power by reference to presumedly inherited racial qualities. While further investigation confirmed the moral sense of men in rejecting these views it remained true that no authoritative science of race was at hand to replace them. Rather, the long-established and intellectually respectable anthropological criteria for the measurement of racial differences revealed new theoretical and practical weaknesses. Under these circumstances the recent elaboration of a new science of race according to the principles of genetics is an event of tremendous moment in the modern world. That the study of human genetics is still in its infancy Professor Dobzhansky and his colleagues who are the pioneers in this work are the first to insist. But that it holds the promise of a rational account of the facts of racial divergence as a dynamic process they are equally certain. In this chapter Professor Dobzhansky lays down the principles of racial genetics and indicates the radically revised attitudes toward an age-old interest which the new approach entails.

S. P.

THE GENETIC NATURE OF DIFFERENCES AMONG MEN[1]

THEODOSIUS DOBZHANSKY

INTRODUCTION

IT IS pleasing to fancy oneself, one's family, class, nation, and race as being intrinsically superior to any others. The gentle art of rationalizing this self-gratification is a very ancient one. Aristotle was convinced that the nations which lived eastward from the Greeks were "intelligent and inventive but wanting in spirit," while the western Europeans were, on the contrary, "full of spirit but wanting in intelligence and skill." Among the Greeks, intelligence and spirit were mixed in just the right proportions, and according to Aristotle this gave to the Greeks a manifest right to lord it over all the barbarians. Some 2,300 years after Aristotle, Professor Ellsworth Huntington argued that the inhabitants of northwestern Europe are the masterpieces of natural selection with respect to high intellectual and moral qualities, that the cream of this superior race moved across the Atlantic to form the "Old American stock," and that the optimal climatic conditions for the flowering of this stock are to be found in southern New England. Is it necessary to add that Professor Huntington was domiciled in New Haven and was connected with Yale University?

The belief that some races or classes are of gentler birth or are nobler and worthier than other races or classes of men has always appealed to many people. It would be wrong to say that people who hold such beliefs invariably belong to a certain political party or parties, or that such beliefs have a necessary logical connection with any political doctrines. Nevertheless, it is a matter of observation that these beliefs usually go together with the political "right," with conservatism, aristocratism, class exclusiveness, national aggressiveness, and recently with all brands of fascism. The opposite type of belief, which assumes that all men are inherently equal and that any human being is of the same intrinsic worth as any other, is probably just as ancient as its alternative. In Western civilization this type of belief stems particularly from Christianity, although the organized churches have not always espoused it in practice. In the political field these beliefs go most frequently, although by no means exclusively, with "leftist" views, with liberalism, radicalism, and the aspirations of the lower and underprivileged classes and nations to a greater share of worldly goods and social equality.

Although all humans may be born equal in rights, everyday experience tells us that they are most certainly not all alike. It is therefore natural that we should want to ascertain the nature and extent of the differences among men. Since the function of science is to describe things as they are, we have the right to expect that biologists and anthropologists will be able to tell us in what ways humans differ, and what causes these differences. Unfortunately, the beliefs that people hold are frequently based on emotions rather than on objective scientific data. One of the functions of popular beliefs is the defense of the real or fancied interests of their holders. Men have an urge to make their interests seem not only respectable but even necessary by pretending that these interests are founded on irrefutable "scientific" truths. Scientists themselves are by no means immune to such temptations. It is possible that science will eventually bring to light a complete and incontrovertible account of human differences. However, it would be presumptuous on the part of scientists to assume that their discoveries will cause everyone to alter his beliefs overnight and bring them into accord with established scientific facts. As things actually stand, scientific study of human differences is still in its infancy. Many critical facts about human biology and evolution remain to be discovered. Much humility and willingness to adjust one's opinions to evidence are therefore required of scientists who work in this field. Nevertheless, it is useful to survey from time to time the extent of our knowledge of these problems in order to determine the promising directions for further work.

SOME BASIC FACTS CONCERNING HUMAN VARIATION

Before considering the nature of human variation one must clarify the meaning of certain fundamental concepts of biology in terms of which the discussion will be conducted. The full meaning of the pattern of human variation and evolution which is emerging in modern biology can be understood only within the framework of the changing system of biological thought.

We are planning to study the biological, genetic, or hereditary differences among men. It is customary to contrast hereditary with environmental or cultural differences, that is, those which are brought about by climate, diet, upbringing, schooling, or language. But this distinction is much less simple than it seems. What is biological heredity? At first sight, heredity is the transmission of characters or traits from parents to offspring. It is sometimes defined as the cause which makes children resemble their parents. A moment's consideration will show the inadequacy of such a definition. One of the most striking differences between the inhabitants of different parts of the world is their skin color. People of north European descent have pale skins, those living around the Mediterranean tend to be more swarthy, and those on the upper Nile have black skins. The color of the skin is obviously inherited, and yet it is also well known that the color of the skin depends often to a considerable extent on the degree to which it is exposed to sunlight. The heredity of an individual obviously does not change every time he is exposed to the sun but his skin color may change appreciably. What, then, is the real meaning of the statement that skin color is inherited? What is inherited is evidently not a skin color as such but rather a capacity to react to the ultraviolet radiation impinging upon the skin by developing this or that pigmentation. Some people react to ultraviolet radiation by sunburn instead of by pigmentation. Others have heredities which cause the skin color to vary within wide limits, depending upon exposure to light. Still others have pigmented skins regardless of exposure.

The genotype, that is, the sum total of inherited potentialities, determines the responses of the organism to its environment. The characters and traits that an individual has, that is, his phenotype, are the result of interactions between the genotype and the environment in which the individual develops. Heredity is not a status but a process. What is inherited is not a "trait" but a capacity to develop certain traits under certain conditions. Heredity begins at conception and ends at death.

Heredity is not destiny or fate. Since the expression of heredity is a function not only of the genotype but of the environment as well, it is to a certain extent subject to human control. To be sure, the plasticity of traits of the organism is not unlimited. For example, the hereditary elements, genes, which give rise to the blood groups in man produce these characteristics of the blood in all known environments; no methods of changing one's blood group are available, and the blood group which one has does not depend upon one's will. But, the heredity of skin color permits considerable flexibility in its expression, since skin color is influenced to a certain extent by exposure to sunlight. Still more so are hair color and hair form. Both are assuredly controlled by heredity, and yet the beauty parlors enable their patrons to display hair colors of their choosing, and to have the hair either curled or straightened at their discretion. The expression of the heredity of hair color and hair form is, therefore, easily manageable. But not one iota of the heredity transmitted by a mother to her children will be altered by the "permanents" she has had. The "permanents" change the expression of heredity, not heredity itself. The extent of control over the expression of heredity may depend upon our knowledge. Diabetes is an hereditary disease, and yet it was found a few years ago that a carrier of this heredity may enjoy normal health if regularly supplied with the drug insulin. Insulin treatment does not alter the "diabetic" heredity but it makes the physiology of carriers of this heredity normal instead of abnormal. Comparable methods of control of the manifestations of other types of heredity may eventually be discovered.

According to a widespread popular notion, heredity is transmitted from parents to offspring through "blood." This notion was conceived in folklore, yet until the beginning of the present century it was shared by scientists, including Darwin. Even now this notion continues to bedevil the thinking of many biologists and anthropologists. It suggests, quite wrongly of course, that the "bloods" of the parents are mixed in their children, and that the "bloods" of individuals are mixed in the "race." It leads us to expect that all children of the same parents must have similar heredities, and that a population left to reproduce by free intermarriage will eventually become uniform in heredity, i.e., will become a "pure race."

The falsity of these views was demonstrated some eighty years ago by Gregor Mendel. Mendel showed that heredity is transmitted from parents to offspring by discrete units now called genes. The hereditary endowment of an organism as complex as man consists of numerous genes, thousands and possibly tens of thousands. In each individual most genes are in duplicate, one gene of each kind having come from the mother and its partner from the father. However, and this is most important, the paternal and the maternal genes (alleles) do not fuse or influence each other. When sex cells are formed the paternal and maternal genes separate and are assorted in such a way that different sex cells receive different sets of genes. Therefore, brothers and sisters do not have identical hereditary endowments. This assortment can be likened to the multitude of "hands" that can be dealt from the same deck of cards. But because of the much larger number of genes involved, the number of different sets of genes that the parents are potentially able to transmit to their offspring is staggeringly great. It is virtually certain that, with the sole exception of identical twins, no two persons, unrelated or related, now living or having lived, have ever had the same genotype. Each person has a hereditary endowment of his own, unique, unprecedented, and unrepeatable.

It would follow from the "blood" theory of heredity not only that the genotype of a child is a blend of those of his parents, but also that intermarriage of carriers of different heredities in a population would lead to a gradual decay of the variability present in the population or race. But this is not so. Suppose that an island is populated by a large clan in which some individuals have brown and others have blue eyes. Suppose further that marriages are concluded at random with respect to eye color, so that there is no preference for selecting marriage mates with either similar or differently colored eyes, and finally that the blue- and brown-eyed persons are on the average equally vigorous in health and successful in parenthood. If these conditions are fulfilled, then the proportions of brown- and blue-eyed individuals within the clan will remain constant indefinitely; there will be no tendency for the eye color in this population to become uniform. No "race" pure and uniform for eye color will result.

How may we explain this fact? Let us assume that the difference between the brown- and the blue-eyed conditions is determined by a single gene pair. This is an oversimplification, but we will adopt it for convenience' sake. The gene for brown eyes may be written simply as A, and the gene for blue eyes as a. Individuals who receive the gene A from one parent and a from the other have brown eyes (since the brown eye color is dominant and the blue is recessive). Now the original population contained a certain proportion of brown- and blue-eyed persons; the genes *A* and *a* have therefore certain definite *frequencies* in the clan under consideration. Let *q* stand for the fraction of the sex cells with the gene *A,* and $(1-q)$ for the fraction with the gene *a,* in this clan. Hardy and Weinberg independently demonstrated in 1908 a very important theorem, namely, that the frequencies of *q* and $(1-q)$ will remain constant generation after generation, and that the proportions of persons with brown and blue eyes will in all generations following the original mixture remain as follows:

$$q^2AA \text{ (brown eyes)} : 2q \ (1-q) \ Aa \text{ (brown eyes)} :$$
$$(1-q)^2aa \text{ (blue eyes)}.$$

In different populations the proportions of brown- and blue-eyed persons may, of course, be different. These proportions will depend on the gene frequencies *q* and $(1-q)$. Some genes occur commonly while others are rare. But whatever the frequencies of the genes concerned, we have now a tool for description of races in man and other organisms. This description of races in terms of gene frequencies makes the race concept appear in a new light. Let us study an example of human races with the aid of this method.

THE BLOOD GROUPS IN MAN—A TEST CASE

Instead of the imaginary "blood" which popular fantasy charges with the task of transmission of heredity, we shall now discuss certain proved properties of the real blood flowing in human veins. As shown first by Landsteiner, all humans can be classified into four blood groups which are designated O, A, B, and AB. If the red blood corpuscles of the A, B, or AB types are mixed with the serum (the liquid part of the blood) of an O person, they agglutinate, i.e, clump in large masses. Similarly, A cells clump in B serum, B cells in A serum, and AB cells in all sera but their own. Blood of O type can be safely transfused into anybody, because O cells do not clump in any serum; O persons are called universal donors. On the other hand, AB persons are universal recipients because they can safely receive blood of any group.

Three variants (alleles) of the blood-group gene, designated *a, A,* and *a^B,* govern the inheritance of the blood types. Persons

receiving the gene *a* from both parents (*aa*) have blood of group
O. Two *A* genes, or one *A* and one *a* (*AA* or *Aa*), give blood of
group A. Two a^B genes, or one a^B and one *a,* give blood of group
B. Finally, one *A* gene and one a^B gene give blood of group AB.
Knowing the proportions of persons of different blood groups
in any given population, it is easy to compute the frequencies of
the genes *a, A,* and a^B in this population. In other words, a population can be characterized in terms of the frequencies in it of the
blood-group genes. During the last thirty years many populations
in all parts of the world have been examined for blood-group
frequencies. The results obtained are of great interest.

Only very few peoples, among them some American Indian
tribes, have proved to be "pure" for a given blood group, i.e., to
consist of persons all of whom belong to the same blood group.
With the exception of these few tribes, representatives of the four
blood groups, O, A, B, and AB, occur in all parts of the world.
But this is not to say that the distribution of the blood groups is
uniform throughout the world. Quite the contrary. Not only
populations living far apart but even neighboring tribes usually
differ. These differences are, however, not absolute, they are
differences in the incidence, or relative frequency, of persons who
belong to the four blood groups. This is to say, differences in the
frequencies of the genes for the blood groups, rather than presence or absence of these genes, characterize human populations.
A summary of the available data on the frequencies of the *A*
and a^B genes in different parts of the world is shown in Figures
1 and 2. (The numbers in the Western Hemisphere refer to the
Indians and not to the now much more numerous populations
of European descent.)

Taking the Old World first, we find that the a^B gene, giving
rise to the B and AB blood groups, occurs most frequently among
the inhabitants of central and southern Asia. In Mongolia,
southern Siberia, and in parts of India up to 40% of the population have B blood and 10% have AB blood. It can be computed
that the frequencies of the gene a^B in these countries is as high as
25% (0.25) or higher (Fig. 2). Asia, then, is the "center" of the
distribution of the a^B gene. As one travels away from this center
in any direction, the incidence of the a^B gene decreases. Thus,
among the Russians only about 15% of the sex cells carry this
gene, among the Poles 11%, in Germany and Italy 9%–10%,
in Scandinavia and England 6%–8%, and in Spain and Portugal

only about 5%. Similarly, the concentration of the gene a^B falls to about 20% among the Japanese, Filipinos, and Sumatrans, and finally to below 5% among the Australian aborigines. The concentrations of a^B gene in Africa are not known as well as one might desire, but it is clear that it is found in relatively high concentration along the Nile and in the Sudan, while the periphery of that continent has lower concentrations.

The distribution of the *A* gene which gives rise to the A and AB

p%

☐ 0-10 ⫶⫶⫶⫶ 10-15 ▥ 15-20 ▦ 20-25 ░ 25-30 ▨ 30-35 ■ 35-45

Figure 1. Percentage frequencies of the gene *A,* for the A blood group, in human populations of the world. (After B. Lundman.)

blood groups is a different story (Fig. 1). It is frequent in Europe, in the Nile Valley, and in the Sudan in Africa, and again in the Far East, among the Japanese, Koreans, and in some parts of China. A remarkably high concentration of this gene is reached among the aborigines in south-central Australia.

The blood grouping among the American Indians has not been studied nearly as well as the interest of this topic would justify, and most unfortunately the time when such a study might be

Figure 2. Percentage frequencies of the gene q^B, for the B blood group, in human populations of the world. (After B. Lundman.)

done is running short because of the rapidly progressing mixture
between the Indians and people derived from the Old World.
Nevertheless, the Indians show a most remarkable situation (Figs.
1 and 2). Many tribes living in Central and South America show
such high frequencies of the blood group O (determined by the
a gene) that it seems very probable that before they started to mix
with the European invaders they may in fact have been "pure"
for the O blood group (the frequency of the *a* gene 100%). Yet it

r%

| | 75- | | 70-75 | | 65-70 | | 60-65 | | 55-60 | | 50-55 | | 45-50 |

Figure 3. Percentage frequencies of the gene *a*, for the O blood
group, in human populations of the world. (After Lundman.)

is also among the American Indians that the world's highest frequency of the A blood group occurs. Thus the Blackfeet and Bloods tribes in Montana and the adjacent part of Canada show frequencies of the gene *A* exceeding 50%, and neighboring tribes similarly show high frequencies of *A* (Fig. 1). Fairly high frequencies of *A* occur also in Eskimos in western Greenland. In South America a small sample of the representatives of the Caraja tribe living in equatorial Brazil quite unexpectedly showed around 30% of the gene a^B. If these findings are confirmed by further investigations, it would follow that certain tribes among the Ameri-

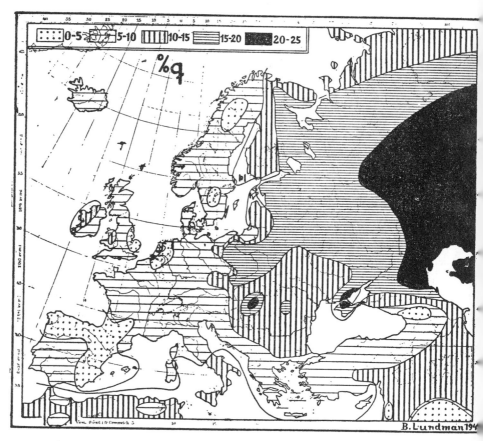

Figure 4. Percentage frequencies of the gene a^B in populations of Europe. (After Lundman.)

can Indians hold the world records for the frequencies of all three blood group genes a, A, and a^B.

We can now describe the races of which mankind is composed in terms of their blood groups and the genes producing them. But we are then brought face to face with a most perplexing question: just what shall we call a race? At first sight it may seem simplest and easiest to unite in a "race" everybody with the same blood type, and thus to have four races which may be designated as O, A, B, and AB. Such a course would indeed have the advantage of eliminating once and for all any possibility of doubt as to which race any individual might belong, all one would have to do to determine his race would be to test the blood group. Unfortunately this course has such drawbacks that it cannot be accepted. It would mean not only that all four races live side by side almost everywhere in the world, but, worse still, that parents and children, and even brothers and sisters, quite frequently would belong to different races. For example, if one parent had AB blood and the other O blood, then according to Mendel's law about half of the children would have A blood and the other half B blood. To put it in a different way, the children would belong to two different races, neither of which would coincide with the races to which their parents belong. Moreover, one must not forget that many genes vary in the human species, apart from those responsible for the blood groups. As stated above, no two persons (disregarding identical twins) are at all likely to have exactly the same genes. If we define a race as a group of persons having identical genes, this would amount to saying that every individual belongs to a race of his own, which is manifestly absurd.

To arrive at a reasonable solution we must recognize that individuals and their heredities evidently cannot be considered in isolation but only as members of biological communities or populations, within which intermarriage takes place. Man is a sexual and cross-fertilizing species; his lines of descent are not isolated from each other as they are in asexual forms, but on the contrary form an intricate mesh due to marriage. The gene complexes belong to individuals, but the genes from which they are composed are drawn from the common stock of reproductive communities or populations. The most important truth we are called on to recognize is that *the concept of race refers not to individuals or to their genotypes but only to populations.*

Our problem, then, is how to describe human populations. All men are, as the saying goes, brothers under the skin. Regardless of blood groups, skin colors, head shapes, or any other differences, intermarriage and interbreeding occur whenever different kinds of men live in the same territory and meet each other. Sooner or later genes of one group find their way into other groups, and this gene flow unites all mankind into a single very large population. Furthermore, this genetic unity of mankind is not anything new which arose with human civilization. Interbreeding has always been taking place. A most elegant proof is afforded by the findings by McCown and Keith in Palestine that Neanderthal man and the so-called "modern" man hybridized there at the dawn of mankind. All living mankind is a single biological species which shares a common fund of genes.

The genetic singleness of mankind does not mean however that the whole human species interbreeds at random. Despite trains, boats, and airplanes, a boy growing up in New York is more likely to marry a girl from New York than one from China, California, or even from Philadelphia. Aside from sheer distance, human marriage is influenced by national, linguistic, religious, economic, educational, and other social factors. These factors act as obstacles to free gene flow through the human species, even though they are far too weak to stop this flow altogether. Hence the species population is divided into a hierarchy of imperfectly delimited subpopulations. These subpopulations vary in size and extent from those indigenous to a continent and easily recognizable by different skin colors, hair shapes, and the like, down to castes and clans, and finally to circles of personal acquaintances.

Now a population of any size may be described in terms of the frequencies in it of the blood groups or of the genes that determine them. Thus, according to Haldane, among the 22,120 blood donors in the city of Barcelona, Spain, in 1937–38 were 41.6% of persons with blood of group O, 45.6% with group A, 9.4% group B, and 3.5% of group AB. These figures describe the population of the city of Barcelona at the time specified, provided, of course, that the blood donors were a fair sample of the whole city population. With this proviso, we may compute that the collective heredity of the Barcelona population consisted of 64.3% a genes, 28.9% A genes, and 6.9% a^B genes. Populations of territories larger than a city can be described similarly. For example, Fisher and Taylor give the following figures for the populations of different parts of Great Britain:

Region	Frequencies of the blood groups in per cent				Gene frequencies in per cent			Number of persons examined
	O	A	B	AB	a	A	a^B	
Scotland	52.0	34.2	10.4	3.3	72.2	20.8	7.0	10,969
Northern England	48.6	40.3	8.5	2.5	69.6	24.6	5.9	8,716
Southern England	45.2	43.2	8.5	3.1	67.2	26.7	6.1	106,477

Among the 20,000 Americans studied by Snyder, 45.0% belonged to group O, 41.0% to group A, 10.0% to group B, and 4.0% to group AB. These figures correspond to the gene frequencies $a = 67.0\%$, $A = 25.9\%$ and $a^B = 7.3\%$.

Examination of the figures for the five populations discussed above will show that each population has blood-group frequencies peculiar to itself. The blood group O (the gene a) is most frequent in Barcelona, less so in Scotland, still less in northern England, and least in southern England and in the United States. The blood group A (and the gene A) is most frequent in Barcelona, less so in the United States and in southern England, and least in Scotland. It may be noted that the population of the United States resembles those of the English regions more than it does the others, which is not at all surprising in view of the former having arisen in large part from immigrants from England.

Populations of some countries differ from the five just cited far more than the latter differ among themselves. Thus, among the 301,959 Japanese examined for blood groups there were 30.5% of group O, 38.2% of group A, 21.9% of group B, and 9.4% of group AB (after Wiener).

A DEFINITION OF RACE

Races may be defined as populations which differ in the frequencies of some genes. A population is a group of individuals cemented by intermarriage, and hence sharing a common treasury of genes.

A race is not the gene complex, still less the physique, of any individual or of any group of individuals chosen solely because these individuals attract the attention of an observer as being interesting or "typical." Unfortunately, such a misuse of the race concept is not at all rare. It is not legitimate to pick out one or several types within an interbreeding population and to declare them to be "races" and to style the remainder of the same population "intermediates." One must always remember that such races and intermediates merely represent different dice throws from the same pool of genes, and that their genes are in every generation returned into the pool. Blue-eyed persons arbitrarily chosen from a mixed population do not constitute a race distinct from the brown-eyed persons, even though the eye color may be very strikingly different and easily recognizable. And yet, populations may be regarded racially distinct if they contain different proportions of blue-eyed and brown-eyed individuals. For example, blue- and brown-eyed individuals occur both in Norway and in Italy. It is a fallacy to unite into a single race the blue-eyed Norwegians and the blue-eyed Italians, and in another race the brown-eyed Norwegians and the brown-eyed Italians. The Norwegian and the Italian *populations* may, nevertheless, be considered racially different because they contain different proportions of blue- and brown-eyed individuals. The attempts of Count Gobineau and his imitators to represent the populations of various countries as consisting of a noble "Nordic" race which lives side by side and intermarries with a nondescript plebeian race are deceptive. Such things can appear plausible only to those who ignore the basic facts of modern biology. Interbreeding leads to fusion of races.

Racial differences need not be absolute and qualitative; they are usually relative and quantitative. Individuals may occur in one race that resemble the representatives of another race. Some Norwegians are as dark-eyed as many Italians, and some Italians are as blue-eyed as many Norwegians. One cannot distinguish all Norwegians from all Italians by their eye colors nor by their blood groups, but the Norwegian and the Italian populations can be distinguished by the relative frequencies in them of persons with different eye colors and different blood groups.

Races may be of different orders. We have seen that the population of Scotland differs in blood-group frequencies from that of northern and of southern England. The Japanese population has a still different set of blood-group frequencies. The difference between the Japanese and the three British populations is, however, obviously greater than the differences between the latter. At least as far as the blood groups are concerned, the racial distinctions between the populations of different parts of Britain are smaller than the distinction between the Japanese and the British populations.

One may perhaps question the desirability of applying the term "racial differences" to distinctions as small as those that can be found between populations of neighboring villages and as large as those between populations of different continents. Might one modify the definition of race by specifying that the differences in gene frequencies be above a certain minimum magnitude? Such a modification is undesirable for two reasons. First, since all magnitudes of difference are found among populations, any specified minimum can be only arbitrary. Second, it is most important to realize that the differences between the "major" human races are fundamentally of the same nature as the relatively minute differences between the inhabitants of adjacent towns or villages. This does not mean, of course, that one should proceed to give separate names to the races that occur in every village or district. The practical task of describing and delimiting races is distinct from that of defining the essence of race as a general phenomenon. We shall return to consideration of these matters later.

THE EVOLUTIONARY PROGRESSION

Variations in the magnitude of racial distinctions cause difficulties in classifying the races of mankind as well as of other species of animals and of plants. The bright and shining dream of a classifier is a system of pigeonholes which would contain neatly packaged races and species; nature ignores such pigeonholes and mixes their contents. Hence, depending upon their personal predilections, different anthropologists recognize from two to several dozen human races. It is easy to see that the populations of England and of Japan are racially distinct. But shall we also consider the populations of different parts of England to belong each to a different race? There is no reason why this might not be done, but if it is done where shall the process of race splitting end? This indefiniteness has plagued biology and anthropology for more than a century, and permitted crackpots and adventurers to indulge their fancy in building "scientific" theories.

The difficulty is not entirely due to insufficient information which could be supplied by more detailed studies. Its root lies far deeper than that. The evolutionary process is continuously in operation, and evolution takes place through accumulation of small changes instead of by cataclysmic upheavals. Race classification would be a relatively easy matter if the races of man or other organisms were either static and self-contained units of creation, or if they arose from time to time as finished products, remaining stable and unchanged for long-time intervals. Such races would be easily separable, countable, and describable. But in reality a race is merely an episode in the process of evolutionary divergence of populations.

Without going into this matter in detail, it must be stated that according to prevailing views it is possible to distinguish in the evolutionary process three stages or levels. First, gene mutation supplies the evolutionary raw materials; accumulation of mutants and their manifold recombination by the process of sexual reproduction results in a variable but spatially undifferentiated population. Second, natural selection and genetic drift transform the originally spatially uniform populations into a group of diverging geographic races. This is the process of race formation strictly speaking. Divergence is a gradual and in many cases a slow and fluctuating process. Third, geographic races develop reproductive isolation, and thus become distinct species; this is the process of species formation, sometimes styled speciation. Distinct species are able to inhabit the same territory without losing their identity and separateness through interbreeding and gene exchange. Except in man, any given territory can be inhabited by only one race of a sexually reproducing species. It is man's social structure and cultural heritage which permits two or more human races to live side by side without at least immediate fusion into a single variable population.

Races observed on our time level in the human species represent various stages of the evolutionary process. Some races differ only slightly in the frequencies of certain genes, as we have seen above in the example of the British populations. Such differences are not noticeable at all without the aid of statistical methods, and are not usually referred to as racial differences in popular parlance. Other populations show more or less striking differences in gene frequencies, as we have seen in the case of the blood-group genes in the British populations on the one hand and in the Japanese on the other. Yet these race differences remain quantitive rather than qualitative, because the same blood groups occur in England and in Japan though with different frequencies. In further race divergence some genes present in one race may be completely lost in another. This may have happened in some American Indian tribes which consist of individuals having blood group O only. Still further divergence, not exemplified among human races but known on the biological level, has led to the development of various obstacles to hybridization and gene exchange. Such races have entered the road to speciation. The obstacles to gene exchange are referred to as reproductive isolating mechanisms, and they should be distinguished from geographic isolation which prevents gene exchange between populations by physical distance alone.

Reproductive isolating mechanisms are diverse. Populations may be strictly adapted to different climatic or other environments, and individuals belonging to these populations may not have the chance to meet and to cross because the milieu in which one population lives is quite unsuitable for the life of the other (ecological isolation). The sexual maturity or the breeding periods of representatives of two populations may fail to coincide in time (seasonal or temporal isolation). Males of one population may cease to be sexually attractive to females of another, or vice versa (sexual or psychological isolation). The hybrid offspring, if produced, may be poorly viable (hybrid inviability) or incapable of further procreation (hybrid sterility). Any one or a combination of several of these isolating mechanisms may reduce the frequency of the gene exchange between diverging races, or may make such gene exchange completely absent. When gene exchange between populations is greatly reduced or eliminated altogether by reproductive isolation, these populations have ceased to be diverging races and have become distinct species.

It should be emphasized that the above outline of the evolutionary process does not imply that every race of any species is destined to pass through the entire sequence of stages of evolutionary divergence culminating in the attainment of species distinction. A race is a potential or incipient species, but many races do not progress very far in that direction, and many incipient species never attain the stage of complete reproductive isolation from other species. It is fair to speculate that some human races might, under certain conditions, have become transformed into species. But in reality no existing human race even approaches the status of a species, independent from the rest of mankind. Mankind preserves its specific unity.

More than that, the process of racial differentiation is reversible. As stated above, the maintenance of race separation is, except in man, based on territorial separation. If such a separation lapses the races may intercross and exchange genes. Gene exchange leads to convergence, and to eventual fusion of the races into a single greatly variable population. There can be no reasonable doubt that just such a process of race breakdown and fusion has been going on for several centuries in mankind. The trend toward race divergence which must have prevailed in the remote past has not only come to a halt over most of the globe but has actually reversed itself. It is very likely that race fusion will continue in the future.

CASTE AND CLASS

The development of civilization, the consequent expansion of populations, and particularly the enormous growth of the means of communication, have destroyed the geographic isolation which in the dim past made possible the divergent evolution of human races. Whenever two or more races meet in the same country some interbreeding takes place. The extent of geographic overlapping which now obtains among human races would, on the animal level, have led to race fusion within a few generations. However, the development of culture has introduced into the human species many elements unknown on the biological level. The evolutionary pattern of man differs sharply from that of any wild species. In the first place, man shares some evolutionary peculiarities with the domesticated animals and with plants that he cultivates. That is, genetically distinct populations that are perfectly able to intercross and fuse into a single population may, in man as well as in domesticated species, coexist for some time in the same territory without breakdown and fusion. For example, a dozen or more "pure breeds" of dogs, plus the highly variable breed called mongrel, live in close proximity to each other in most American towns. The intercrossing of these breeds is restricted because of a deliberate effort on the part of the owners to control the reproductive processes of their pets. Similar conscious effort on the part of man keeps apart the breeds of horses, of cattle, corn, garden flowers, etc. Here man supplies isolating mechanisms which accomplish the same results accomplished in nature by geographical isolation of races of one species and by reproductive isolation among distinct species. Although man is vastly less efficient in controlling his own reproduction than that of animals and plants he has domesticated, human reproduction is to a certain extent under deliberate or spontaneous social control. To this extent the assertion of some anthropologists that man is a "domesticated" animal is justified.

Probably nowhere else is human reproduction socially controlled to a greater extent than in India, where a complex and rigid caste system has persisted for many centuries. A combination of customs and religious and social taboos functions here in a way analogous to incipient reproductive isolation on the biological level. Indian castes are populations that in at least some cases differ in gene frequencies, and hence are racially distinct. These populations frequently live in the same territory without fusion. Yet history shows that even the Indian caste system in the long run fails to approach the effectiveness not only of biological species barriers but even of the barriers maintained by man for the purpose of keeping apart the breeds of domestic animals. Enough illicit gene exchange seems to have taken place between the castes in the course of time so that they show a trend toward genetic convergence rather than divergence. The intent of the "race segregation" as practiced in the southern United States is, of course, the same as that of the Indian caste system, but the biological efficiency of the American model is low even by comparison with the Indian system.

Unacknowledged castes exist in most societies. Any rule, custom, or prejudice which causes people to marry exclusively or predominantly within only a part of the population of a given territory tends to split that population into sub-populations which may under certain conditions become different in gene frequencies. For example, marriages are concluded chiefly within an economic stratum, so that families that become united by marriage bonds tend to have bank accounts of the same order of magnitude. On the other hand, quite a number of marriages are unions of members of different economic strata. Whether or not different economic strata will under these conditions become repositories of different genes will depend upon many factors, one of which is, of course, the frequency of intermarriage. Genetic divergence is possible only if gene exchange through intermarriage is not rapid enough to cancel the effects of differentiating agents discussed below.

This is a part of the problem of whether or not social classes are genetically different. This problem has been debated for many centuries, from Plato to our day. It is evidently much older than the science of genetics or of biology itself. Partisans of the ruling or otherwise privileged classes frequently seek to rationalize and vindicate the position enjoyed by the members of these classes by claiming that they are genetically superior to their less fortunate brethren. Care in the preservation of the upper classes would in such cases amount to conservation of the biologically valuable heritage of mankind. The opposite contention, that all men, or at least all social classes, are biologically of equal value, appeals more strongly to those who for altruistic or for selfish reasons prefer a more egalitarian structure of society. We shall not consider here the question of what qualities make men more or less valuable or desirable; a biologist has nothing to contribute to its solution, at least in his professional capacity. We shall limit ourselves to a discussion of general biological principles which underlie differentiation of populations.

In the first place, different classes of a society may be derived from peoples of different geographic and racial origin. History knows many instances when the upper classes are descendants largely of foreign conquerors while the lower classes stem in the main from the conquered aborigines. Or else some trades or professions in a country may be wholly or in large part monopolized by a group of people of a different geographic origin from the rest of the population. If intermarriage between such classes is for any reason infrequent we have in effect a caste system, and the class boundaries will for a time coincide with race boundaries. But since intermarriage across the class barriers is never completely excluded, the differences in the gene frequencies that may exist at the beginning will progressively diminish and eventually disappear. The speed of this process will of course be a function of the frequency of intermarriage. Introduction of a caste system, as practiced in India, will slow down the process but hardly avoid it completely. Sooner or later the upper classes come to differ from the plebeian mass only in having foreign sounding names and an imaginary nobility of descent.

Perhaps the most striking example of a semi-isolated sociobiological group is the Jewish "race" which lives almost always side by side with other peoples and almost nowhere by itself. Religion and customs proved to be sufficiently strong barriers to intermarriage, so that some differences in gene frequencies between the Jews and the peoples among whom they live have been retained after centuries of proximity. At the same time, gene exchange has been taking place to an extent sufficient to make the Jewish colonies residing in different countries differ more markedly from each other in their anthropological characteristics than some of these colonies differ from their respective non-Jewish neighbors. The situation is, then, a paradoxical one. In many countries the Jewish populations are to varying extents racially distinct from the peoples among whom they live. Yet the Jews from different countries do not constitute a biological population, and therefore the application of the word race to the totality of the Jews is misleading. The Jews are a cultural or a linguistic group, not a biological race.

Classes of a society are by no means always derived from different groups of immigrants. Another way in which socioeconomic classes take their origin is through a gradual differentiation from a single population under the influence of economic and political forces. Class structure of this origin is profoundly different biologically from that based on descent from geographically as well as genetically different populations. Its genetic corollaries will depend on the method of perpetuation of the class distinction.

Social stratifications in the human species are rationalized by means of the following assumptions. First, man's capacities, aptitudes, weaknesses, and defects are assumed to be inherited through "blood" from immediate or remote ancestors. In societies in which this belief is current an individual's social position tends to be transmitted to his offspring regardless of what personal merits or demerits the latter may show. An implied justification of this procedure is that a scion of an illustrious family is made of biologically superior stuff, even if he himself happens to show no signs of the imputed superiority. This is the principle of hereditary aristocracy in its extreme form. Second, it is believed by many people that the qualities of an individual which determine his fitness for this or that social station are independent of biological heredity and are brought about by environment and training. This belief may serve as a basis of a social stratification in a democracy, in which the position of an individual in the social scale is determined by his personal merits, regardless of his origin or antecedents. A social stratification of this kind presupposes an equality of opportunity which permits individuals best endowed for a given function to reach a position where this function can be exercised most effectively.

An assumption that human personality is wholly or largely determined by a mechanism of heredity (such as Mendelian genes) which permits great variations within a line of descent harmonizes best with the democratic, and not with the aristocratic, type of social stratification. If members of the same family, and even brothers and sisters, may carry gene combinations different enough to make their endowments and capacities radically divergent, it is reasonable to evaluate a person according to his own deserts and not according to those of his ancestors.

An aristocratic social structure can only perpetuate, for a time, the genetic distinctions already present at the inception of the social stratification. The different classes in such a society may be genetically different either because of different geographic origin, or because the stratification originally involved a selection, whether deliberate or unintentional, of persons with different genetic endowments. If so, the genetic differences between the classes will be perpetuated for a shorter or a longer time depending upon the frequency of intermarriage of representatives of different classes. These differences will, however, of necessity decline and finally disappear with time. Of course, high standards in an aristocracy may be maintained through careful upbringing and education of the scions of certain families, but then the social stratification will be based ultimately on training and not on genetic differences. Thus aristocratic systems of the extreme type can only conserve, but never create, a biological distinction.

In a society based on complete equality of opportunity the situation will be radically different. In such a society every individual becomes a member of the class to which he is best fitted by his personal qualities, regardless of the situation of his ancestors. It is sometimes wrongly supposed that social classes may be genetically distinct only if founded on aristocratic principles. This is not necessarily so at all. It is, of course, true that if the merits which cause an individual to go up and down on the social scale are not controlled by biological heredity then the social stratification based on an equality of opportunity will have no biological counterpart.

Suppose, however, that the merits of an individual are determined in part by the combination of the genes he carries, and that the gene combinations which are likely to be encountered in the relatives of that individual may produce very different "merits" or "demerits." Such a supposition is by no means farfetched if heredity is transmitted through genes rather than through "blood"; all that this supposition involves is to grant the possibility that brothers and sisters may carry different gene combinations. Given equality of opportunity, the carriers of certain gene combinations, regardless of whether they are or are not close relatives, will fall into a certain class, profession, or occupational group. These classes and groups then will be to some extent genetically different from each other. For example, the profession of musicians would include everybody who has a genetic endowment helping him to become a successful musician; but some near relatives of musicians may be genetically more fitted to become engineers or truck drivers, and they would be engineers or truck drivers by profession. Theoretically, such classes and groups in a "democratic" society may come to reflect the genetic variability present in a population to an extent much greater than what would occur in a society built on aristocratic principles. It must, however, be clearly understood that such classes and groups do not form distinct biological populations any more than do blue-eyed and brown-eyed persons, or persons belonging to the O and the A blood groups. Classes and groups in a society based on equality of opportunity are not racially distinct.

In reality, a social stratification always involves a compromise between what has been designated above as the aristocratic and the democratic principles. The position of an individual in any existing society is probably determined in part by his own merits and in part by the attainments of his parents and ancestors. It is usually the case that an individual can move up into a more privileged class only by overcoming the resistance of a class barrier; on the other hand, the sinking of an individual down to the less privileged strata is hindered by the social prestige or wealth handed down to him by his ancestors. Complete equality of opportunity has never existed, but neither has the aristocratic principle been practiced rigidly.

Compromise systems of social organization do not in general permit social classes to become biological populations, and hence do not make them racially distinct. The only exceptions to this rule are possible in societies close to the extreme aristocratic end of the range. In such societies racial differences, if present in the beginning because of different geographic origins of the social strata, may be conserved for a shorter or a longer time. The Indian castes are the best example of this, but they show a tendency to become transformed into a purely social institution without any biological basis whatever.

If human skills and aptitudes are in part conditioned by genes, then the different occupational and professional groups formed in a society that permits a fair degree of equality of opportunity may become genetically distinct. In so far as there is a preference for marriages between persons of like tastes and abilities, certain gene combinations that would arise only rarely in an aristocratic society may be formed relatively more frequently in a democratic one. Coupled with this biological agent is the fact that parents possessing special abilities are likely to pass their skills to their genetically conditioned offspring by means of specialized education. This creates favorable circumstances for the manifestation of special gifts and talents. A social or professional group in a democratic society involving a high degree of division of labor may, then, contain a high concentration of certain kinds of genes. And yet, as pointed out above, it would be a fallacy to confuse this type of genetic differentiation with the racial type.

CHARACTER COMPLEXES WHICH DISTINGUISH RACES

The human blood groups have been chosen above as a test case to clarify the genetic nature of racial differentiation and to evolve a definition of race that makes sense in the light of modern biology. The obvious limitation of this test case is that it concerns only a single trait controlled by a single gene having three main variants (a, A, a^B). Many other variable traits exist in the human species, however. Suffice it to mention skin color, eye and hair colors, hair form, stature, and body proportions. The reason for the choice of the blood groups as the test case is that this trait is the one best known genetically. Just how many genes are involved in the production of the other traits mentioned above is uncertain, except that several to many genes are involved in each trait. The total number of genes that vary in the human species is likewise uncertain, but one can make guesses ranging from hundreds to thousands and even tens of thousands.

According to the false "blood" theory of heredity, the maternal and the paternal heredities blend and fuse in the offspring. Actually the genes of the parents preserve their identities, and the offspring receives various combinations of the parental genes. Supposing that the parents carry respectively the genes *ABC* and *abc*, among the grandchildren the combinations *ABC, ABc, AbC, aBC, Abc, aBc, abC*, and *abc* may occur. If parents differ in n genes, there may be 2^n kinds of sex cells with different sets of genes formed in the progeny. As an illustration of the effects of the gene recombination on the variability in human populations one can recall the diversity of types observed among the "colored" people in the United States and particularly in Brazil. Among them the skin color varies from quite fair to black, the nose from very prominent to very broad and depressed, the hair shape from straight to frizzled, etc. Furthermore, these characters are occasionally united in what from the standpoint of persons of pure European or of pure African descent appear to be odd combinations. Thus individuals may be encountered having fair skins but broad and depressed noses, with black skins but prominent noses, with frizzled hair but thin lips, with nearly straight hair but protruding lips, etc.

The independence of genes in inheritance causes enormous difficulties in race classification. Pioneer anthropologists emphasized differences in skin color as race criteria. Very soon, however, nose and hair forms attracted attention. Later in the nineteenth century the shape of the head became very fashionable, first among anthropologists and then among political propagandists. Presently it became apparent, to the great discomfiture of the race classifiers, that classifications built on different traits simply fail to agree with one another. Characters vary independently. Thus in northern Europe longheaded people have fair skins, but the central African longheads have black skins. Yellow and brown skins go together with straight hair in the Asiatic Mongols and American Indians, but some of the natives of South Africa have yellowish skins and extremely frizzled "peppercorn" hair.

If we were to classify mankind on the basis of the distribution of the blood-group genes (Figs. 1 and 2), we would probably distinguish a European race with 25% or more of gene A and 15% or less of gene a^B, an Asiatic race with generally less than 25% of A but more than 15% of a^B, an Australian race with very little a^B but up to 40% of A, and an American race in which the gene a (the blood group O) decidedly predominates but which has minor enclaves of races with very high frequencies of A (the Blackfeet and Bloods in the United States and Canada) or of a^B (in South America). The African populations would cause us some difficulty. Along the Nile there live peoples with rather high frequencies of both A and a^B, West Africa shows moderately high frequencies of A and moderately low ones of a^B, while in southeastern Africa the frequencies of both genes are low. We might thus be forced to unite the West African populations with the European, and to place the southeastern Africans in a race of their own. Such classifications, while possibly adequate as far as the blood groups are concerned, are not much good otherwise. They unite together some peoples who have identical or very similar frequencies of the blood-group genes but who are otherwise quite dissimilar. Indeed, the blood-group frequencies are similar in such different pairs of peoples as the Labrador Eskimos and the aborigines of western Australia, the Chinese from Canton and some Negro tribes from the Belgian Congo, and even the inhabitants of Scotland and the Bushmen of South Africa. Yet one need not be an anthropologist to distinguish a Scot from a Bushman.

There is no very convincing reason however why a classification built on the blood groups should be any better or any worse than one built on skin color, or on head shape, or on hair form, etc. To escape this predicament it has been decided that classifications which take into account the greatest number of characters are the most trustworthy ones. Accordingly, an enormous amount of labor has been invested in careful studies of the living persons as well as of skeletal remains from many parts of the world. Measurements of numerous traits and recordings of traits that are difficult to measure (such as shades of color) have been accumulated by anthropologists. This imposing array of data is then treated with the aid of statistical methods which serve to arrive at averages of the characters measured or recorded. As a result of these measurements and calculations, a system of averages is arrived at for each population or each "racial type," which is a kind of morphological center of gravity toward which the population or type gravitates. One may, for example, invent an "average American," an actually nonexistent person of a certain stature, with a certain cephalic index, chest circumference, length and proportions of the extremities, nose shape, etc.

It would be impertinent to treat the imposing material collected by classical anthropologists with anything less than respect. Indeed, for the purpose of making a descriptive catalogue of the races of man, the systems of averages furnish simple and reasonable entries. And yet the fact remains that none of the many proposed classifications of the human species and its races is regarded as satisfactory by all anthropologists.

There still exist some human body characters insufficiently studied by anthropologists, and there remain some tribes waiting to be investigated. Race classification can be improved by further research along classical lines. But the reason why a satisfactory classification has not yet been developed lies much deeper: the methods used to delimit and describe races are inadequate. These methods were invented in the eighteenth century and they reflect the status of science at that time. An assumption which is implicit in these classifications is that mankind is divisible into a finite number of discrete races. Another implicit assumption is that back of each of these races there is an ideal prototype which the investigator can and should discover and describe. The race prototype is embodied only more or less imperfectly in the concrete representatives of each race, and the imperfections give rise to the annoying phenomenon of variation. Since the race prototypes are difficult to discover, a supplementary hypothesis is made that the discrete races sought for existed as such only in the Golden Age of race purity which is now long past. Humanity is at present mainly a collection of mongrels. Most of us are "race intermediates." But here and there, it is believed, the rare survivors of the pure types can still be discovered.

The above theoretical construction does not agree with the now undeniable fact that race mixture, though doubtless accelerated by the growth of civilization, has been taking place ever since remotest antiquity. It is quite certain that pure races have never existed in man. The idea of racial prototypes stems, unconsciously for the most part, from the "blood" theory of heredity. If that theory were correct, then a population left to reproduce in isolation from other populations would become gradually more and more uniform, and eventually would reach the status of a pure race. At least in theory the ideal racial types could exist in some long isolated populations. But Mendel's discovery has demonstrated that the concept of a pure race is a fallacy, because the variety of genes once present in a population is not consumed or even depleted in the process of sexual reproduction. Human populations have always been variable, although the variability has waned during times of race differentiation and waxed in times of race fusion. The diversity of human genotypes is accordingly immense, practically coextensive with the number of individuals.

Human populations can be described in terms of the relative frequencies of different genes in them, such as the gene for the blood groups. An anthropologist of the future will possess data on the distribution in populations of many different genes for different characters. Such data can be collected if enough scientists realize the need of collecting them. It will then be possible to describe populations with precision simply by stating that they contain so many per cent of the gene A, so many of B, C, D, etc. And it will then also be possible to compare populations quantitatively by indicating the differences in the gene frequencies that exist between them.

Unfortunately, no human gene has been studied nearly as well as the blood-group gene. Hence, the best that can be done at present is to describe the distribution of separate human traits. Although most nonpathological traits are known to be determined by several genes each, it remains true that the genetic mechanisms which underlie the differences in single traits are less complex than the differences between whole organisms.

The data on the distribution of a given trait in various populations can be conveniently summarized in the form of geographic maps similar in principle to those showing the distributions of the blood-group genes in Figures 1 and 2. Such maps for the distribution of stature, cephalic index, head size, and pigmentation of hair and eyes in the populations of Europe and the adjacent parts of Asia and Africa can be found in the excellent book of Coon.[2]

The geographic distributions of different genes are frequently independent. Suppose that we wish to classify European populations according to their average stature. In two regions the inhabitants are very tall, 172 cm or taller on the average. One of these regions embraces Iceland, Scotland, northern England, Scandinavia, and parts of Finland and northwestern Russia. The second region lies in the mountains of southern Yugoslavia. At the opposite extreme, most of Portugal, Spain, France, and Italy are inhabited by peoples who, on the average, are short (165 cm or less). Short peoples also live along the coasts of the Polar Sea, in the extreme north.

The distribution of the cephalic index is completely different from that of stature. The inhabitants of central Europe and the part of Western Europe from southern France across northern Italy to Yugoslavia and Hungary are roundheaded or brachycephalic on the average (cephalic index above 83). Britain and Scandinavia are relatively longheaded or dolichocephalic (average cephalic index below 78). Similar dolichocephalic populations are also found in Portugal and Spain, while the inhabitants of northern Africa are pronouncedly dolichocephalic (cephalic index below 74).

The pigmentation of hair and eyes is again a different story. In parts of Britain, most of Scandinavia, northern Germany, Poland, and western and central Russia light hair and eye colors predominate. In Portugal, Spain, Italy, the Balkans, Turkey, Caucasus, and parts of Russia east of the Volga dark colors predominate. In the territories lying between those just named, light, mixed, and dark pigmentations occur with about equal frequency.

With respect to the blood groups, the European populations show a differentiation principally from west to east.

A skeptic however may ask: what difference does it make whether the human populations are described in terms of ideal race averages or in terms of the distributions of separate characters? Consider, then, the following hypothetical situation. Suppose that you need a blood transfusion, and that you can pick anyone to be your blood donor. Whom should you select for that important function? It is known that blood transfusions are most likely to be successful if the blood of the donor is similar to that of the recipient. Now the whole structure of thought fostered by the classical anthropology would suggest that one should look for blood similarity among members of the same race, tribe, or caste to which the recipient belongs. The solicitude of some people during the war that the blood plasma of white persons be kept separate from that of colored shows this thought clearly. The brothers or sisters of the recipient are, from this point of view, most likely to have blood identical with his. But a familiarity with the principles of genetics shows that the above expectations are far from necessarily correct. Brothers and sisters are quite frequently carriers of different blood groups. On the contrary, it is safe to choose as the blood donor a native of any part of the world quite remote from that of the recipient, provided only that he has similar blood genes, i.e., that he belongs to the same blood group. It does not matter that the donor and the recipient may differ in many other genes. Individuals within a population frequently differ among themselves with respect to genes which are similar in individuals from different populations.

Persons with blood of O, A, B, and AB groups occur almost everywhere on the globe, although some blood groups are relatively more frequent in some geographic regions than in others. Persons with blond hair and blue eyes, and persons with dark hair and brown eyes, also occur in many countries, although the frequency of blondism is high in some and low in other territories.

Moreover, the distributions of the blood groups on one side and of the types of pigmentation on the other are not correlated. In any case, the genes which an individual inherits are not completely determined by the race in which this individual is born. To be certain, if races differ in gene frequencies, then the probability that an individual taken from a given population will carry a given gene may be either greater or smaller than it would be for an individual from another population. However, a complete biological, as well as social, evaluation of an individual can reasonably be made only according to the qualities of this particular individual, and not according to those of his ancestors, his caste, or his race.

RACE BOUNDARIES

Suppose that a blood sample of an individual is given to a specialist on blood grouping. The donor of the blood is otherwise completely unknown to the specialist, but the latter is asked to determine from what part of the world the blood donor or his ancestors have come. Assume that the blood is tested and found to belong to the group AB. An individual with AB blood must carry the genes A and a^B (see p. 91). Examination of the maps in Figures 1 and 2 shows that both these genes occur almost everywhere. It may be noted, however, that American Indian tribes seldom have frequencies of the genes A and a^B sufficiently high to produce many persons with AB blood. Our blood donor is therefore unlikely to be a "pure" American Indian, but beyond that the problem cannot be definitely solved.

Suppose that the same specialist is given not a single blood sample but a collection of blood samples of 100 persons native to the same country and district as the single AB individual mentioned above. The blood samples are analyzed, and 42 of them are found to belong to group O, 42 to group A, 11 to group B, and 5 to group AB. With such or similar frequencies of the different blood groups, the probability that the population from which the samples came is a tribe of "pure-blooded" American Indians has decreased very greatly. Moreover, one may now entertain serious doubts that the population in question is native anywhere in Asia, because in that continent greater proportions of individuals with B and AB blood, and fewer with O and A groups, are likely to be encountered. It is also unlikely that we are dealing with a tribe of

Australian aborigines, because fewer B and AB samples are likely to be found among them. The specialist will probably say that a collection of blood samples such as these is most likely to come from a population native somewhere in Europe or in Africa.

If the collection of the blood samples is increased from 100 to about 10,000 the situation will be still more definite. Assume that the number of O group samples is about 4,500, of A group about 4,100, of B group 1,000, and of AB group about 400. Such a collection is most likely to come from a population native to western Europe, to Britain, the Low Countries, France, possibly but not likely from Spain or Portugal. Of course we might be dealing with a group of western European descent residing anywhere, for example with Americans or white Australians, or with a group so much mixed with the western Europeans that it has acquired the characteristic gene frequencies.

Mankind is less differentiated geographically with respect to blood-group genes than with respect to some other characters. For example, we shall be right far more frequently than wrong if meeting any blue-eyed person we suppose that person to come from a population of European extraction. This is because the genes for blue eyes occur chiefly in Europeans and only in some exceptional tribes of presumably non-European descent. If, however, a majority of a group of ten or more persons from a given population have blue eyes, then it is very probable that this population is native somewhere in the territory stretching from England in the west to central Russia in the east. If a person has the combination of genes which cause his skin to be black, it is certain that this person himself or at least some of his ancestors came from Africa, or from certain tribes in southern Asia, or from Melanesia.

Mankind is racially differentiated. Because of this fact the geographic origin of individuals or groups of individuals can be determined with a higher or lower degree of probability depending upon how many and which ones of their genetically determined traits are examined. By and large, the more traits examined in an individual, and the more individuals examined in a population, the more precisely can be inferred the part of the world from which these individuals come. Scientifically, this is all there is to the "race problem." Beyond this there remain chiefly nomenclatorial issues. Man likes to have a name attached to everything. It is an easily ascertained fact that populations of Africa differ in the frequencies of many genes from the populations of Europe. Africa is inhabited mostly by Negroes and Europe by whites. But where do the Negroes end and the whites begin?

Suppose that one travels from Scandinavia in northern Europe southward through Germany and Italy, to northern and finally to central Africa. The characteristics of the human populations encountered on such a journey will change gradually. The skin color of most Scandinavians is pale, but some individuals have more swarthy skins and the proportion of such individuals increases as one moves southward. In southern Italy most inhabitants have tawny skins, although some individuals with pale and some with darker skins are met with. Across the Mediterranean, the North African Arabs and Berbers continue to vary greatly in pigmentation, ranging from very fair to olive skinned and to medium brown. The desert-dwelling Tuaregs of the Sahara are also variable, but among them the skin color increases to reddish bronze and to dark brown. Still farther south, in Nigeria, the skin color is dark brown to black. Similarly, starting with fair to tawny skins among the Egyptians of the Nile Delta, the incidence of darker coloration increases and lighter coloration decreases as one ascends the Nile. In the Sudan one finally encounters the tall and slim Nilotic Negroes with black skins. Interestingly enough, in South Africa the skin pigmentation again diminishes in intensity, with brown and yellow-brown becoming the predominant colors among the Hottentots and Bushmen.

This gradual change in the incidence of traits in human populations is responsible for what is at first sight a paradoxical situation. Although it is quite clear that Negroes are racially distinct from whites, it is nevertheless difficult to delimit the Negro and white races. For gradual changes in gene frequencies, gene gradients, occur not in the skin color alone but in other traits as well. The transition from the white to the yellow or Mongolian race is even more gradual than that from the white to the Negro race.

There are few places in the world where anything approaching a line of demarcation can be drawn to separate geographic populations sharply distinct in gene frequencies. This absence of sharp dividing lines is often ascribed to centuries of race hybridization. As a general explanation this is misleading; for although gene exchange between geographic populations has become more rapid in modern times, some hybridization has always taken place. The diffuseness of race boundaries is not something accidental or introduced by the advent of civilization or any other peculiarly human phenomenon. Races merge into each other because a race, as it is observed at our time level, is only a passing stage in the process of evolutionary differentiation of populations. Speaking metaphorically, a race is like a stream flowing from a single geographically uniform species into a complex of several derived species. A race starts as a mere ripple on the surface of the population genotype, but it becomes progressively a more and more tangible, discrete, and substantial entity as it approaches specific distinction. Owing to the fact that human races are very far from this stage of speciation, the boundaries between them are very vague. This vagueness is enhanced by the increasing frequency of hybridization in historical times. Hybridization sets back the races further and further from the status of species.

Just as branches of a tree subdivide into ever smaller twigs, so races are susceptible of successive subdivision into races of lower orders. No acute observer is needed to distinguish most natives of Europe from those of central Africa and those of central Asia. It takes more experience to differentiate the populations of northern Europe (so-called Nordics) from those of central Europe (Alpines) and from those of southern Europe and northern Africa (Mediterraneans). It may be impossible to tell apart all individual Norwegians from all southern Germans, and the latter from all southern Italians. Some individuals will be classified wrongly, although the populations to which they belong are readily recognizable as such. The populations of different districts in the same country, or even of neighboring villages, may become distinguishable by the use of statistical methods. We have seen above that the geographic origin of a group of blood samples can be more easily and more exactly defined as the number of samples increases.

A race distinction may be, therefore, as large as that between Negroes and whites, or as small as that between Norwegians and Italians, or as minute as that between inhabitants of neighboring villages. The wisdom of applying the same term "race" to distinctions of such different orders of magnitude may, perhaps, be questioned. The fundamental nature of race differences is however the same regardless of their magnitude, so that a common name has at least the advantage of emphasizing the dynamic nature of the process of race formation and race divergence. No biologically meaningful distinction can be drawn between major, minor, and micro-races, just as the distinction between limbs, branches, and twigs of a tree is quite arbitrary.

The transitions between different races are not, however, absolutely uniform and gradual. For example, in the gradient of skin pigmentation discussed above, some parts of the gradient are steeper than others. Though there certainly is a very considerable difference in the average skin color between the Norwegians and the southern Italians, the really striking change in the incidence of different skin colors occurs as one crosses the Sahara Desert. The inhabitants of the lands south of the Sahara have decidedly dark skins, and those of the countries north of Sahara are relatively much more light skinned. Gradients between the European and the African populations are observed in traits other than the skin color (hair form, nose shape, etc.), and again the changes are most rapid, and hence the differences between adjacent populations most striking, on either side of the Sahara Desert. This fact validates the conventional distinction between the white and the Negro races. In other words, compared to the numbers of persons who can be placed without hesitation either in the white or in the Negro race, individuals and groups that are intermediate between the races are relatively few, and these intermediates occur (or occurred) in only a relatively limited territory.[3]

The fact that character gradients between races are more gradual in some territories and more abrupt in others makes the racial variation of man discontinuous. These discontinuities permit in many cases an approximate delimitation of racial groups, thus making the latter to a certain extent natural, rather than arbitrary, entities. The sharper the discontinuities, the more "natural" the races.

Moreover the breaks in character gradients do not occur at random. Such breaks usually have geographic or historic causes behind them. Abrupt changes in gradients may coincide with natural obstacles to travel, such as great expanses of water, deserts, mountain ranges, forests, etc. The Sahara which separates the territories occupied by the white and the Negro races is even now not easily traversed except by airplane. The population density in the Sahara itself is very low since only few people can eke out an existence from the nearly waterless waste. This makes the diffusion of genes across the Sahara slow, and permits genetic divergence of the populations which live on either side of it. Less than a millennium ago, the inhabitants of the Eurasiatic steppe were able to penetrate the forest expanse bordering the steppe to the north only with great difficulties. Hence a racial boundary separated the forest dwellers from the nomads of the steppe. This boundary is gone at present, because travel in this region is now easy. But the rampart of the Himalayas still remains a formidable obstacle to travel, and hence an ethnographic barrier. The growth of technology erases obstacles to travel and to gene exchange, with the consequent blurring of racial boundaries in recent time.

ORIGIN OF RACE VARIATION IN MAN— PREFATORY REMARKS

The study of races of man or any other biological species may be approached in two ways. First, the morphological, physiological, and other differences between races may be described. Second, the mechanisms that bring about race divergence may be examined and the causes which are responsible for the origin and maintenance of racial differentiation analyzed.

The first approach is predominantly comparative and descriptive. Its goal is definition of the status of racial variation as it exists at present and as it existed in the past. The second approach is, to a greater extent than the first, analytical and dynamic. In organisms other than man it makes wide use of experimental methods. It is concerned not so much with the sequence of events that actually took place in the history of a given species as with the agents which produced these events and which may continue to shape the events of the future. In its application to man, the first approach tells us how human races differ from each other and how they can be classified and arranged in a rational system. In the foregoing pages we have discussed the biological foundations of the methods with the aid of which a classification of races can be made. In the following presentation the agents that have brought about the divergence of human races will be examined.

Few problems in any field of knowledge can rival in fascination that of the mechanics of the origin of human diversity. And yet, far from being solved, the problem is at present receiving very little attention. Even the best books on general anthropology devote only perfunctory pages to this subject; and comparison of modern books with those written as far back as half a century ago discloses that little progress has been made in this field. This unfortunate situation seems to be due largely to a lack of mutual understanding and cooperation between anthropology and biology, particularly genetics.

The biological outlook of most anthropologists is still dominated by a mixture of Lamarckism and Darwinism of a kind which colored the evolutionary thought of the late nineteenth century. Anthropologists are aware of the fact that this concoction of Lamarckism and Darwinism has outlived its usefulness and is derelict, but most of them have had no opportunity to become familiar with modern theories of evolution, just as most geneticists have never acquired the rudiments of anthropology. Unfortunately the effect of this situation has been to arrest the progress of work on the mechanics of evolution in man.

In the nineteenth century it seemed permissible to speculate that Negroes have black skins because many generations of their ancestors had the pigment formed in them owing to exposure to the tropical sun. The scarcity of pigment in the natives of Europe was, according to the same view, ascribed to the bleaching of the skin induced by the paucity of ultraviolet radiations in high latitudes. In our day such views are untenable because they imply a belief in the heritability of characters acquired under the direct influence of the environment. This belief is devoid of experimental foundation and is based on a misunderstanding of the essential phenomena of heredity (see p. 88). For similar reasons, it is no explanation at all to say that inhabitants of deserts have been modified by their environment in a direction different from the inhabitants of wet jungles. What is required is an account of the mechanisms by which the desert and jungle environments modify the heredities of the populations exposed to them. It is misleading to say that races of short stature have been formed because the diet of their ancestors was meager; diet, however meager, does not induce specific changes in the genes that control stature.

The inadequacy of Lamarckism has prompted some anthropologists to explore in other directions for possible explanations of race differentiation in man. It has been suggested, for example, that some of the differences between the major human races resemble those produced by different levels of the hormonal activity in various parts of the endocrine system. According to this hypothesis, many racial characteristics might be merely outward signs of the more fundamental distinctions in the endocrine organs. It is undeniable that an important step forward in the understanding of race physiology would be made if this hypothesis could be substantiated (although actually it is still very far from proven). It must, however, be noted that the problem of the origin of races would not be solved thereby. However desirable it might be to know how different endocrine levels in the human organism change certain bodily proportions, it remains necessary to ascertain the causes which bring about such endocrine differences. Indeed, the endocrine glands, just as all other bodily traits and functions, are in the last analysis governed by the genes.

Perhaps equally or more important than the suspected endocrine differences between human races is the finding that in certain morphological characters man resembles the embryonic and infantile stages of development of the great apes more than he does the adult apes. The evolutionary process giving rise to the human species seemingly involved so-called fetalization or infantilism. Furthermore, in some human races, which from this standpoint are considered to be the "advanced" races, the process of fetalization has gone further than it has in the supposedly more "primitive" races. Thus a low but elongated (dolichocephalic) braincase and a prominent lower part of the face, perhaps together with a rugged bodily build, are the presumed "primitive" features, while a high and rounded (brachycephalic) braincase, reduction of the lower part of the face, and perhaps a more rounded and delicate bodily build are the "advanced" infantile traits.

If confirmed, the theory of fetalization would permit an anthropologist to see a functional connection between the various differences which he finds among human populations. It would then be unnecessary to look for explanations of each of these differences taken separately, but it would still be necessary to find what genetic mechanisms induce fetalization and why fetalization has progressed further in some races than in others. The theory of fetalization is at the bottom only a restatement of the fact of race diversity in comparative morphological and embryological terms. Such a restatement may, to be sure, be very helpful in the search for a causal explanation of this diversity, but it does not in itself constitute an explanation.

Modern biology knows only four agents which, singly or in combinations, may be involved in the formation of race differences, in the maintenance of the race distinctions, and in race fusion. These agents are mutation, selection, genetic drift, and hybridization. The origin and subsequent fate of the human races can be understood causally only in terms of these agents. This is far from saying that the specifically human features of the evolutionary pattern of man should be left out of consideration. On the contrary, civilization has undoubtedly exerted, and is bound to continue to exert, a profound influence on the evolution of mankind, so much so that any attempt to treat the biology of human populations without reference to cultural factors is fallacious from the start. But it must be realized that as far as biologically inherited race differences are concerned, no cultural factor can influence them directly. Such influence can be and actually is exerted only through the medium of the four biological factors named above.

In our consideration of the origin of racial differentiation in man the physical characters will be discussed first and the mental or psychical characters thereafter. The limitations of the traditional distinction of the physical versus the psychical are fully realized. Yet this distinction is convenient at least for the purposes of presentation. Physical and psychical characteristics are subject to somewhat different regularities in human evolution. It is most desirable to clarify these differences, because the failure to appreciate them is responsible for a part of the confusion that exists around the "race problem."

MUTATION

A mutation is a sudden change in the genetic materials, and hence in the heredity of an organism. The extent of the outwardly perceptible alterations produced by a mutation varies all the way from changes drastic enough to kill the organism (lethal mutations), down to modifications so slight that they can be detected only with the aid of statistical methods. For technical reasons, mutations can be studied most conveniently in organisms whose breeding is easily controlled in experiments. Man being least favorable for such control, very little is known directly about mutations in the human species. There is, however, no ground to suppose that the regularities of the mutation process in man are different from those in other organisms. The basic genetic processes are surprisingly uniform throughout the living world, including man.

All body parts and all kinds of traits are subject to mutational change. Mutations may influence the seemingly "superficial" characters, like shades of pigmentation or sizes and proportions of this or that body part. On the other hand, some mutations alter characters as "fundamental" as the key processes of embryonic development. The outwardly visible parts, such as skin and hair, as well as internal body organs, are influenced by mutations. Changes may involve visible structures or physiological processes which have no perceptible morphological effects (such as variations in the metabolism, e.g., diabetes in man). Mutational changes may produce chemical alterations of the blood (e.g., the blood groups), or of the reflexes, "instincts," and behaviors. In other words, any type of difference that may occur between individuals and populations may arise by mutation, or at least it may be compounded of several mutational steps.

Since mutation is the only known way in which hereditary changes arise, it is regarded as the mainspring and fountainhead of all organic evolution. This does not, however, mean that mutation and evolution are synonymous. The role of mutation in evolution may be likened to the delivery of raw materials to a factory. It is evident that no factory can operate for long without raw materials, but raw materials alone are not the manufactured products.

At first sight it may seem that mutation is a very rare event. With the aid of ingenious mathematical calculations, Haldane has computed that 1 in approximately 100,000 haemophilia genes in man mutates in every generation from its normal state to the state that gives rise to the pathological symptoms of haemophilia. However, taking into account the fact that every egg cell and half of the spermatozoa carry this gene, the number of new mutations to haemophilia that arise in every generation in mankind is not inconsiderable. Furthermore, there are probably thousands of genes in man that undergo mutation from time to time; if the mutation frequencies in these genes are of the same order of magnitude as in the haemophilia gene, the numbers of mutations that arise in every generation in the human species must be quite large.

More important still, the mutant genes do not mix with the normal ones, and hence the products of the mutation process do not become dissolved and lost in the sea of normal nonmutant genes. According to Mendel's law, each gene preserves its identity in hybrids. Since mutation takes place relentlessly in every generation, mutant genes accumulate in the population. The genetic variability present in any population has arisen by mutation, but it does not arise anew in every generation. Thus among the mutant genes that now exist in the sufferers and carriers of haemophilia

some appeared in the sex cells that gave rise to the present generation, others in the preceding generation, others two, three, or many
generations ago. In such a way even very small mutation rates will
result in the accumulation of great numbers of mutant genes after
many generations. The mutant genes may in time become as common as the ancestral normal genes, and eventually may supplant
the ancestral genes and come to constitute the new "norm."

As a matter of fact, distinction between the "normal" and the
mutant genes in a population may be impossible. We call "normal" things that we see frequently around us, while rare things are
"abnormal" or exceptional. Yet a gene frequently met with in a
population may be newer than a less frequent gene. For example,
nobody knows for certain the eye color of the ancestors of the
human species. If, as seems probable, our ancestors had brown eyes
then the genes for the blue eye color must have arisen from the
brown genes by mutation. However, in some parts of Europe blue
eyes are now the "norm," in the sense that they are the most frequent condition in the population, while brown eyes are less
common. The same problem arises in connection with skin color
—man's ancestors may have had black, brown, yellow, or white
skins, but in any case some of the now existing genes for skin
color must have arisen at some time by mutation from other genes.
Any other variable nonpathological human character may fluc-
tuate in the same way.

It is most desirable for the understanding of human evolution to
accumulate data on the mutation rates in man, i.e., on the frequencies per generation with which various human genes give
rise to altered variants. Such data are at present very scarce. Nevertheless, at the present level of biological knowledge the best working hypothesis is that the entire hereditary diversity present in the
human species arose through accumulation of mutations.

A theoretical example of how the mutation process could bring
about diversification of human populations may now be discussed. It is known that in most human populations individuals
are encountered who possess the blood groups O, A, B, and AB.
Therefore the three variants of the blood-group gene, a, A, and
a^B, occur in most human populations. The question at issue is:
what is the origin of this diversity of the blood-group genes? It
may seem at first sight simplest to suppose, and such a conjecture
has actually been made, that the three blood-group genes arose
in different parts of the world and gave rise to three different

"pure races" in which every individual belonged to the blood groups O, A, and B respectively. These "pure races" have subsequently hybridized, and the resulting mixed populations have spread to nearly all parts of the world. Since the gene a^B is commonest in central Asia, it has even been suggested that the ancestors of the modern Mongolians had only the blood group B. The gene a^B is supposed to have been introduced into Europe and in other regions by the Mongolian invaders during the population movements issuing from central Asia and invading Europe.

The conjecture just outlined is, however, very improbable. For the sake of the argument, suppose that at some time mankind did consist of three races "pure" for the blood groups O, A, and B respectively. These races must, however, have arisen from some more remote common ancestor. Now, regardless of what blood group this common ancestor belonged to, one must face the problem of how the three "pure races" appeared. This is precisely the problem of the origin of the diversity of the blood groups in the human species which the above conjecture pretended to explain. The assumption of a stage of three "pure races" in the development of mankind is clearly superfluous, since it merely pushes the problem back into the dim past. This assumption becomes hopelessly farfetched if one takes into account the fact that a similar diversity of the blood groups exists not only in man but in the anthropoid apes as well. Blood groups O and A have been found in chimpanzees, A, B, and AB among orangoutangs, A and B among gorillas, and A, B, and AB among gibbons. Must we suppose that the races "pure" for the blood groups existed even before the species ancestral to both man and the anthropoid apes had split into the branches leading to the modern species?

No such supposition is necessary. Populations mixed with respect to the blood groups can arise anywhere, at any time, if the blood group genes a, A, and a^B are occasionally converted into each other by mutation. It is unknown how frequent such mutations actually are, but it is virtually certain that they do occasionally take place. Suppose, then, that the mutation rate from the gene a to A and a^B is about 0.000,005 (this would mean that approximately one gene in every 200,000 a genes mutates to the A or a^B states in every generation). Now let the genes A and a^B be in turn subject to mutation to the state a at a rate of about 0.000,010 (one in every 100,000 per generation). The mutation rates to and from a given gene are symbolized by v and u respectively. It can be shown mathematically that, with mutually opposed mutation rates v and u, the frequency, q, of the gene a in the population will become:

$$q = \frac{v}{u + v} = \frac{0.000,010}{0.000,005 + 0.000,010} = 0.67, \text{ or } 67\%$$

It can therefore be seen that if the blood-group genes are in fact subject to mutation, human populations will come to contain different blood groups. With the mutation rates assumed above, the frequency of the gene a (for the O blood group) will eventually become about 67% of the total gene pool. The combined frequency of the genes A and a^B will then amount to the remaining 33% of the gene pool. These are the approximate frequencies of the blood-group genes that are actually found in the populations of western Europe and some other countries.

Human populations vary with respect to many traits besides the blood groups. Suffice it to recall the variations in eye and hair colors, in stature, cephalic index, etc. The hypothesis used to account for the origin of the diversity of the blood-group genes can be applied to other genes as well. If mutations to and from a given gene take place with finite frequencies, the populations will become mixtures of individuals carrying the different variants of that gene. Diversity of genes will produce diversity of traits.

Though the mutation hypothesis can account for the origin of the heritable diversity within a species, it does not necessarily explain how the species becomes split into diverging races. In general, the same mutations occur in all populations that compose the species. This will make different individuals within each population different from each other, but will not make the incidence of the mutant and the normal genes different in different populations. Thus the mutation pressure is enough to account for the existence of several blood groups in human populations. However, human races are not simply collections of individuals with a certain blood group. Races are populations which differ in the incidence of the blood groups and of other heritable traits. The mutation process has brought about the differences within human populations, but it does not alone produce racial differences between the populations.

One can conjecture that the mutation rates are greater in populations that inhabit some countries and lower in other countries.

If so, the frequencies of certain genes will become different in these countries. Thus the mutations toward the gene a^B may be more frequent, or mutations away from that gene less frequent, in Mongolia than elsewhere; this would explain the high incidence of the blood group B in Mongolian and other Asiatic populations (Fig. 2). In this case, the problem of the origin of human races would turn upon the origin of the differences between the mutation rates in these races. But this is like trying to solve an equation for one unknown by introducing another unknown. Still another conjecture may be that the environments prevailing in different countries modify the relative mutation rates of some genes and thus cause racial differentiation. At the present level of biological knowledge such a supposition can neither be proven nor definitely disproven. Fortunately, other evolutionary factors exist which can bring about race differentiation and make these conjectures unnecessary.

GENETIC DRIFT

It has been stated on page 91 that one of the basic theorems of genetics is that the frequency of a gene in a sexually reproducing population tends to remain constant indefinitely, generation after generation. For example, the frequencies of the blood-group genes a, A, and a^B in the United States population are respectively 67%, 26%, and 7%. If the population of the United States should be examined 100 years from now, the frequencies of the blood-group genes will be very much the same as they are now, unless one or both of the following things happen: (1) relatively more persons of certain blood groups than of other blood groups emigrate from or immigrate to the United States, or (2) individuals that belong to some blood groups live longer and produce more or healthier offspring than those of other blood groups. In reality, the second of these contingencies is improbable since all the attempts to correlate the blood groups with health, disease, or any other externally perceptible traits have so far been unsuccessful. The first contingency cannot be excluded, but it is not important for the theory presented below.

The expectation that the incidence of the blood groups in the United States population will remain constant generation after generation is, it must be noted, based on the fact that this population is numerically very large. It so happens that in populations that consist of small numbers of individuals the gene frequencies need not remain as constant as they do in large populations. A complete mathematical proof of this assertion is a rather abstruse matter, but a simple example will show the essence of the argument.

If a coin is tossed it is as likely to fall heads up as tails up. Therefore if a coin is tossed, say, 1,000 times, there will be *approximately* as many heads as tails. To be sure, exactly 500 heads and 500 tails will be obtained rather rarely; in about half of the coin-tossing experiments there will be between 489 heads and 511 tails or vice versa. However, if we express these results in percentages, it will be found that they fall mostly within 1% or 2% of the "ideal," i.e., 50%. Only rarely will as few as 45% or as many as 55% of heads or of tails be obtained.

If the same coin is tossed only 10 times, instead of 1,000 times, one still expects about half heads and half tails. Ideally, this would mean 5 heads and 5 tails. But a 4–6 result will be quite frequent, and 3–7 and 2–8 distributions will not be very rare. One may obtain, though seldom, even 10 heads or 10 tails in succession. Now, expressed in percentages a 4–6 distribution means 40% to 60%, a 3–7 distribution 30% to 70%, and a 0–10 distribution 0% to 100%. Hence the results of tossing a coin 10 times are relatively far more variable than the result of tossing the same coin 1,000 times. On the whole, the greater the number of tosses the closer the frequencies of heads and tails are likely to be to the ideal 50%.

The transfer of genes from a preceding to a succeeding generation is, in a sense, a process somewhat akin to tossing coins. Suppose that in a certain population 500 babies are born from 500 parents. Since each individual has two genes for the blood group (one maternal and one paternal gene), this means that 1,000 genes are incorporated in each generation. Assume that among the parents 500 genes, or 50%, are *a* and the other 500 genes, or 50%, are *A*. What will be the proportions of *a* and *A* genes among the offspring? An approximate answer to this question is given by the above experiment of tossing a coin 1,000 times. The numbers of the genes *a* and *A* will be in the neighborhood of 500 each, mostly within one or two dozen genes from the ideal figure. Except very rarely, the proportions of each of the two genes will remain between, say, 45% and 55%.

If the numbers of the parental genes and of genes in the offspring are both 10, instead of 1,000, the probable fate of the population will be approximately described by the experiment of tossing a coin 10 times. In other words, the frequencies of the genes *a* and *A* in the offspring are liable to deviate quite widely from the ideal 50%. Though rarely, it may even happen that either the gene *a* or *A* will be lost altogether.

It is justifiable to conclude that perfect constancy of gene frequencies can be expected only in ideal, infinitely large, populations. In reality gene frequencies are variable. This variability of gene frequencies is known as genetic drift or the Sewall Wright effect.

Variations in gene frequencies are trifling in very large populations but important in small ones. Most human populations in our time are so large that the variations of the gene frequencies in them are of little consequence, except in terms of very long time intervals. Unless some human strains expand greatly at the expense of other strains, the frequencies of the blood groups in the populations of most countries will remain for a long time to come approximately what they are now. There exist however in some remote places tribes of primitive peoples which are numerically so small and so isolated from other peoples that important variations of gene frequencies may take place in their populations. Such small and isolated tribes are of interest especially because in the past large numbers of mankind probably led the life of small endogamous groups scattered in large sparsely settled territories. If so, the genetic drift may have been far more important in the differentiation of the human species in the past than it is now.

Some examples illustrating the action of genetic drift may nevertheless be observed even in a country with so highly advanced a civilization as the United States. Those who are acquainted with the rural areas of this country may have encountered villages or small towns in which a startlingly high proportion of the inhabitants have some one family name, often a name which is not particularly common in the country as a whole. The origin of such high local concentrations of family names is usually not far to seek. An inquiry discloses that most of the persons having the same name are derived from a prolific early settler who raised a family with many boys, who in turn had large families. Such a multiplication of a single clan may occur also in a large city, but it will produce no striking results; in a village or a small town it is remarkable. A family name is, however, only a label which indicates that the genes of a certain individual have become spread in a number of persons which is large enough to constitute a perceptible fraction of a population.

An important difference between the lives of primitive and of civilized men is that the former enjoy even less security than the latter. Crop failures and fluctuations in the abundance of game may spell disaster and extermination to once large and prosperous tribes. For example, the survival of certain nomadic tribes in Turkestan may be jeopardized within a week by freakish weather. These people subsist on products of animal husbandry alone; hence the formation of a hard ice crust on the soil surface prevents the livestock from reaching at the pasturage, causing staggering destruction of the animals and consequent starvation of the humans. Only a few centuries ago infectious diseases, such as the black death, killed most of the inhabitants of some districts in Europe.

Conversely, periods of abundance, good health, and peace may lead to rapid population growth. A small tribe may increase in numbers and overflow from its old territory into the surrounding lands. Particularly striking expansions of populations have occurred when relatively small groups of people have discovered and settled previously uninhabited territories. The genes present in a small group may thus become multiplied many times. The same effect of rapid expansion of small groups and consequent multiplication of their genes could also come about without discovery of new territories. An invention which would exploit previously inaccessible natural resources might furnish a livelihood for many persons who could not exist otherwise.

The genetic effect of such fluctuations in numbers of different human strains is that the genes of large populations may have descended from a relatively few ancestral genes. In general the human beings now living have not descended uniformly from all the persons who were living, let us say, in the year 2000 B.C. Many individuals who lived in that year died without producing offspring; the offspring of many other individuals died before they could breed further; many families, clans, tribes, and whole nations were destroyed in the course of history by famines, wars, and other calamities. But the genes of some individuals living in 2000 B.C. have, on the contrary, become multiplied and spread in many persons now living. This funneling of the heredity of large numbers of human beings through relatively small numbers of ancestors intensifies genetic drift.

Genetic drift leads to the increase in incidence of some genes in some territories and of other genes in other territories. In this way the frequency of the blood-group gene *a* may have become stepped up in the ancestors of the present American Indians, most of whom have the blood group O. The incidence of the gene *A* may have similarly increased in the ancestors of the Australian aborigines, and of the gene a^B in the ancestors of the Mongols. But it should be remembered that possession of more *a* genes, or more *A* genes, or more a^B genes, neither helped nor hindered the ancestors of these races in survival and propagation. It was essentially a series of cumulative accidents, of drifting in the direction of increasing the frequencies of certain genes more than in the direction of increasing the frequencies of other genes, that led to the differentiation of mankind into races which differ from each other in blood-group frequencies.

It must be conceded that the hypothesis of race differentiation through genetic drift is for the time being only a speculation; it is a working hypothesis that must be tested by observations on actual populations. To test this hypothesis one needs data on population numbers and on the degree of endogamy of various human groups, particularly those living in sparsely inhabited and primitive countries. No less important would be data on the numbers of the actual parents, and if possible of grandparents and other ancestors, from whom the living members of the different tribes and clans are descended. Such data are important because, as stated above, only a fraction of the members of a preceding generation become the actual progenitors of a succeeding generation. The intensity of genetic drift may depend on how large that fraction is. Possibly critical data on the role of genetic drift in the race differentiation of mankind might be obtained through careful genetic studies of isolated tribes of primitive people. If genetic drift is important in racial differentiation, such isolated tribes would be expected to show appreciable differences in the incidence of various genes, particularly of those genes which are neither useful nor harmful for the survival and propagation of their carriers. The blood-group genes are, it appears, a good example of such "neutral" genes. Here is a virgin field for anthropological studies.

A few facts which seem to speak strongly in favor of the importance of genetic drift in the formation of human races are nevertheless known. One such fact concerns the remarkably high variability of the blood-group frequencies among the different tribes of American Indians (see pp. 94). As mentioned above, most tribes show a decided preponderance of the gene *a* (blood group O). Some tribes seemingly consist (or consisted before having been mixed with the white conquerors) of O individuals only, thus showing the highest frequency of the gene *a* found anywhere in the world. Yet the Blackfeet and Bloods in Montana have extraordinarily high proportions of persons with the A blood group; these tribes may, in fact, hold the world's record for a high incidence of the gene *A*. Finally, a tribe in South America seems to contain an extremely high frequency of the blood group B (the gene *a^B*). Taken as a whole, the American Indians display, therefore, a greater variability in the blood-group frequencies than all the rest of mankind together.

This high variability is expected because of the mode of origin of the American Indian populations. It is established beyond doubt that the ancestors of the American Indians have moved into the New World from northeastern Asia, across the Bering Strait. We need not enter into consideration of the less firmly established contention that some migrants came in the pre-Columbian days across the Pacific Ocean to the west coast of South America. Both the Bering Strait route and the possible transpacific routes were surely so difficult and inhospitable that the total number of individual migrants from whom the pre-Columbian populations of the Americas were descended must have been small. All the blood-group genes of the American Indian populations have, before the advent of the European settlers, been derived from the genes of these migrants, plus whatever mutations may have occurred since.

The offspring of the original migrants became spread over the vast land area which extends from Alaska to Tierra del Fuego. It is certain that many territories were settled originally by small groups of pioneers. This circumstance favors genetic drift, which would result in the very high variability of the blood-group frequencies that is actually observed in the aboriginal American populations. It would be most interesting to know if American Indians show high variabilities not only in the blood groups but also in other genetic characteristics of a similar kind. It is to be hoped that data of this sort will be collected in the near future. Because of the rapid development of communications even in the most remote corners of the world, and the consequent mixing of previously isolated tribes, such investigation cannot be long postponed. In fact, it is possible that our generation is the last one which can still secure data of momentous significance for the solution of the problem of the origin of human races.

SELECTION

Regardless of the degree of importance which will eventually be ascribed to genetic drift, it is very improbable that the entire racial differentiation of the human species can ever be satisfactorily accounted for by genetic drift and its interactions with the process of mutation. The differences in blood groups are only a small part of the genetic differences between the human races. Furthermore, the variability of many traits is in some respects different from that of the blood groups.

Probably the most commonplace distinction between human races is that of skin color. Variation in skin color differs from that in blood groups in at least two ways. First, most human populations all over the world are mixtures of individuals of all four blood groups. Racial differences in terms of blood groups are clearly differences in the relative frequencies of the different blood-group genes, not in the presence or absence of this or that blood group in the inhabitants of various territories. This is the reason why the blood groups have been used above as a test case for clarification of the race concept. Racial differences in skin color are much sharper. With the exception of a few albinos, all natives of central Africa have more or less dark skins, and all natives of Europe have more or less pale skins. Secondly, the inheritance of blood groups is much simpler than that of skin color. The blood groups are in the main conditioned by the three variants, a, A, and a^B, of a single gene. The genetic basis of skin color is quite complex, so much so that the genetic mechanism underlying skin pigmentation is far from adequately understood at present. All one can say with assurance is that several genes for pigment formation, some having more striking effects than others, are involved.

Even so, racial variation in skin color does not differ in principle from that in the blood group. Anyone can observe persons with lighter and with swarthier skins in almost any population of European descent. A part of this variation is obviously due to varying degrees of the exposure of the skin to the sun's rays, but a part is hereditary. Individuals in a European population may, therefore, differ among themselves in that some of them carry pigment-forming genes which other individuals do not carry. Populations of different countries in Europe may differ in the incidence of these pigment-forming genes, for example, such genes are more frequent in the population of Italy than in Norway. The same is probably true for populations of different parts of Africa. The racial variation in skin pigmentation is, like that in the blood groups, due to differences in the incidence of pigment-forming genes in human populations.

The fact that a native of central Africa always has a much darker skin than a European means, however, that 100% of the individuals in African populations have enough pigment-forming genes to produce a decidedly dark skin. One hundred per cent of the individuals in European populations have so few pigment-forming genes that their skins are light. It is conceivable (although certainly not proven) that most of the genes whose interaction makes the Negro skin black occur scattered in the European populations as well, but the concentrations of each of these genes are so low in Europe that no individual is at all likely to inherit more than a few of them. The skin color of Europeans is sometimes swarthy but never black.

The problem is, then, to visualize the origin of human populations differing in skin color. There is no difficulty in understanding the origin of the pigment genes. No matter what was the skin color in the ancestors of mankind, the process of mutation can give rise to gene variants that either increase or diminish the pigmentation. There may arise genes which intensify or suppress pigment formation in the skin. The more numerous such mutations in a population, the greater will be the variation in skin color among the members of that population. As an extreme result of a long-continued accumulation of such mutants one can imagine a population somewhat resembling "colored" people in the United States. Pale and black skins, as well as all intergrades between them, would occur in such a population, but the extreme color would be very much less frequent than the intermediate conditions.

The process of mutation is, then, capable of producing the gene variants from which race differences can be built. This is just as true for skin colors as it is for blood groups or for any other heritable trait. However, the presence of the genetic raw materials from which race differences can be built does not explain how these differences become established. In the case of blood groups genetic drift appears to be the probable agent of race differentiation. But to imagine that race differences in skin color arise by a similar method is next to impossible. Every native of central Africa carries enough pigment genes to make his skin very dark, while every native of Europe has so few pigment genes that his skin is more or less light. In other words, the degree of race differentiation in skin color is much greater than that in blood groups.

The origin of racial differences in skin color through genetic drift alone would require so improbable a succession of evolutionary accidents that the hypothesis of genetic drift in this case succumbs under its own weight. One would have to imagine that the respective ancestors of the Negro and white races were repeatedly reduced during their history to single pairs of progenitors, recurrent racial Adams and Eves. Furthermore, every time such a reduction happened the progenitors of the Negroes by chance possessed more pigment genes than the population whence they came, while the progenitors of the whites by chance carried fewer pigment genes than their ancestors. If we assume that the racial differences in the blood groups show how great may be race differences due to genetic drift in the human species, it is obvious that the divergence in skin pigmentation is far too great to be so accounted for.

The only evolutionary agent other than genetic drift that can be invoked to further the process of racial differentiation is selection. Suppose that individuals who carry more pigment-producing genes, and hence have darker skins with equal exposure to sunlight, are healthier or more prolific in the environment of central Africa than are individuals with few pigment genes. Conversely, individuals with few pigment genes, and hence with light skins, are healthier or more prolific in the European environments. Such differential survival and fertility would result, generation after generation, in a gradual but steady increase of the incidence of pigment-forming genes in the African populations, and in a decline of the frequencies of such genes in the European populations. The concentration of pigment genes may eventually approach 100% in Africa and 0% in Europe.

It must be emphasized that to be effective, contrary to the assertions made by some writers, Darwinian natural selection does not require wholesale destruction in Africa of every person with little skin pigment, nor of everybody with a dark skin in the European environments. Racial differences can arise from very slight viability or fecundity differentials in different environments. In other words, natural selection is not an embodiment of "Nature red in tooth and claw." Selection may fail to perpetuate genes rather than destroy them, and may multiply other genes by making their carriers more prolific rather than by inducing these carriers to devour the possessors of less favored genes. Genetic drift is merely a series of accidental displacements of gene frequencies which may or may not add up to an appreciable net change; selection is a directional process which is likely to be more efficient than genetic drift.

The validity of the hypothesis of building up race differences in skin pigmentation by natural selection depends upon whether or not the presence or absence of the pigment in the skin confers upon its possessor some advantage or disadvantage in certain environments. If the hypothesis is correct, it should be possible to prove that individuals with dark skins survive or reproduce in the environments of central Africa and other countries in which black-skinned races have arisen more successfully than people with white skins. Likewise, it should be possible to prove that a pigmentless skin is somehow advantageous in the environments of Europe, or at least that it was advantageous at the time when the white race was in the process of formation. Unless the adaptive significance of skin pigmentation is demonstrated the hypothesis cannot be regarded as proven.

The anthropological, physiological, and medical literatures contain dozens if not hundreds of papers dealing with skin pigmentation in man. Yet no incontrovertible evidence that pigmentation genes have survival value seems to be available. Of course, it is well known that prolonged exposure of scantily pigmented skin to intense sunlight leads to dangerous burns. However, most persons of the white race can develop enough protective tanning by means of a gradual adaptation to enable them to withstand further exposure without harm. It is not obvious, then, that primitive men with moderately pigmented skins were at any disadvantage in climates with strong sunshine compared to black-skinned persons.

It is of course quite possible that the disadvantages of scanty pigmentation in sunny climates are not directly related to the protection against exposure to ultraviolet radiations. One can read many, and hear even more, assertions that the "white man" is ill adapted to tropical environments, and hence suffers bodily and psychic injury as a result of tropical residence. Much of the literature containing these assertions hardly deserves being regarded as scientific. This is not to deny the possibility that there may indeed exist physiological maladjustments in persons of white race in the tropics. But it remains to be shown that such maladjustments are caused even in part by deficiency of skin pigment.

The converse proposition, namely, that scarcity of skin pigment favors survival or reproduction in climates with low intensities of sunlight is even less securely established. A possibility has been pointed out that the ultraviolet radiation impinging upon an unpigmented skin produces greater quantities of vitamin D than it does in a dark skin. The importance of vitamin D for health is certainly beyond doubt. Its deficiency causes serious pathological symptoms, among which rickets in growing children are most widely known. If the alleged relation between skin pigmentation and vitamin D requirements could be ascertained, the hypothesis that natural selection led to a depigmentation of the populations living in territories with little sunshine would be very greatly strengthened. Such a demonstration is, however, a matter for future investigation.

There is even less positive knowledge about the adaptive significance of human racial characters other than skin pigmentation. For example, does frizzy hair favor perpetuation of human strains in Africa and coarse and straight hair in most of Asia? What is the survival value of the "Mongolian" fold on the upper eyelid, a character very constant in some races? Why is it advantageous for the inhabitants of central Europe to have round (brachycephalic) heads and for the natives of northern Europe and of most of the Mediterranean region to have long (dolichocephalic) heads? There are no known answers to these questions.

In a most interesting recent paper by Weidenreich[4] it is shown that the human species as a whole, or at least considerable sections of it, exhibits a steady trend toward rounder and rounder heads. For example, during prehistorical as well as historical times the population of central Europe has been developing more and more brachycephalic heads. According to Weidenreich, this is not caused by immigration of strongly brachycephalic human strains from outside this region. Having established this important fact, Weidenreich did not even raise the question about the possible survival advantages of the different head shapes, nor did he offer any other suggestion concerning the cause of the trend toward brachycephaly.

This attitude is rather general among anthropologists, human physiologists, and medical scientists. The bodily characters that distinguish human races are implicitly, or even explicitly, assumed to be of no significance in survival and reproduction. Such a point of view could have been maintained in the nineteenth century, when it was believed that the environment changes hereditary traits by direct influences. But it is known at present that the influence of the environment on evolution is exerted not through direct modification but through natural selection, genetic drift, and possibly through altering the mutation rates. The assumption that human racial characters are neutral for survival makes the origin of racial differentiation in man an apparently insoluble puzzle. A geneticist can only most respectfully suggest to his colleagues in the sister disciplines that this assumption is very probably wrong and that the problem deserves more careful study.

This should not be construed as a denial of the existence of truly neutral traits. It so happens that the blood groups in man are probably the racial trait most carefully studied for possible correlations with other physiological and pathological characters, and that these studies have failed to discover such correlations. But if the blood groups are a neutral trait it certainly does not follow that other racial traits are also neutral. Many racial traits, such as skin color, show far too much divergence in the human species to permit race differentiation to be accounted for by genetic drift alone, and without intervention of natural selection.

In a sense, our discussion has thus reached an impasse: a process of selection seems to be necessary to account for racial differentiation, and yet positive data which would warrant the assumption that racial traits have selective value are lacking. The realization of this difficulty, regardless of whether the impasse will finally prove to be real or only apparent, may in the final reckoning be most fruitful. This realization definitely points toward the necessity of careful studies in the fields of comparative human physiology, pathology, and genetics. Studies of this kind have never been undertaken.

There is a possibility which, though it can hardly be imagined to remove the above impasse, may make it somewhat less formidable. There exist forms of selection on the animal level, and even more on the human level, which do not require the traits selected to be either conducive or detrimental to physical health or survival. They are related to Darwinian sexual selection. Ideals of beauty and sexual desirability vary to a surprising extent in different lands and at different times. A lady with small feet may be considered attractive among Westerners, although the addiction to the smallness of feet which leads to mutilation by binding the feet from infancy seems preposterous to us. But the Chinese thought otherwise for centuries.

Here, then, is a factor which may initiate a selective process which, if long continued, could bring about considerable divergence of the gene frequencies in human populations. A circumstance which militates against the effectiveness of a selective process of this kind is that among primitive peoples there are usually but few spinsters and bachelors, most adult persons thus having opportunity to become mothers and fathers. Nevertheless, an individual who is regarded as good looking by his fellows may have indirect but very real survival advantages, as well as advantages in productive parenthood. Cultural anthropologists may have data that would permit estimation of the magnitude of the genetic effects of such selection. In any case, such data could be collected.

A brief mention should be made here of other selective processes which, though probably of little importance in racial differentiation, are nevertheless very significant in human evolution. As indicated above, it seems probable that numerous mutations in many genes arise continuously in the human species. Now, in all organisms studied in this respect a majority of mutations are deleterious to their carriers. Many mutant genes in man doubtless belong to the category of hereditary disease producing factors. A disease is, however, a condition which hinders the survival and propagation of its carrier. This hindrance is automatically a selective process that tends to eliminate the "diseased" genes from the gene pool of the population. The only exception to this rule are diseases of old age, which develop after the completion of the reproductive life; natural selection is powerless to eliminate them.

The usefulness or harmfulness of a gene is, however, not independent of the environment prevailing at a given place and time. The qualities that are useful in the intellectual circles of an American city might be of very doubtful value in the jungles of New Guinea and vice versa. A gene may be useful in combination with some but harmful in combination with other genes. As the environment in which the species lives changes, the adaptive values of various genes change also; mutants that were deleterious may become neutral or even useful, and those useful of old may become neutral or harmful. This is even more true for man than for any other species, because surely no other species ever changed its environment as completely as man did when he developed civilization. This was bound to cause radical upsets in the working of natural selection.

Strong teeth were quite important for the prehumans and the primitive humans who tore and ate rough uncooked food. The processing of food, and particularly the use of fire for cooking has made teeth less indispensable. Modern dentistry promises to make them quite dispensable. In our remote forebears the mutations that weakened teeth were accordingly kept in check by natural selection. This selection was relaxed in our less remote ancestors, and the mutation pressure weakening teeth may be able to assert itself. This relaxation of selection against such mutations may explain the reduction not only of the teeth themselves but also of the whole lower part of the face which has taken place in human evolution. The Lamarckian explanation of these reductions, which supposes that teeth and jaws were weakened by lack of strong functional use, is, of course, invalid.

HYBRIDIZATION

Since the parents of any human individual are always different in some genes, everybody is, strictly speaking, a hybrid. In this sense, hybridization in man is universal. On the other hand, the term "hybrid" is sometimes used in a more restricted sense, meaning the offspring of parents who belong to different races or, on the biological level, to different species.

Crossing of individuals which differ from each other in some genes is very important in evolution. The genes recombine in the hybrid offspring, and the sex cells formed by a hybrid carry diverse combinations of the parental genes. As pointed out on page 90, the variety of gene combinations produced in man is so immense that no two human beings, except identical twins, are at all likely to have identical heredities. The gene combinations embodied in different individuals are exposed to the action of natural selection which eliminates some but preserves and multiplies others. Mutations favorable for the survival of the species may arise in different individuals born in different localities. Since mutant genes are not lost among nonmutant genes, they may be preserved in the population and eventually may find their way into the same territory. Hybridization can then combine these favorable genes and thus create new gene complexes more favorable for survival than the old ones. Combining mutant genes is particularly important when these genes produce no very favorable effects when present singly but do so when present together in a gene complex.

The genes that distinguish a given race from other races need not have arisen in the race for which they are now characteristic. Some of these genes may as well have appeared in other populations, and only subsequently may have combined by hybridization and thus become established as racial features. Man as a species may be said to have a collective gene pool, and the genetic processes that are taking place in a part of mankind are potentially of importance to the whole.

Hybridization of different races has two aspects. First it accomplishes the same result as does crossing of individuals within a population, namely, formation of innumerable new gene combinations. Since individuals who belong to different races are likely to differ on the average in more genes than members of the same race, the diversity of gene combinations which may result from race crossing is potentially greater than without such crossing. In so far as some of these gene combinations are likely to be potentially favorable for survival, race crossing may further evolutionary progress.

Second, race hybridization leads to the breakdown of racial differences previously accumulated by selection and genetic drift. It is easy to see why this happens. Races are populations which differ in the frequencies of some genes. If race hybrids join the population of either parental race the gene frequencies in the races are likely to become more and more similar. This is the way toward race fusion.

Desirability or undesirability of race hybridization in man is frequently the subject of passionate controversy. Most of the opinions advanced in this debate are plainly rationalizations of the prejudices of the debaters. Looked at from a biological viewpoint the situation is fairly simple. So far as genetic differences between races have been built by natural selection, the gene complexes of the respective races favor optimal survival and reproduction in the environments in which each race was formed. Hybridization may, then, lead to emergence of less well adapted gene combinations. However, since we have been unable as yet to detect with complete assurance any adaptive differences between human races, the fear of "disharmonies" among human race hybrids is farfetched. Indeed no such disharmonies have been found even by investigators with an acute desire to find them.

Neither is there any reason to think that hybridization of very distinct races leads to beneficial results, such as "rejuvenation of the blood," whatever this expression may mean. On the contrary, wider intermarriage may be distinctly favorable in some populations. Until the advent of the modern era of cheap transportation, a great majority of people the world over led a sedentary existence. In remote places one may find even now many persons who have never been outside the neighborhood of the village or town in which they were born. The circle of potential marriage mates under these conditions was further restricted by all sorts of social and religious considerations. Hence generation after generation marriages occurred among members of a few families living in a small territory and closely related in their pedigrees. Marriage of relatives is known as inbreeding, that of unrelated persons as outbreeding.

Inbreeding may lead to manifestation of recessive genes with unfavorable or even distinctly pathological effects; inbred families are said to "degenerate." However, if scions of inbred families intermarry with those of other families, also inbred but coming from afar and having no common ancestors in recent generations, their offspring may be biologically more vigorous than the parents.

The recent history of mankind is characterized among other things by steadily increasing mobility of populations. Not only has the process of urbanization spread to most lands, but traveling has become safer, easier, and cheaper in rural districts as well. Coincident with this has been a breakdown of customs that used to restrict marriages to narrow circles of potential mates. The consequence of all this has been an increase in the degree of outbreeding which may be expected to stimulate the vigor of populations. One of the manifestations of this increased vigor may be the increase of the average stature of people achieved in countries with advanced civilizations. People have been becoming progressively taller for at least a half century in all countries in which statistical data bearing on this topic are available. Although a part of the increase may doubtless be accounted for by improved nutrition and other non-genetic causes, the transition from inbreeding to outbreeding has probably also contributed its share.

However, one must not jump to the conclusion that the increase in vigor will continue indefinitely as greater and greater masses of people intermarry. "Hybrid vigor" occurs only when marriage of close relatives is replaced by unions of persons who are less closely related; but as more and more human strains enter the interbreeding population, the vigor which accrues from this source very rapidly approaches an upper limit.

INHERITANCE OF PSYCHIC TRAITS

Probably no other problem in the fields of biology, psychology, and anthropology has produced more stubbornly divergent opinions than that of the heredity of psychic traits in man. Hundreds of investigations aimed at the solution of this problem, some of them exceedingly detailed and painstaking, have been made from the time of Galton in the last century to our own day. Nevertheless, the views of different writers still range from the contention that heredity has nothing to do with human behavior to the contention that man's personality, tastes, abilities, and inclinations are rigidly determined by biological inheritance. So great a disagreement suggests two things. First, that opinions on this subject are likely to be colored by biases powerful enough to make people imagine that they have found what they are looking for. Scientists are not immune to this human failing. Second, that there may be something wrong with the way the problem is stated. The same words frequently mean different things to different people. It is with the statement of the problem of inheritance of human behavior that the following paragraphs are concerned.

Heredity determines the reactions of the organism to its environment (see page 88). It is, therefore, a fallacy to argue that a trait is not influenced by heredity because its manifestations are different in different environments. It seems to be proven that environmental influences can modify the intelligence quotient (IQ) to a very appreciable extent. But it does not necessarily follow from this fact that heredity does not enter into the determination of the IQ's. There are good reasons to think that it does. Thus adopted children show significant correlations in their IQ's with their foster parents as well as with their real parents. The IQ's of identical twins reared apart differ on the average more than those of identical twins reared together. This demonstrates that the IQ's are influenced by the environment. Yet fraternal twins reared apart show a still greater average divergence of the IQ's than identical twins raised separately, and fraternal twins living together diverge more than do identical twins in similar circumstances. This indicates that the IQ's are conditioned by heredity.

The conclusion which seems inescapable from the work on the IQ's taken as a whole is that, in the populations so far studied in this respect, part of the observed diversity of the IQ's is caused by heredity and part by environmental influences. Every person inherits from his or her parents a certain gene complex, and is exposed to a certain succession of environments. What IQ a person has in a particular environment is determined by heredity. This statement does not conflict in any way with the assertion that the same person, or other persons with identical or similar heredities, may show very different IQ's if brought up in a different succession of environments.

Although some writers express doubts regarding its validity, the proposition that human behavior is influenced by genetic causes is very easy to prove. To do so one does not even need to mention the gross pathological conditions such as some forms of insanity which are positively known to be caused by mutant genes, or the hereditary diseases that cause blindness or deaf-mutism accompanied by obvious peculiarities in the behavior of the afflicted persons. Let us consider a known inheritable character which at first sight has no relation to the psychic sphere. A certain recessive gene produces a condition known as albinism—absence of pigment which makes the skin pale and incapable of developing a protective coat of tan, and eyes with a pink iris and hypersensitivity to strong light. In general, there is nothing in the behavior of an albino to set him apart from ordinary people. But nobody need be surprised if an albino acts noticeably differently from non-albinos on a hot summer day at a beach resort. Albinos must protect themselves from too strong sun exposures, and most of them are aware of this need and act accordingly. The behavior of an albino on a sunny day is obviously influenced by the gene for albinism. The fact that no peculiarities may be noticeable in the behavior of the same albino on a cloudy day does not change the fact that the gene for albinism modifies the behavior of its carriers. Examples of this kind can be multiplied at will.

In a sense any gene is potentially capable of influencing behavior. In southeastern United States, anyone who carries genes of African origin which appear in his features is forced to display certain peculiar forms of behavior when he comes in contact with representatives of the white race. The whole mentality of carriers of Negroid genes becomes permeated from childhood on with the consequences of the necessity of these forms of behavior. The effects of these genes on the psychic traits of their possessors are indeed tremendous. This statement is not in the least contradicted by the fact that the carriers of similar genes exhibit different behavior if they grow up, for example, in northern or western United States. The same genes produce different effects in different environments. The blood-group genes are not known to influence the behavior or any other externally visible trait. But if a crazy dictator should make the carriers of blood group AB aristocrats and those of blood group O day laborers, then the blood-group genes might become very important in the determination of psychological reactions.

The above statements should not be confused with the widespread but erroneous notion that individuals or races which show variations in their bodily structures must necessarily show correlated differences in their mental make-up. It has been argued by many popular as well as scientific writers that inasmuch as human races differ in visible bodily features they must differ in their psychological reactions as well. This implies the belief that any physical trait has its necessary mental corollary. This belief is bolstered by analogies with races and breeds of wild and domestic animals. Indeed, breeds of dogs and horses have strikingly different temperaments. Compare a high-strung and active fox terrier with a placid and dignified Saint Bernard. Although horses can be trained to perform this or that kind of work, it is difficult to have an Arabian charger draw a milk wagon, and a milk wagon horse will hardly make a good showing on the track. If animal races are so different in their behavior, should human races be any more alike?

As general propositions these arguments are certainly false. Even though mutations in many genes may change several traits at once, there is no necessary connection between every change in externally visible structures or physiological functions on the one hand and psychic traits on the other. Moreover, whether or not a trait undergoes a change or remains constant in evolution depends upon several factors. In the first place, mutations that alter the trait in question may or may not arise. But even assuming that many mutational changes affect a certain trait, such as intelligence or memory, it does not follow that these mutations will necessarily become established as normal properties of the race or species in question. Mutant genes spread if they prove useful for survival or reproduction of the organism. A neutral mutant may or may not be established. The spread in a population of a deleterious mutation is hindered by natural selection. To be sure, natural selection may be powerless to prevent a harmful mutation from arising from time to time in the species and appearing in some individuals as an hereditary "disease." But on the whole the direction of evolutionary changes is rather effectively controlled by natural selection. Therefore, a priori judgments that races of man or of any other species must differ in a certain category of traits, such as mental traits, may be misleading. Analogies and inferences from species to species are even more hazardous, because the evolutionary patterns of different species are variable, and the pattern of the human species is a singular one.

THE EVOLUTIONARY PATTERN OF THE HUMAN SPECIES

The idea of the biological uniqueness of man was clearly set forth more than two thousand years ago in the Platonic myth of the distribution by Epimetheus of protective qualities to the living beings created by the gods. Epimetheus gave strength to some species, to others swiftness, or high fertility, or means of defense such as flying through the air or burrowing in the ground. Only man was forgotten and left unprotected. Prometheus then took pity on man, and so stole fire and the mechanical arts from the gods and gave them to men. Finally, Zeus sent to men reverence and justice, lest they fight and exterminate each other. Aristotle stated the same idea even more concisely in his famous dictum, "Man is by nature a political animal." Strangely enough, the bearing on the biological evolution of the human species of the truth of which this myth is the vehicle is still incompletely realized.

When man's ancestors evolved reasoning abilities and became "political" animals they gained a mastery of the environments on our planet never before approached by any other species. This mastery is achieved through the possession of a highly developed brain. Therefore, the gene complex that permitted the extraordinary development of the brain has automatically, and probably irrevocably, become the key to all subsequent evolutionary developments in the human species.

Natural selection encourages the propagation of those gene complexes which are *as a whole* best adapted for survival in the environments in which their carriers live. Perfection of a single organ or function may confer so high an advantage on a race or a species that it may outbreed and supplant races or species competing with it, even though the losers may have minor advantages over the victor in other organs or functions. This is understandable because natural selection is an agent not endowed with foresight. Selection cannot apprehend advantages or imperfections of separate organs of the body; it is concerned only with over-all fitness or unfitness, and that regardless of whether the fitness is permanent or only temporary. In other words, natural selection is opportunistic.

The opportunism of natural selection explains the strange fact that highly successful species sometimes possess traits lacking in excellence. The human species unfortunately abounds in such traits. The muscular strength of the human body is far below that in many animals of similar bulk. Although difficult to establish with assurance, it seems probable that the ancestors of the human species were relatively brawnier than men now living. If so, degenerative changes in bodily prowess have taken place in man's evolution. The extreme painfulness and hazard connected with childbirth in man are biological absurdities. There is no need to continue this recital of imperfections in man's body. Clearly, control of the environment by brain power has permitted man to get along with weaker bodily power. Of course, this does not mean that all degenerative changes in the human body are tolerated by natural selection. The brain powers being equal, stronger and healthier bodies are selectively advantageous. However, just as the specialization of bats for flight has allowed them to lose the ability to run on the ground possessed by their remote flightless ancestors, similarly the specialization of man for thinking permits him to get along with a weaker body. Animals and plants become adapted to their environments by changing their bodies, while man becomes adapted largely by making inventions that alter his environment. The artificial temperatures in which men live on the equator and near the poles are more nearly alike than the natural temperatures of these regions.

Nevertheless, the human environment is not uniform throughout the world. The natural and especially the social environments in which men live in different countries are quite diversified. No less different may have been the environments at different historical times in the same country. Now an animal or a plant species which inhabits territories with diverse conditions usually responds to this diversity by becoming differentiated into geographic races, each of which is genetically adapted to the conditions prevalent in the particular territory it occupies. There is no apparent reason why race differentiation should not occur in the human species as well, and indeed we observe that human populations of different countries often differ in skin color, hair form, head shape, blood groups, and other physical traits. The supremacy of mental over physical development in human evolution might lead us to expect further that the human races might differ from each other not only in physical but also in psychic traits adapting them to the environments which each of them occupies. This apparently reasonable inference has indeed been made by many nonbiologists as well as by biologists. Nevertheless, a closer examination shows that this inference is probably false.[5]

There are two ways in which biological adaptation can be attained: by genetic specialization and by evolving a favorable norm of reaction to the environment. For the sake of argument let us assume that skin pigmentation protects from sunburn and that the lack of pigment reduces the requirements of the body for vitamin D. The adaptive reaction of the human species to the climates that prevail in different countries may then be twofold. First, in countries with intense sunshine natural selection may favor mutations that increase skin pigmentation, while in countries with little sunshine mutations decreasing the amount of pigment in the skin may be favored. The populations of different countries may therefore come to possess different shades of skin color which are optimal for survival and comfort in the climates that prevail in the respective countries. Second, natural selection may favor genotypes which respond to intense solar radiation by quickly developing a protective coat of tan, but which react to the absence or shortage of sunlight by losing the pigment. The possessors of such genotypes might, theoretically, be equally at home in any climate.

Which one, or what combination, of the above two methods of becoming adapted will be resorted to depends, apart from the kind of mutations that arise in the species, on how stable or variable is the environment. Having a permanently fixed amount of pigment in the skin is desirable if the intensity of sunlight in the territory in which men live is fairly constant. Indeed under moderately constant conditions plasticity of the trait may be undesirable, because the organism would respond to fluctuations in the milieu that are freakish and evanescent. Since any response takes time to become realized, the return of the normal conditions might catch the organism unprepared. Perhaps even more important is the consideration that plasticity implies a complex and unstable physiological mechanism which can easily be disarranged by environmental and by genetic accidents. Studies on the mechanics of development disclose numerous safeguards possessed by the organism that absorb the shocks emanating from the environment and keep the course of development within "normal" bounds. Environmental fixity favors fixity of traits of the species or race.

In many climates the sunshine is, however, abundant at one season of the year and deficient at another season. Or else tribes of people may wander at intervals from territories with heavy cloudiness to lands with clear skies and vice versa. No fixed skin pigmentation will then be suitable, while genes that permit the pigment to appear when called forth by sunshine and to disappear when the solar radiation is deficient will be advantageous. Unstable environments favor genetically determined plasticity of the traits concerned. Indeed, the "white" race which developed in the notoriously changeable climate of Europe is capable of changing its skin color to a remarkable extent when exposed to or protected from solar radiation. The inhabitants of tropical lands in which seasonal variations of sunshine are fairly small have relatively fixed skin colors regardless of sun exposure.

Civilization brings about greater and greater homogeneity of the physical environment in which men live, and at the same time a heterogeneity of the social environment which is truly prodigious and which leaves behind anything known on the animal level. Moreover, the social environments are heterogeneous both in space and in time. To overlook the paramount importance of this fact in human evolution is very shortsighted. It is primarily in the psychic sphere that the adaptation of man to his social environment takes place. Hence the most consistent feature of the human evolutionary pattern must be a trend away from genetic fixity of response and toward environmental plasticity of man's intelligence and behavior. Natural selection in the human species should bring about the development of educability in the broadest sense of that word.

Genetically determined educability is to be sure not indispensable to existence of some forms of social organization. Highly developed societies exist on the animal level, particularly among insects, but the behavior of the members of these societies is, in contrast to human society, more or less rigidly determined and fixed. Though bees, termites, or ants perform marvelously complex and objectively strikingly purposeful series of operations, they are unable except to a very limited extent to modify their actions to suit the circumstances that do not regularly arise in the environment in which the species normally lives. As could be expected on theoretical grounds, species and races of social insects often show genetically fixed adaptive differences in their behavior; these differences are the product of the action of natural selection in the history of the species. Social life on the human level is, however, built on the overtly stated or implicit principle that every normal individual is able to vary his behavior and to fit his actions to either recurrent or unprecedented circumstances and situations. Natural selection would probably eliminate a race of ants that showed a tendency toward varying their behavior under closely similar circumstances, because such variations might be adaptive only by accident. An experimenter endowed with the brain power of an ant can hardly profit by the results of his experimentation. On the human level, the ability to choose paths of behavior on the basis of learning by experience is highly adaptive. This educability furthers survival in any human society.

A mind that runs always in the same groove, a person who evinces the same behavior at all times, whether of meekness or of pugnacity, is gravely handicapped, and in general the more so the higher the organization of the society of which he is a member. It is hardly necessary to stress the obvious point that in primitive as well as in advanced societies a successful individual is one who adjusts his behavior to circumstances. An occasional nonconformist may succeed in following his own inclinations with less regard to circumstances than is expected in ordinary men, but unless in so doing the nonconformist produces something which is socially valuable to his fellow men he is more or less handicapped in life. Even the most uneventful biography of a member of a modern industrial society involves a succession of situations that require adaptive responses to enable the individual to secure his livelihood. Situations that demand reactions of different kinds, sometimes aggressive and at other times submissive, some leading to perseverance and others to relaxation, follow each other in everyday life in a scarcely predictable succession from hour to hour. Natural selection on the human level favors gene complexes that make their possessors adjust their behavior to any conditions in the light of previous experience. In short, it favors educability.

Circumstances vary not only in the life of an individual but also in that of a family, clan, class, or nation. Where aristocracy is hereditary, a majority of the noble families have usually been so regarded for a century or less; the few families that trace their descent from the nobility of a thousand or more years have passed through periods of ascendancy and adversity. On the other hand, some genes of ancient noblemen are now carried in many a humble peasant or worker. The ruling and privileged classes of times gone by were repeatedly overthrown and supplanted by upstarts from the lower classes or by foreign invaders. An assumption stoutly defended by many partisans is that certain genes are selected among the ruling classes which transform these social groups into biological strains specialized for the function of being leaders and masters. The question arises however: are these genes adaptive also in the descendants of the leaders who are now divested of the rulership? If so, natural selection would favor such genes among those who obey as well as among those who rule; if not, then a genetic constitution which permits sufficient plasticity to develop traits useful to patricians as well as to plebeians in various social environments would have an obvious and permanent selective advantage.

Since the average length of a generation in man is close to 25 years, it follows that only about 78 generations have lived since the beginning of the Christian Era. Counting 20,000 years from the time Cro Magnon man appeared in Europe, and reducing the estimate of the generation length to 20 years, it turns out that about 1,000 generations of men of the modern type, Homo sapiens, have lived since the beginning of the known record. Unless powerful selective pressures are applied to, or removed from, the genotype of a species, 1,000 generations are not enough to accomplish important evolutionary changes. Except for the extinction of many animals and plants, free living species seem to have changed little in more than 1,000 generations. On the other hand, domesticated animals and plants change greatly, sometimes within only a few generations, when intense selection is, either consciously or unconsciously, applied to them.

Now, as far as can be discerned at present, the only strong selective pressure to which the human species has been subjected continuously and unremittingly since the inception of culture down to our day is the selection for educability, i.e., for the capacity to modify one's behavior under the influence of experience and reasoning. The result accomplished by this selective process has been the replacement of biological heredity by social heredity (or social tradition) as the most important determining agent of human behavior. This replacement is a trait common to all normal men, and it differentiates man as a species from other organisms.[6]

The above arguments should not be construed to mean that the genotypes of all men have become alike so far as psychic traits are concerned. This is certainly not the case. Even disregarding grossly abnormal and pathological changes, there can be little doubt that psychic traits are influenced by many genes. What is referred to above as genetically determined educability constitutes a problem somewhat different from the conventional nature-nurture controversy. Genes that condition or modify special abilities, intelligence, emotional reactions, and other psychic traits vary from individual to individual and from group to group. Man is still not far removed from his biological past, when his evolutionary pattern was distinct from what it became later and from what it is now. Most of the genetic differences now found among men had biological significance in the past as adaptations to the then existing environments; many of these differences however have lost their meaning because the environments to which they were adapted exist no longer. This is particularly the case with genetic differences in psychic traits because the psychic sphere underwent by far the most radical changes in the course of evolutionary development from the prehuman anthropoids to modern Homo sapiens. These differences are retained like so many other rudimentary organs and traits, the more or less innocuous remainders of the evolutionary path traversed by our forebears. Their retention is possible chiefly because they are all but engulfed in the far more important diversity due to cultural heredity and to the immediate social environments. Cultural inheritance is the "Superorganic" (Kroeber) which has entered the Universe with man. The origin and the development of this Superorganic is, however, made possible only by the unique pattern of the biological evolution of the human species.

NOTES

1. The manuscript of this chapter was submitted in May, 1946. The writer wishes to express his sincere appreciation to the following colleagues who have kindly read the

manuscript of this chapter and offered many valuable suggestions and criticisms: L. C. Dunn, Karl Koopman, James King, M. M. Rhoades, and Bruce Wallace of Columbia University; C. Pittendrigh of Princeton University; E. Mayr of the American Museum of Natural History; M. Demerec of the Carnegie Institution of Washington; M. F. Ashley Montagu of Rutgers University; Carl Epling, Carl Sauer, and G. Ledyard Stebbins of the University of California; C. Pavan of the University of São Paulo, Brazil; and C. C. Tan of Chekiang University, China.

2. C. S. Coon, *The Races of Europe* (New York, Macmillan, 1939). Coon's race concept is, however, very different from that expounded in these pages.

3. This, of course, should not be interpreted as supporting the system prevailing in the southern United States, where anybody who admits any African ancestry is considered a Negro regardless of his appearance. "Negro" so defined is evidently a sociological and economic but not an anthropological category. Furthermore the Negroes in most of the Western Hemisphere are not identical with the African Negroes, since the former represent a hybrid population in which the processes of Mendelian recombination have not yet reached an equilibrium.

4. F. Weidenreich, "The Brachycephalization of Recent Mankind," *Southwestern Jour. of Anthropology,* I (1945), 1–54.

5. Gobineau and many of his followers contended that "mankind is thus divided into unlike and unequal parts, or rather into a series of categories, arranged one above the other, according to differences of intellect." At the same time he denied that racial differences in intellectual qualities are adaptations to the environments of their possessors. In fact, the followers of Gobineau see no inconsistency in claiming that "the immense superiority" of the races idolized by them is combined with so extreme a fragility that these precious races must be protected from competition with "inferior" races. The origin in evolution of so strange a "superiority" is a mystery which is discreetly left in the dark.

6. Only the barest rudiments of what could be called social heredity are known on the animal level. Thus some species of birds are broken up into geographic races which differ in their songs. The differences in songs seem to be determined in these species not so much by the biological heredity as by training, since juvenile singers copy the songs of other birds of the same species which reside in the neighborhood. The food habits of some species are also subject to modification by such "training."

PART II

EVOLUTIONARY THOUGHT
IN AMERICA

INTRODUCTION TO CHAPTER IV

EVOLUTION AND AMERICAN SOCIOLOGY

IN no field of thought was the impact of evolutionary ideas more incisive yet episodic than in American sociology and anthropology. The school of "Social Darwinism" centered in the sociology of William Graham Sumner has received considerable attention, although its sources are to be found more immediately in Malthus and Spencer than in evolutionary science. It was in anthropology, however, that the evolutionary influence made its greatest impression upon social thought. Here, as Professor Faris shows, organic evolution was not only taken to confirm the older faith in progress, but it furnished several specific concepts for the measurement of the stages of social evolution. Besides adopting the notions of the struggle for existence and survival of the fittest anthropologists noted vestigial social remains of more primitive institutions, which, together with presumed recapitulation of earlier traits in each generation, seemed to attest the fact of social evolution in a series of invariant stages.

The limited utility of these concepts was soon realized, and few of them survived into the twentieth century. The dogmatic approach of the social evolutionists gave way to a more empirical spirit which is prepared to discover in social change its own unique dynamic.

S. P.

EVOLUTION AND AMERICAN SOCIOLOGY

ROBERT E. L. FARIS

I

SOCIOLOGY is in one sense more ancient than history itself, for we find that even the simplest of peoples habitually generalize about human behavior in its collective aspects. The social wisdom of a folk society is expressed in the storehouse of proverbs and myths which are parts of a living and unbroken thread of culture, linking contemporary generations with their ancestors of thousands of years ago. This "folk sociology" is not, of course, scientific in character. But, since cooperative life was as essential to the survival of prehistoric man as it also is to modern man, there had to be an adequate degree of soundness in his knowledge. If we observe the folk wisdom of contemporary pre-literate peoples, we may find examples of judgment and eloquence which compare not unfavorably with some of the best of our modern heritage. We treasure such thoughts as Shakespeare's re-flections on responsibility, contained in Cassius' statement, "The fault, dear Brutus, is not in our stars, but in ourselves, that we are underlings." The preliterate but not unsophisticated natives of the Gold Coast of West Africa express the same thought in their own metaphor. They say, "A mouse as large as a cow would still be the slave of the cat."

Following the development of writing and therefore of civiliza-tion, human knowledge, like other aspects of culture, became more organized and complex. The Egyptians and later the Greeks sought an integration of knowledge in a general philosophy, and thus made attempts at an organic, if not a truly scientific, formula-tion of the subject matter of sociology. But today sociologists read Plato and Aristotle, if at all, to understand the thought of an ear-lier day rather than to discover the truth. And from the early days to the nineteenth century the philosopher contributed little more than speculation, elaboration, and organization to the social field of inquiry. General science had flourished for many centuries before there arose any significant conception that it could embrace the study of the social behavior of mankind.

Auguste Comte introduced the term "sociology" more than a hundred years ago. But the time was not yet ripe for the development of a real social science, and Comte, recognizing this, took as his task the preparation of the ground for the science to come. His work was broad and philosophical in nature, and was something of a culmination of the work of his predecessors. Sociology had hitherto been undifferentiated from the general inquiry that had been thought of as a "philosophy of history," and that was taught for a time in American colleges under the name of "moral philosophy." Comte conceived of a plan of the relations of the sciences to one another, and assigned a logical field to the new discipline. Astronomy, physics, chemistry, biology, and sociology were seen as developing in that order, and in turn passing through theological, metaphysical, and scientific stages of development. Sociology was to be concerned with the principles of interaction among persons, but it was recognized that there would have to be an adequate body of knowledge, gathered by proper methods, before this matter could be considered to be a science.

It should not be understood that the idea of evolution came more abruptly to sociology than to biology—there were in fact evolutionary aspects to Comte's work. But the publication of Darwin's findings had a vitalizing effect on sociology which was to remain active for three quarters of a century. The new, stimulating conception of a grand process which reveals the relations of all living things to one another presented an irresistible temptation to scholars who were in search of unifying principles. Not only the physiological structure of man, but his characteristic actions and his social life could be understood, as it then seemed, as a part of this cosmic development, and able men to make this interpretation were not lacking.

Herbert Spencer had been thinking and writing on aspects of evolution before Darwin made available his carefully elaborated hypothesis of the mechanism of differentiation of species. But Darwin, in impressing the scientists and other intellectuals, could not fail at the same time to provide further impetus to the social philosopher to study the evolution of the social behavior of man.

Spencer applied himself to such an endeavor for more than half a century and became the dominant figure in sociology during a large part of his productive life. His conceptions were cosmic in the manner popular during the nineteenth century when it still seemed conceivable that the knowledge of one man could with reasonable adequacy embrace all of the sciences.

It was natural that Spencer, like others of his century and even later, would attempt to make sociology scientific by directly transferring the conceptions and methods of older sciences. He chose to build his system upon the physical law of the conservation of energy, and attempted to view the universe as an expression of a grand evolutionary process in which reality becomes ever more highly complex. The formation and development of the earth, the origin and differentiation of living species, the evolution of the human mind and of social organizations were for him all illustrations of the operation of this general process.

Not all that Spencer drew from evolutionary theory was derived from Darwin, for Spencer also read Lamarck and Malthus, and was impressed by their suggestions regarding the effect of severe competition on selective survival. There was some parallel to and even anticipation of Darwin in Spencer's phrase, "survival of the fittest," applied to the human and social field. In this latter realm, as in the jungle, the laws of nature are inescapable and heartless, and in the long run presumably are to lead to a happier state of things. Man and society must adapt to conditions, and those unable to achieve a successful adaptation will and should be eliminated. It is useless in the long run, and immediately harmful, according to Spencer, to attempt to escape the harsher aspects of the process. For that reason he opposed governmental rescue of the weakest classes of the population, the poor, the crippled, the ignorant, and the mentally deficient. For those who are unable to survive without such aid, death was held to be only proper. Even the milder forms of state interference were offensive to Spencer, and he opposed, on evolutionary grounds, state-supported education, regulation of housing conditions, tariffs, state banking, government postal systems, and other measures to which we have since become well accustomed.

This policy of noninterference with harsh evolutionary competition has come to be known as Social Darwinism. It survived for a time in sociology—conspicuously in William Graham Sumner—and escaped to a wide and influential circle of intellectuals of the late nineteenth and early twentieth centuries. Prominent in this group were John Fiske, Benjamin Kidd, and Walter Bagehot. Their sociology was congenial to such business leaders as Andrew Carnegie, James J. Hill, and Elbert H. Gary, who found in it formidable justification of their competitive methods. The elder Rockefeller spoke for this big business group most eloquently, in a Sunday-school address in which he found the highest beauty and morality in the prevailing business methods of the times. He said, "The growth of a large business is merely a survival of the fittest . . . The American Beauty rose can be produced in the splendor and fragrance which bring cheer to its beholder only by sacrificing the early buds which grow up around it. This is not an evil tendency in business. It is merely the working-out of a law of nature and of God."

The laissez faire policy of Social Darwinism had one of its most articulate opponents in Lester F. Ward, who for a time was referred to as "the father of American Sociology." However ingenious the arguments of Spencer, they were at a disadvantage in the United States, where the liberal reform movements were gaining in popularity. Theodore Roosevelt's "trust-busting" policy had a wider appeal than did the more traditional political philosophies, and Ward's "teleology," if not his terminology, was more in harmony with the times than was the crusty conservatism of men like Sumner. Ward's arguments further drew strength from the fact that their author was a biological scientist of high reputation, and could refer to biological evolution without incurring the suspicion of lack of qualification. He held that in human life competition not only does not guarantee that the best results will emerge, but rather that it prevents the really fittest from surviving. He urged the active intervention of human intelligence and foresight in order to take control of the processes of evolution, rather than to continue to depend on the slower, less sure, and more wasteful, processes of natural selection.

Social Darwinism in time virtually disappeared from American sociology. Contemporary knowledge does not support the assumption that the lower income classes are necessarily biologically inferior, nor is there any indication that artificial support of these classes does any damage to present or to future society. Modern knowledge of human genetics does not verify the contention that the traits which hinder persons in competition are biologically transmitted. Furthermore, archeological and anthropological study supports the conception that man has never been at the mercy of pure individualistic competition. The process of cooperation has always been necessary for survival, and it has been as fundamental a process in human evolution as has competition. The human animal, in fact, evolved into a creature with the longest period of infancy, and one of the most helpless without an organized society.

But Social Darwinism did not wither away entirely upon its abandonment by sociology. It had too great a value as a rationalization, not only to the more predatory commercial leaders, but also to aristocrats and imperialists who conceived their "white man's burden" and "manifest destiny" as expressions of the law of nature. To the extremists of this point of view no policy, whether of legal discrimination, religious persecution, military conquest, or even racial extermination, was too harsh to justify. The culmination of this philosophy occurred among the "scientists" of the National Socialist movement in Germany, where the most brutal of policies was given the moral support of eugenics by official biologists. An illustration of the degree to which the sophistry was carried is furnished by an officer in the German aviation corps in a paper contributed in the middle 1930's to the *Archiv fuer Rassen und Gesellschaftsbiologie,* in which it is explained that aerial bombing of cities is eugenic in its effects. The bombs, argues the writer, are dropped on crowded cities where the undesirable slum-dwelling populations constitute the major group requiring elimination. Furthermore, after an air raid a certain amount of pillaging and disorder occurs, thus presenting to the police a convenient opportunity to eliminate criminals by shooting. The terror of the raid also brings out the instability of the more nervous persons, thus exposing them for segregation or elimination. And finally, fear reduces the productive capacities of the nervous elements in the population, thus allowing the stronger and bolder to survive and propagate the race.

II

Darwin's study of the *Descent of Man* provided an apparently logical basis for the new science of anthropology, which, in its early period, was considered to be the study of "man in evolution." Its four divisions were physical anthropology, archeology, linguistics, and cultural anthropology. It was believed that the lines of development were interrelated, so that for any given stage of human evolution there could be specified a characteristic physical development, a state of material arts, a level of language achievement, and a stage of social organization. The controlling factor in the movement from stage to stage was believed to be the unfolding of successively higher levels of intelligence.

In 1877 Lewis Henry Morgan published his systematic study, *Ancient Society,* in which he organized in such fashion the anthropological information then available to him. The grand periods of savagery, barbarism, and civilization were each divided into the subdivisions lower, middle, and upper. For each of these periods Morgan described the leading inventions, the characteristic family and tribal organization, and the conception of property. He specifically recognized that it sometimes did occur that a primitive society learned through contact with more advanced peoples but he did not put the emphasis on diffusion which later prevailed, for he stated in the preface, "It can now be asserted upon convincing evidence that savagery preceded barbarism in all the tribes of mankind, as barbarism is known to have preceded civilization. The history of the human race is one in source, one in experience, and one in progress."

Modern theory does not deny that the natural order of technical development is from simple devices to complex machinery. But in the nontechnical culture the sequence is not so uniform, and there is no such obvious reason to assume that such a marriage custom as polygyny, for example, by virtue of its nature, must precede monogamy, or that matrilocal residence of the married pair must precede patrilocal residence. It has been reasoned, however, that a particular family style, not in itself more primitive, might be best adapted to a simple technology.

William I. Thomas, in his extensive treatise, *Primitive Behavior,* finds that there is a tendency, among cultures in which hunting is important to subsistence, for the residence of a married pair to be matrilocal for a period, after which the husband takes his wife to his own group. He further observes an association of matrilocal residence and matrilineal descent with agriculture which is in the care of women, and of patrilocal residence and patrilineal descent with cultures in which cattle keeping, continued agriculture, political heads, and organized war are characteristic. Thomas does not imply that there is necessarily a fixed order of development from one type of residence and lineage to another—it is not family residence customs that are evolving, but the state of invention.

However unconvincing the attempt may appear today, the extension of the principles of biological evolution into the study of the origin and development of societies and institutions was for a time a flourishing practice. Even before Morgan's *Ancient Society,* there appeared a work by McLennan on *Primitive Marriage,* in which the stages of the development of marriage were stated to be promiscuity, matrilineal descent, and finally, patrilineal descent, and in which prehistoric customs were traced, partly by imagination, through various modifications to modern vestigial survivals. Around the turn of the century Wundt began to expound his evolutionist approach to language, myths, morals, religion, art, and law. He believed that he was revealing, through his inspection of these aspects of behavior in societies of varying degrees of complexity, an evolutionary sequence of the unfolding of the traits of the human mind. In his view this progress had passed through the grand stages of "primitive man," the "totemic age," the "age of heroes and gods," and the "development of humanity" which was in the process of emerging.

Some of this tradition has been carried well into the twentieth century through such writers as Hobhouse, Haddon, McDougall, Frazer, Westermarck, and Briffault. Not all of these men held to the conception of single sequences of development or single causes of progress. Hobhouse, for example, merely maintained that there must be some relationship of the social institutions to the stage of technology and economic life, and, although he found such relationships to be loose and irregular at best, he held to the conception that he was illustrating the process of social evolution. Frazer and Westermarck mainly concerned themselves with tracing specific customs and institutions from ancient and contemporary primitive expressions to modern forms. Briffault, however, without training or particular qualifications for his task other than his training as a physician, boldly set out to prove the priority of the matrilineal and matriarchal form of family in a unilinear evolutionary sequence. Freud, on the other hand, just as confidently maintained that the patriarchal family was the original form. It is the almost unchallenged verdict of modern sociology and anthropology that the methods employed, particularly in the latter two cases, are totally unsatisfactory and incapable of demonstrating the predetermined conclusions.

The proliferation of living forms was not the only type of evidence on which the fact of evolutionary transformation was based.

There was confirmatory evidence both from the study of vestiges and from the process of recapitulation. Examples are well known to scientists. The semilunar fold of the human eye, the mammalian pineal gland, the limbs of the whale, and many other vestiges are the now useless remainders of formerly serviceable organs of remote ancestral beings. Plant life yields similar examples in the leaves of the parasitic dodder reduced to tiny scales, and in the staminodia, or functionless stamens, of pigworts and other flowers. The temptations to look for similar sociological evidences of earlier forms of social behavior could hardly be expected to be resisted, and in fact the early and superficial quest brought to light many interesting examples which were called "popular antiquities" by the dilettanti.

Edward Burnet Tylor and later social evolutionists, combing through an enormous literature, found a great many picturesque customs which were presumed to represent cultural survivals in a sense analogous to such biological vestiges. There are societies, for example, in which the marriage ceremony is accompanied by some sort of make-believe fight between the bridegroom and the relatives of the bride. The presumption was that there must have been at some earlier time a practice of seizing brides by force—some writers actually postulated a universal custom of violence in the early stages of the development of man. On the basis of the observed custom of dividing the hair of the Roman bride into six locks with the point of a lance, Sumner and Keller drew the conclusion that people ancestral to the Romans must have used a spear to cut the hair from a bride. The same authors cite a statement regarding tribes in Assam, India, in which complete sexual liberty was allowed all persons until marriage, after which fidelity was expected. The interpretation was that in the history of these people morality began with marriage, and that in this custom the individuals epitomize their own race history.

The early sociologists were similarly stimulated by the findings of the biologists with respect to recapitulation. There was spectacular confirmation of the general theory of evolution in the embryonic development of living things. In the process of development of the higher vertebrates, including man, each individual develops gill slits and an arterial system capable of supplying blood to them, only to have them disappear—thus recapitulating the fish and amphibian stages of evolution. Even before Darwin there had been discussion of the theory that each person in his behavior recapitulates the history of the human race. Wundt later took an interest in the conception, but it never gained wide popularity in modern sociology or anthropology. Through G. Stanley Hall's interest, however, it spread to psychologists, educators, and to the general public. In his influential work on *Adolescence,* Hall stated the relationships of the periods of childhood and youth to the evolutionary stages of the human race, finding, for example, that in the prepubescent years the child is essentially in the stage of savagery and has a disposition toward active outdoor pursuits such as hunting, fishing, fighting, roving, as well as toward play, idleness, and predatory activity. He recommended that these tendencies be given as full expression as possible, on the theory of Aristotelian catharsis, for if this were not done, the suppressed, perverted, and delayed organs of the soul would crop out in menacing forms in later years. Such educators as were impressed by the ring of scientific authority in this viewpoint set out to modify the curriculum and the ancillary activities in the schools to conform to the laws of evolution and human nature. Some reflections of the belief are even now to be found in the policies of schools, and even Sunday schools, possibly because such a theory tends to support itself— that is, if small boys are believed to be savages, and are thus treated as savages, they have little disposition to behave in a manner to challenge the hypothesis.

Today, more than forty years after the publication of Hall's *Adolescence,* metropolitan Boy and Girl Scouts are organized into totemic groups, trained to track wild animals, rehearsed in the savage's methods of making fire, and in other ways saturated with the activities, lore, and symbolism of forest life. There are to be seen, of course, some challenging instances of children who prefer to play with model trucks, tanks, and planes, to spend Saturday afternoons at the motion pictures, and in other ways to behave in defiance of the older laws of evolution and recapitulation. In fact, when the sociologist takes a wider view than Hall appears to have done, he finds that children in other lands and other times do not behave alike. Not only are the Samoan adolescents, described by Margaret Mead, unlike those of early twentieth-century New England, but those of present-day America also observe new and puzzling ways.

Through the influence of Freud, who made an early excursion into anthropology in *Totem and Taboo,* a somewhat cruder form of the recapitulation idea made a deeper though possibly not yet so wide an impression in some circles in sociology and anthropology. Although biological science had abandoned the belief that acquired characteristics could be inherited, Freud apparently retained this notion as an important part of his explanation of human motivation. His position is understood to be that some such event as the Oedipus drama must actually have occurred—that a group of sons conspired to kill their tyrannical father who monopolized all the women, and that in remorse they renounced marriage with women of their own clan. Freud traced from this event not only the origin of the incest taboo, but also the supernatural awe of a father-god, which from that time was presumably transmitted by biological inheritance even though acquired in a single event.

In Freud's conception of recapitulation each person normally passes through fixed stages in his own sexual development, in a progress which reflects the phylogenetic stages. The principal levels of development are the autosexual, the homosexual, and the heterosexual—each with its characteristic instincts and directions of interest. It was assumed that any interference with the natural expression at each level would produce complications that would remain to cause trouble at some future time. The influence of this conception is most pronounced in certain branches of child psychology, social work, and pediatrics. Freud's disciples hold that the infant should be permitted free expression of each type of interest while passing through these stages, and that frustration of virtually any sort involves the possibility of psychological damage. The extremists recommend that thumb sucking be allowed to go unchecked, that crying of infants be rewarded with attention, that babies be cuddled as much as possible and rocked to sleep if they seem to wish it. The instinct theory involved here is more extreme and rigid than ever prevailed in the "instinct school" of psychology itself.

Although sociology on the whole has never been greatly influenced by Freud, there has arisen in anthropology an interest in ethnological contributions to psychoanalysis. It could hardly be expected that Freud's narrow experience among selected neurotic European personality types would yield principles equally valid among the varying cultures of the world, and early criticism of his work arose on this basis. Observations made over a wide range of peoples failed to confirm many of the principles which had been originally set forth as universal in the human species.

As a consequence, the attention of members of the psychoanalytic school of anthropologists has been turning away from the fixed instinctive and recapitulationist conceptions, and these scientists have instead begun to investigate processes of family interaction to show how aspects of various cultures produce distinctive personality types. The archaic evolutionary theory of Freud is thus being replaced by a direction of interest in, and a method of investigation of, the genesis of personality traits in intensive social psychological processes of family relations.

III

There is no implication in the present discussion that such prominent investigators of social evolution as Spencer, Morgan, Tylor, Freud, and others were wrong merely because of meager intelligence. If we reject their leading contributions today, it is because the information available to us is incomparably more abundant and superior in quality. Spencer, for example, suffered from poor health and had little or no opportunity to travel. He attempted to make a synthesis of such an enormous amount of material that he had to rely on a staff of secretaries to aid in the gathering and selection. The larger part of the material available to him, as well as to others of his time, was not gathered by scientists or qualified observers, but by such amateurs as travelers, missionaries, traders, sailors, and the like. The notable triumph of Darwin in organizing enormous masses of botanical and zoological observations into a convincing theory of evolution, though not equaled by social scientists in respect to quality, nevertheless could not fail to inspire the most able men to attempt a similar task for human society.

The intensive ethnographic investigations by trained professional anthropologists did not get well under way until the twentieth century. When a sufficient mass of the newer and sounder type of information became available, reinterpretations of earlier observations were inevitable. Activities which had been recorded in widely separated cultures, but which in the earlier anthropology had been considered to be of essentially the same nature, were revealed by the intensive investigations of the qualified anthropologists to have entirely different meanings and only superficial resemblance. McLennan, Frazer, Freud, and others, for example, made attempts to interpret the widespread but not universal trait of totemism. Later anthropologists, however, have suggested, on the basis of fuller information, that what had been referred to as "totemism" in Australia may have had a different origin and may in fact be a form of behavior unrelated to that which is known in North America. An important aspect of the Australian belief is the idea that the totem ancestor exudes the spirits of children, and that when a woman passes the place where the totem resides, one of the spirits enters her and in time causes a child to be born. In the North American totemic complex a prominent feature is the idea that the totem animal is a super-natural guardian of the individual. It may have been an error resulting from the superficiality of early information that caused such different patterns to be designated by the same name of totemism.

The information available to Spencer and his contemporaries did not present a challenge to the accepted belief in the mental inferiority of preliterate peoples. Apart from the simplicity of material culture, there were many observations cited to support this contention, though every type of evidence eventually had to be reinterpreted in the light of later knowledge. For example, Spencer and others pointed to the lack in certain primitive languages of any numerals above five, arguing that this may be considered evidence of a deficiency in the capacity to deal with higher numbers. But in some of the cultures where no single *word* is found for a numeral greater than five, it has been found that six is expressed by saying "three and three," seven by "four and three" and so on. The lack of a word is no more an indication of mental inability than is the French term for seventy—"sixty and ten"—an evidence of Gallic mathematical deficiency.

The early evolutionists have on occasion misinterpreted what appeared to be primitive ignorance of common matters, such as the physiological role of the father in paternity. This ignorance was presumed to represent the low state of logical and observa-tional powers characteristic of early and primitive man, and surviving examples of the ignorance were apparently to be found in Australia and in New Guinea. Later information, however, suggests that the natives are not ignorant, but that they maintain a dogma and fiction in order to support other features of their social systems. Strehlow, a German missionary in Australia, re-ported that the old native men admitted that they knew this fact, but they said nothing about it to the young men or to the women. He further reported that even the young understood the relations between copulation and offspring among animals—no primitive inability obstructed the comprehension of this principle. Malinowski reported that the Trobriand Island natives among whom he lived are ignorant of the same matter, but Reo Fortune made inquiry of some neighboring peoples who claimed that "they (the Trobrianders) are lying."

In such fashion the new knowledge has forced revision of the early conceptions of the savage of low ability, until at present it is a matter of general consensus that there is no fundamental difference in kind, and even doubtful that there is on the average any considerable difference in degree, in innate mental capacity between preliterate and civilized peoples. The similarity of mental processes and of ability is more plausible in the instances when the translations of native statements are made to sound not like pidgin English of a half-wit, but are instead rendered freely into equivalently graceful and idiomatic English—a practice which was rare in the days of early anthropology and insufficiently observed even today.

Morgan, Tylor, and their colleagues were aware of the process of diffusion, and even made research contributions toward our knowledge of the process. The greater emphasis on the importance of diffusion in determining the state of a culture, however, came after their time, and in consequence of the accumulation of a large fund of research. Anthropologists learned that it was not contact that was exceptional, rather it was isolation. In fact, it could not be said that any existing society had achieved its stage of culture in complete isolation. Diffusion turned out to be much more widespread and to move much more rapidly than had hitherto been recognized.

The complex and highly useful bow and arrow, earlier regarded as an indication that the tribe possessing it had evolved the mentality required to invent it, was discovered to be widely distributed over an area which was contiguous, and that there was little or no relation between the general state of advancement of the culture and the presence of the bow and arrow. The highly developed Polynesians who had kings, nobles, commoners and slaves, and who built great ocean-going canoes and made voyages of more than a thousand miles—these were without the instrument. On the other hand, the very primitive Andaman Islanders as well as the natives of northern Australia did have it. The modern conclusion is that the bow and arrow was invented at one time and in one place, and from there diffused over the whole large area.

Such a process is not unusual but typical. Alphabetic writing also developed once—the Latin alphabet, the Greek, Russian, Arabic, Mongolian, and others were all borrowed and altered from that one source or from other people who derived it from that source. The same statement can be made concerning iron, the use of tobacco, the true zero numeral, printing, and many other inventions and discoveries.

There have been a few cases of "independent invention" which for a time were employed to support one side of a controversy between the "evolutionists" and the "diffusionists." An instance is furnished by the occurrence of strikingly similar musical pipes in the Solomon Islands and in northwest Brazil. In the sets of pipes not only are the intervals approximately the same, but so is the absolute pitch of the notes. Kroeber is inclined to accept this as a genuine coincidence, although it has also been accepted by other scholars as evidence of a historical connection between the western Pacific and South America. Another example is the presumably independent development of bronze in the Eastern Hemisphere and in or near the Bolivian highlands. Some cases offered as examples of parallel inventions are devices with certain similar aspects but different in form and function, such as the number symbol for zero which was apparently an invention of the Hindus and also of the Mayas of Yucatán.

It has been an approved practice to conclude that highly similar devices which occur in two places separated by great distances, and found nowhere between, must have been invented independently. The possibility that a culture trait could diffuse over continents and across oceans, and then die out in all but the two separated places seemed too remote to be accepted. Such a process, however, is not entirely impossible. A contemporary anthropologist has related an interesting example. A traveler returning from the Philippines brought with him a silver breast ornament with a distinctive design and showed it to an anthropologist on the staff of a leading museum. The expert identified it at once as a product of the Sac and Fox Indians. But the true origin of the design was at neither place. It originated in Scotland, diffused to France, then to Spain, and from there to North America where it reached the Sac and Fox Indians, and also from Spain to the Philippines. The pattern was eventually forgotten everywhere but in the two widely separated places in North America and the Pacific, and presented what could easily be mistaken for a true case of independent development. One of the differences between the early organizers of anthropological knowledge and the contemporary experts is that the latter have been able to profit by such lessons.

It has been recognized that diffusion is not a mere passive process—the receiving culture does not accept every type of available trait with the same hospitality and at the same speed. The rate depends on the function the new trait may play in the culture to receive it. While the alphabet, paper, and printing are hardly likely to appeal to members of the extremely simple cultures, such elements as iron, cereals, beads, whisky, and tobacco are readily accepted. The objects of most immediate appeal diffuse rapidly and extensively. Tobacco spread from America in both directions to encircle the world in recent historical times. When Stanley discovered the Equatorial tribes on the Congo he found that they were growing manioc and tobacco which had been diffused from Brazil, although no white man had previously been closer than 700 miles from the region. In the Hopewell Mounds near Chillecothe, Ohio, there were found sea shells from Mobile Bay, hematite from Lake Superior, mica from North Carolina, and minerals from the Rocky Mountains. Here again, the relatively meager information available to the nineteenth-century students of social evolution gave no hint of the extensiveness of this process of diffusion.

The richer knowledge available to present-day scholars has also had the effect of eliminating a minor method formerly employed in the search for explanations of origins of culture traits. This was the method of inventing a plausible fable, such as the Freudian account of the origin of the incest taboo in the murder of the tyrannical father of a tribe by his jealous sons. The origin of fire has been attributed to a mythical performance by an early man who persistently sawed with a bamboo splinter until he accidently made fire. Pottery has been accounted for by the experience of primitive savages who walked through soft wet clay for many centuries until their mental ability reached the point where they were able to conceive of molding the clay into useful shapes. The origin of speech has been accounted for by several rival theories which, before their abandonment, came to be called by such pet names as the "bow wow," "pooh-pooh," "dingdong," and the "yo-he-ho" theories. The existence of rival theories, equally plausible, would be sufficient if no other basis existed to call into question the value of this method. Rival theories to account for the existence of the fair skin of the white man may also be found among the darker peoples. The natives of the Belgian Congo say that the white man came *under* the water of the ocean (which the former had never seen but of which they had been told) and that the long journey through the salt water bleached out the originally black skins. The Greenland Eskimos have a less flattering hypothesis—they say that an Eskimo girl was lost and married a dog.

IV

The general conception of evolution is believed to have had an influence on the idea of progress in human history. Darwin provided a mechanism which apparently rendered progress inevitable, and insured, in his belief, that "natural selection works solely by and for the good of each being, (so that) all corporeal and mental environments will tend to progress towards perfection." Spencer elaborated and extended this idea in his systematic works, finding that a grand design was at work to bring all things into order and completeness, "Always towards perfection is the mighty movement—towards a complete development and a more unmixed good; subordinating in its universality all petty irregularities and fallings back, as the curvature of the earth subordinates mountains and valleys. Even in evils the student learns to recognize only a struggling beneficence. But above all he is struck with the inherent sufficingness of things."

The optimistic spirit spread out in all directions. Historians looked at the recent advances and were impressed. There were the explorers who had made possible a map of the entire planet; the mechanical marvels of the Machine Age which put within reach of the peasants cotton textiles that were formerly rarer and more expensive than the silks of India and China; the wonders of medical research which had increased by years the life-span of man. There was a great missionary effort which boldly outlined and initiated a movement to evangelize the whole world, every human being on the planet, in a single generation; there was a conviction that the growing economic interdependence and other ties between nations would make intelligent men find a way to settle international quarrels without wars. These and other visible

triumphs made men believe that progress was certain and pre-
destined by the laws of nature. Man was climbing the "world's
great altar stairs, that lead through darkness up to God."

In the wake of such a spirit it is not surprising that sociologists
for some decades wrote books on "social progress" or "social
evolution." But the troubles of the twentieth century had a dis-
illusioning effect on the scholars. It was still possible to show that
change is continual, and that there is something of a one-way
character to it. The world becomes ever more complex and man
gains increasing control over natural processes, but it is less than
certain that human life is inevitably becoming better. William F.
Ogburn, who has produced or inspired the production of the
major part of recent sociological research on the concept, had
made use of the term "social change," refraining from committing himself on the subject of whether the change is also
progress. There is in fact a growing disposition on the part of
many thinkers to shudder at the consequences of technological
advance, for they see in it the menace of Frankenstein.

The evolutionary conceptions of Spencer and his followers have
all but disappeared from modern sociology. Some traces persist
in the writings of such men as MacIver and Hankins, who employ
the term to refer to the progressive differentiation of units within
the social system. A few scholars who have been most shaken
by the rough events of the times have embraced the relatively pessimistic conception of cyclical change, such as that advanced by
P. A. Sorokin. The rest, however, continue to study as objectively
as possible the way in which changes do take place in society.
The hope is present that a more complete science of such processes
may in time give men a larger control of their own destinies,
but there is little disposition to assume that ultimate perfection
is inevitable, or even to assume that direct exertion, before a
mature science is achieved, will eliminate the major ills of mankind.

Contemporary sociological research has made its principal
contribution to the theory of social change by illuminating the
causes and consequences of technological achievements. Without
contending that all change must stem from this one source,
Ogburn argues that there is a certain primacy in technological
developments from which other kinds of social change flow as
consequences. This theory removes the source of change from
a general law of nature, or from a trait of human nature, and

places it in specific and describable processes. Where technology is at its lowest state of development, as in the most primitive societies, there is no indication that change must take place. Such observations as are available over historical periods, such as the descriptions of the Toda peoples in India by Rivers who visited them in the opening years of the twentieth century, and by a Portuguese missionary who observed them three hundred years earlier, reveal an almost complete lack of change. It is apparent that some external force is required to break up the contentment that man naturally feels for his familiar and successful routines of life.

The inventions that break up customs do not necessarily stem from the foresight of genius. The mass of available knowledge shows convincingly that inventions are normally of slow development, and are made in such small steps that in a large number of cases the process of invention appears both accidental and inevitable. In the earlier stages of prehistoric development innovations in such techniques as the manufacture of flint tools came thousands of years apart. For most of the time since his emergence on the planet man's technical knowledge has grown at an extremely slow pace. But with the gradual accumulation of material devices and with the beginnings of science the possibilities of new combinations of the elements of inventions increased at an exponential rate, so that an acceleration set in that even today shows no tendency to stop. The invention is produced by activity of individual human minds, but it is not at all necessary or even characteristic that the inventors foresee the final perfected state of their own inventions, or that they have any imagination of or desire for the consequences that follow their use. It is also quite clear that other members of the society are far from conscious or desirous of the changes– throughout most of human history the great mass of people have regarded change as unwelcome and have opposed most of the inventions and discoveries while they were new.

It is not possible for a society to make wide use of a new invention without experiencing some adaptations of custom and social organization. The typewriter was not merely a more convenient device for writing letters. As Ogburn pointed out, it created a new social class—the female stenographer (and emancipated the spinster)—and it aided in the women's suffrage movement, and increased business efficiency. A mere listing of the effects of such inventions as the automobile or the radio takes pages. Now and then an invention or discovery virtually transforms the whole society and stimulates a crucial advance in human history. Among such outstanding developments are the invention of writing, the symbol for zero, the wheel, the printing press, steam power, electricity, chemical science, and perhaps nuclear physics.

It is only within the last century or two that the general recognition has come to the masses of civilized people that new inventions mean more than a change in the details of technical operations, and only in the last few years that scientists have tried to analyze the causes and consequences of technological innovations, and to foresee and control their use in the interests of the whole society, as did the Rust brothers following the invention of their apparently successful cotton-picking machine, and the physicists after the demonstration of the power of the atomic bomb. It is too soon to say that we have achieved control of events, or even that we will soon learn how to control, but the new effort to manage events through a well-developed science of society is surely and at last under way.

The foregoing discussion has shown that the evolution concept made a deep penetration into nineteenth-century sociology during the helpless infancy of the science. But the influence so receded during the present century that only traces of evolutionism are now visible in sociology. This does not mean that sociologists are in any way inclined to challenge the findings of biologists and paleontologists regarding the origin of species, including the human animal. The former have, however, found in consequence of a rich accumulation of knowledge of human behavior and social organizations that the principles of behavior of men are not efficiently stated by reference to principles of biological evolution. The century in which the evolutionary influence flowed and ebbed was not by any means lost time for sociology. It should not be considered futile to pursue theoretical problems to their end, even if the answer is not the one expected. Such a rewarding organizing principle as evolution, in view of its success in biology, had to be investigated in sociology as well, and the record of the results of the trial remains to be instructive today.

The sciences of human behavior did not emerge from this experience the same as they went into it. The concept of evolution performed a valuable service to science in helping to shatter the prevailing traditional, mystical, and theological views about the nature of man and his behavior. As long as man was considered to be distinct in nature from all other living creatures, governed only by his "free will," the principles of his behavior could scarcely be subject to scientific investigation. Although present-day human psychology has receded from the instinctivism of fifty years ago, it is forever on firmer grounds for having recognized the biological aspect of man. Sociology and anthropology likewise remain conscious of the limiting influences of biology on behavior, and of the continuous interaction of social and physiological processes.

The evolutionary theory may not be solely responsible for putting the spirit of science into sociology, but it is probable that it played an important part in turning the subject into more fruitful directions. There has always been in sociology a rivalry between the scientific tradition and a point of view, essentially theological, which is characterized by an impatient spirit of reform. While the reform wing debated and exhorted, the evolutionary scientists patiently and laboriously accumulated the volumes of knowledge which made possible much of the solid progress of sociology. The conclusions of Spencer, Morgan, Tylor, and their contemporaries, and even the quality of much of their basic information, have been impugned, but the tradition of seeking information and of organizing it objectively was carried on by Sumner and handed down through him and others to contemporary sociologists and anthropologists. In time the superiority of a theory based on collected knowledge became so clear that the theological reform spirit in sociology has been overshadowed.

Many of the specific problems investigated by the early evolutionists have expanded into fields of research which remain active today. Most of the science of anthropology is in fact still concerned with the development of these early inquiries. The present investigations of social change have new emphases, but the questions were specifically raised by Morgan, and certain aspects of his treatment are still in harmony with modern findings. The lively and developing modern field of population research had direct linear descent from Malthus and Spencer. The evolutionist concern led to the raising of many other questions as well, and to the clearing of the ground for the solid science that was to come.

In recent decades the scientists of human behavior have learned to pursue these questions with the same spirit of patience and diligence, but with improved methods and resources, and of course with the advantages that come from the accumulation of knowledge. It has been found best to abandon the effort to transfer methods and conceptions by analogy from other fields, and to investigate social causes and effects on their own level and by methods suitable to the nature of the subject.

Thus has come and gone from sociology the biological conception of social evolution. For those who regret its loss, and who desire a term for the account, not of the stages through which all societies must pass but of the particular way in which civilization did develop, there is available the traditional and respectable word, "history."

THE IMPACT OF THE IDEA OF EVOLUTION ON THE AMERICAN POLITICAL AND CONSTITUTIONAL TRADITION

IT has become customary to refer to the rationalization of the rugged individualism of the Gilded Age as Social Darwinism. Professor Corwin suggests, however, that this initial social application of evolutionary ideas owed more to the influence of Herbert Spencer, and that the term Darwinian should be reserved for later philosophies of social reform, for which pragmatism provided the theoretical foundations. Thus in the political as in the economic and sociological realms of thought the ultimate influence of evolutionary ideas was fully felt only when adapted to the social life of man and understood as providing fruitful insights both for analysis and for social control.

S. P.

THE IMPACT OF THE IDEA OF EVOLUTION ON THE AMERICAN POLITICAL AND CONSTITUTIONAL TRADITION

―――――

EDWARD S. CORWIN

THE warp and woof of classical American political theory are seventeenth-century English political theory and the political thought of the eighteenth-century Enlightenment. The central motive of the resulting pattern, implicit even when not explicit, is supplied by the notion that man is a creature of reason, and that to this creature had been vouchsafed a revelation—by ratiocination, of course—of certain *final* political and social values. What these were is authoritatively stated in the famous second paragraph of the Declaration of Independence:

We hold these truths to be self-evident—that all men are *created* equal; that they are endowed by their Creator with certain *un*alienable rights; that among these are life, liberty, and the pursuit of happiness. That, to secure these rights, governments are instituted among men, deriving their just powers from the consent of the governed. . . .

In the Constitution the word of the Declaration was made flesh—a too fleshly flesh, some have thought, inasmuch as the Constitution betrays considerable solicitude for the rights of property, which the Declaration does not mention. To compensate, on the other hand, for this concern for property, the quite negative conception of "consent of the governed" of the Declaration becomes in the Preamble of the Constitution positive and creative: "We, the people of the United States" not merely "consent" to a pre-established order, we "ordain and establish" one of our own devising.

Moreover, the Constitution of the United States was deemed by its framers to embody certain permanent principles of correct constitutional structure, a matter not touched upon by the Declaration. After invoking the eternal verities just recited in justification of the Revolution against Great Britain, the American people next proceeded to erect a governmental system capable of giving permanent effect to these—an act of unexampled self-confidence, which sprang from the belief of that generation that it possessed a matured and perfected political science such as the world had never up to that time been blessed with.

Thus Alexander Hamilton wrote in the *Federalist,* No. 9:

The science of politics, however, like most other sciences, has received great improvement. The efficacy of various principles is now well understood, which were either not known at all or imperfectly known to the Ancients, the regular distribution of power into distinct departments; the introduction of legislative balances and checks; the institution of courts composed of judges holding their offices during good behaviour; the representation of the people in the legislature by deputies of their own election; these are wholly new discoveries, or have made their principal progress towards perfection in modern times. They are means, and powerful means, by which the excellencies of republican government may be retained and its imperfections lessened or avoided. To this catalogue of circumstances that tend to the amelioration of popular systems of civil government, I shall . . . add one more . . . ; I mean the *enlargement of the orbit* within which such systems are to revolve.[1]

By its framers and by the generation which received it, the Constitution was regarded, and justly so, as marking the climax of a great, even though brief, period of original political creation. In the words of Lord Acton, the Constitution of 1787 "resembled no other Constitution, for it was contained in half a dozen intelligible articles"; indeed, outside of America, written constitutions did not yet exist. The idea of putting legal restraints upon government in the interest of private rights, while of respectable antiquity, had never before received embodiment in implementing institutions. Even in the early state constitutions the principle of the separation of powers was mere literary theory. Only in Massachusetts and New Hampshire did the executive veto exist even as late as 1787; and although judicial review had been asserted in a few dicta of state courts and in one or two decisions, it was still, when the Federal Convention assembled, the rawest sort of raw idea, unillumined by any practical experience in its operation. In the Constitution of 1789 the executive veto and judicial review are pivotal institutions.

Even more noteworthy was the work of the Convention in adjusting the relations of the states and the nation. There had been confederacies before—the past indeed was strewn with the wreckage of them—but no earlier confederacy had possessed a central government which operated directly upon *individuals* rather than indirectly through the governments of its corporate members and yet without sacrifice of the principle of local autonomy. Lastly, the method by which the Constitution was adopted employed the principle of popular sovereignty on a previously unparalleled scale. For the first time in history the right of revolution appeared as the more positive right of the citizens of a great national community, acting through bodies chosen for the specific purpose, to remodel their political institutions.

The final element of American political thinking is at core a fact rather than an idea—a physical presence rather than an intellectual conviction. I mean the frontier, a term which I use to symbolize those conditions of escape from ancient, inherited controls in which the American adventure was initially cast. The significant fact about these conditions was that they furnished a perpetual reminder and authentication of the possibility of environmental change not only without loss, but with positive betterment—in short, of the idea of *progress*. In the influence of the frontier and in the American talent for mechanical invention, which now and then spilled over into the political field, we encounter those factors of early American social life which most sharply challenged the static premises of classical American political thought and institutional devising, and which offered from the outset a handle to the dynamic presuppositions of the conception of evolution. Thus we come to our question: what has been, to date, the impact of evolutionary ideas on the American political and constitutional tradition?

A subordinate question at once arises: whose conception of evolution are we talking about? Three lines of thought have to be taken account of in answering this question: (a) Spencerian evolutionism; (b) the Darwinian theory of biological descent; (c) modern "pragmatism" or "instrumentalism." But I propose to devote some passing attention also to a fourth line of thought, which, while not the product of evolutionism, has indubitably contributed to the latter's impact upon the American tradition—I mean the Marxian doctrine of *class struggle*—which, besides being a sort of specialized version of the general notion of the struggle for existence, has indirectly contributed to American reformism looking to the economic betterment of the masses.

The brand of the doctrine of evolution to which any considerable part of the American public first inclined a respectful ear was that of Herbert Spencer. This was owing in the first place to the *odium theologicum* which stigmatized the Darwinian doctrine of *biological evolution* on account of its challenge to the notion of special creation and especially its demotion of man from the kingdom of Heaven to the animal kingdom—from the status of fallen angel to the status of mere creature.[2] More than that, the early Darwinians, including Darwin himself, horrified many people by picturing nature as "red in tooth and claw." Even Darwin's great apostle to the Gentiles, Huxley, admitted this, and drew from it the conclusion that the course of biological evolution and that of social or ethical evolution were diametrically opposed, which meant, in effect, that Darwinism had no relevance to social purposes.

Spencer avoided both of these difficulties. His doctrine of the "Unknowable," by making the existence of Deity and its attributes and potencies articles purely of religious faith, gave leave and license to all and sundry to believe in evolution on weekdays and in the first chapter of Genesis on the Sabbath. Nor, in fact, was Spencer specially interested in biological evolution. He speaks, to be sure, of "the struggle for existence," but its outcome was preordained in "the survival of the fittest," whereas Darwin's fittest survivors were obviously fittest only for a particular environment, which might well be a very debased environment from the point of view of human values. While, therefore, evolution might with Darwin actually spell *retrogression,* with Spencer it was quite otherwise.

In short, Spencer's generalized theory of evolution explained *everything*—it was universal. Furthermore, it was a resolutely optimistic theory, whereas Darwin did not profess to pass on ethical or social issues. A great god called Evolution had the universe, at least the habitable part of it, in its grip and was hurrying it toward some far off divine event, willy-nilly. The idea appealed especially to the view that Americans took of their own destiny, and they were too generous a people to resent the discovery that other peoples might have destinies as well as they.

Again Spencer appealed to American individualism; indeed, for a time he virtually took over the American doctrine of rights *versus* the state. Just how Spencer contrived to reconcile the doctrine of evolution with that of natural rights and the utopianism which underlies the latter, would be much too long a story to set forth here. Professor Ernest Barker thinks Spencer failed in his attempt to square the circle, but I am not so sure. Concede Spencer his premises and he is generally fairly logical. Unfortunately, facts were always cropping up to disturb his logic. Hence Huxley's quip, that Spencer's "idea of a tragedy was a beautiful theory killed by an ugly fact."

But at the outset—in the late seventies and early eighties—Spencer seemed to have the facts on his side, and especially in the field in which he was keenest to see evolution get forward with its good work, the industrial field. For here his teaching seemed to be verified by the contemporary teachings of the Manchester school of political economy generally taught at this time in American universities. And the sum and substance of this teaching was that the state, a regrettable residue from feudal militarism, should carefully refrain from action which was calculated to interfere with the struggle for existence in the industrial field.

So Spencer became a sort of tutelary genius to rising big business in the United States and the accepted philosopher of the most influential class in the American community. Nor did his exponents—John Fiske and Professor William Graham Sumner of Yale pre-eminent among them—have long to wait before the Supreme Court at Washington, responding to the guidance of the foremost lawyers of the period, began translating the Manchester-Spencerian doctrine into terms of American constitutional law—the concept of "dual federalism," the doctrine of the separation of powers, the doctrine of due process of law, and others.[3]

Thus was the circle rounded out. The truths of evolution and the eternal verities of the American constitutional system were, it turned out, just different facets of the same thing—or in other words, the initial impact of evolution on the American ideological tradition was to *confirm* the notion of liberty *versus* government, and especially that phase of liberty in which men of property were most particularly interested, the liberty to drive advantageous bargains with labor—what the court of the day baptized "freedom of contract."

Finally, mention should be made of the missionary work for Spencer of John Fiske and Edward Youmans, editor of *Popular Science Monthly,* and especially of the former, who in his *Cosmic Philosophy* popularized the Spencerian sociology, with some improvements of his own, and gave it a decidedly theological cast, as in his little book, *Through Nature to God.* Evolution became a new religion, something for which the American people have always evinced a pronounced tenderness.[4]

Spencer's influence is today extinct. No intellectually respectable person would wish to be caught in the company of the "synthetic philosophy," or—since Professor Giddings and Professor Sumner, both men of great intellectual distinction, passed from the scene —in the company of the Spencerian sociology. It is true that there is still a social science which calls itself "sociology," but it is a very different affair from the Spencerian product. It is no longer greatly intrigued by the general notion of evolution. Indeed, it is often more than a little doubtful as to progress—at least, there is no progress without conscious and planned effort. It, therefore, studies specific situations, and is especially interested in questions of *environment,* "ecology," "demography," social statistics and the like. This sociology owes little to Spencer except the idea that society, or "social groupings," are something of a definite, tangible nature enough to be made subjects of "scientific" investigation. In brief, sociology today owes most of its problems and procedures to Darwinian ideas rather than to Spencerian. Why is this?

For one thing, Spencer had given the idea of evolution favorable advertisement; at least, the expression no longer shocked religious sensibilities unduly. That much at least had Spencer done for Darwin. And meantime Darwin was winning out with the scientists, was becoming intellectually respectable. Eventually he was to be intellectual tops with those who knew, and that helped with the generality, even though the Darwinian thesis was, in its strictly scientific aspect, a comparatively narrow one.

And with the rise of Darwin's prestige in scientific circles, liberal-minded theologians began to cast favorable glances in his direction. Reinterpretations of the first chapter of Genesis began to pour from both pulpit and press, and sometimes the reinterpreters, as in the case of Professor Patrick Macloskie of Princeton, went on to show, at least to their own satisfaction, that the whale's exploit in swallowing Jonah and giving him shelter for three days and nights was feasible biologically and hence scientifically credible.[5]

Darwinism presently gave evidence, moreover, of being itself amenable to the evolutionary process; especially did the "red in tooth and claw" feature of the theory, which had caused Huxley to rule out the notion of Social Darwinism, undergo revision. Thus as early as 1872 Walter Bagehot advanced the notion in his brilliant volume *Physics and Politics* that the triumph of certain societies over others was to be accounted for in earliest times by their superior social coherence, i.e., by the suppression among their members of the struggle for existence; and thirty years later Peter Kropotkin brought out his *Mutual Aid as a Factor in Evolution,* which pointed out the importance of group cooperation as a factor of survival among certain of the lower species. At about the same time, Charles Horton Cooley, in his delightful volume *Human Nature and the Social Order,* which was published in 1902, reduced to absurdity the notion that self-reliant individualism was the fine fruit of evolution by pointing to the gorilla as the one perfect individualist. Human nature as distinct from animalism, Cooley proceeded to argue on the basis of observations he had made of his own children, was the product of social living, not of individual competition.

More important, however, for the purposes of this discussion was the suggestion presently put forth, that so far as civilized societies are concerned, the struggle for existence is not predominantly a struggle between individuals, as Spencer liked to imagine, *but a struggle with environment,* from which it followed that the prerequisite to social improvement was *improvement of social environment*—an idea which was confirmed for Americans in the history of the frontier.

But by what means, through what agencies, was environment to be improved? One means, obviously, was science, whose "conquest of nature," as it was termed, lay at the basis of the vast increase of social wealth since the Middle Ages. Unfortunately, however, this increase in social wealth was not equitably distributed throughout society. So another agency, too, must be brought into operation, viz., government, which thanks to the spread of democratic ideas and institutions, had become adapted to precisely this task. *Darwinian evolutionism, translated into social terms, became reformism.*

One of the first voices to be raised in this behalf in the United States was, fittingly enough, that of the sociologist, government bureaucrat, and paleobotanist, Lester F. Ward, who in 1883 published his large two-volume work, *Dynamic Sociology*. This was at once a systematic attack on the negativism of Spencer's *Social Statics* and a positive demand for governmental intervention in the economic field. Asserting that, quite contrary to the assumptions of the Spencerian laissez faire school, social control had been gradually expanding throughout the history of civilization, Ward continued:

For more than a century the English school of negative economists has devoted itself to the task of checking this advance. The *laissez faire* school has entrenched itself behind the fortifications of science, and while declaring with truth that social phenomena are, like physical phenomena, uniform and governed by laws, they have accompanied this by the false declaration and *non sequitur* that neither physical nor social phenomena are capable of human control; the fact being that all the practical benefits of science are the result of man's control of natural forces and phenomena which would otherwise have run to waste or operated as enemies to human progress. The opposing positive school of economists simply demands an opportunity to utilize the social forces for human advantage in precisely the same manner as the physical forces have been utilized. It is only through the artificial control of natural phenomena that science is made to minister to human needs; and if social laws are really analogous to physical laws, there is no reason why social science may not receive practical applications such as have been given to physical science.[6]

Ward, it turned out, had no monopoly of such ideas. In September, 1885, the American Economic Association was founded at Saratoga, N. Y. Many of its outstanding members, most of whom were comparatively young men, had gone to Germany for their postgraduate work, and had been witnesses to Bismarck's experiments in state socialism, which constituted the German Reich's answer to Marxian socialism. In the new association's declaration of principles the following statement stood out as a challenge to Spencerian evolutionism and Manchester laissez faire-ism: "We regard the state as an agency whose positive assistance is one of the indispensable conditions of human progress."[7]

Four years later David G. Ritchie reiterated to the British public the same challenge to Spencerism in his *Darwinism and Politics;* and in 1907—to omit mention of others—Professor Simon N. Patten of the University of Pennsylvania, succeeded, in his *New Basis of Civilization,* in anticipating the "economy of abundance" theorists of the Coolidge era by more than two decades. Asserting that the world's food supply could easily be doubled, Patten went on to contend that among humans the prime factor of improvement was nurture, not nature. There is no inherent difference, he declared, between rich and poor; and "nature will care for progress if men will care for reform." [8]

Thus we are confronted with two interpretations of evolution for social application: the Spencerian, laissez faire interpretation and the reformist interpretation. Which one was best warranted by the Darwinian doctrine of biological evolution? Inasmuch as Darwin centers his attention upon the struggle for existence among *creatures* and treats the environment in which this struggle takes place either as relatively inert or as changing in response to factors beyond human control, the answer must undoubtedly be in favor of the Spencerian interpretation.

Furthermore, as Darwin himself admits, his attention was originally drawn to the general problem of the struggle for existence by Thomas Malthus' famous *Essay on the Principle of Population,* which was conceived in part as an attack on the younger Pitt's effort through the Poor Law of 1796 to apply governmental relief to the poverty and distress resulting from the emergence of industrialism and the breakdown of feudal society in England. Malthus' contention was, briefly, that humans breed at a geometric ratio, while food supply increases merely at an arithmetical ratio—or more shortly, that population increases always outrun food supply. Nor were remedial measures ever long effective, since any measure of betterment was bound to operate as a stimulus to further breeding. Poverty, in short, was an ineradicable condition of society—a social fate. In a revision of his work Malthus admitted the possibility of moral checks on population increase, a position no more encouraging to the cause of economic reform through governmental action than his original position had been.

Taking, then, this doctrine as his point of departure, Darwin saw all creatures engaged in a struggle for existence, which only those individuals which were best adapted to a particular environment survived to establish new species. From these general premises the laissez faire conclusion of "everyone for himself, and the devil take the hindmost" was perfectly logical if not inevitable. Yet since it was apparent that civilization had advanced, it also followed that the struggle for existence, severely as it bore on particular individuals, had in social terms proved beneficial. At least only a few aesthetes disputed this conclusion at the time.

The transmutation of Darwinism into a gospel of social reform required a complete reversal of the formula of adaptation of creature to environment. In the case of the human creature only the eugenists have ever thought to effect any radical improvements on Darwinian premises. So the formula had to be read backward—instead of the creature being adapted to the environment, *the environment had to be adapted to the creature.* But how adapted? By what methods? Science, of course, was one method, but, as was said before, its benefits had not been spread as they should have been. The *state* must, therefore, be brought into the business, that is to say, the democratically organized state, the state where politically each person counted as one, neither more nor less.

So we are brought to that chapter in the story of the transformation of the Darwinian hypothesis into a creed of social reform which is variously labeled "pragmatism," "instrumentalism," "experimentalism," "functionalism." Part of the argument, which centers chiefly about the names of William James and John Dewey, runs briefly as follows: in biological evolution the supreme problem is that of physical survival. In man's struggle for survival his principal weapon has been his mental superiority, that is, the ability to forecast events and to plan to meet them and divert them to his own advantage. Thus mind, or thought, directed originally to the problem of sheer existence, remains as an instrument of social improvement, and profitable thought to this end is *planning*. It follows that the most valid test of thought is its *planning* value—its anticipation of events and its usefulness in giving them an advantageous turn.

A paragraph from Mr. Hofstadter's excellent book, *Social Darwinism,* is much in point:

While Dewey's interpretation of thinking is more than a simple extension of Darwinism, it is biological in its orientation. Thinking is not a series of transcendent states or acts interjected into a natural scene. Knowledge is a part of nature, and its end is not mere passive adjustment but the manipulation of the environment to provide "consummatory" satisfactions. An idea is a plan of action rooted in the natural impulses and responses of the organism. The "spectator theory of knowledge" is pre-Darwinian. "The biological point of view commits us to the conviction that mind, whatever else it may be, is at least an organ of service for the *control of environment* in relation to the ends of the life process." [9]

The questions arise: what ends are thought of; whose "consummatory satisfactions"; and what is their nature? The answer is that in the process of becoming a gospel of reform, pragmatism has, like Darwinism itself, undergone a profound change. Permit me again to quote some words from Mr. Hofstadter's book, this time words of Professor Dewey himself:

Long after "pragmatism" in any sense save as an application of his *Weltanschauung* shall have passed into a not unhappy oblivion, the fundamental idea of an open universe in which uncertainty, choice, hypotheses, novelties and possibilities are naturalized will remain associated with the name of James; the more he is studied in his historic setting the more original and daring will the idea appear. . . . Such an idea is removed as far as pole from pole from the temper of an age whose occupation is acquisition, whose concern is with security, and whose creed is that the established economic régime is peculiarly "natural" and hence immutable in principle. [10]

These words express the pure spirit of Jamesian pragmatism, which regarded the universe as always "open" and centered its interest on the "open" mind. It is an aristocratic idea, and regards thought as primarily, or altogether, a personal adventure.

But this is not the attitude of present-day social reformers as it is set forth by one of the most eminent of them, Professor Charles E. Merriam, in his recent work *Systematic Politics*. In one respect Merriam is a thoroughgoing follower of James and Dewey, especially the latter. He rejects utterly the idea that inherited institutions have any necessary validity—they must daily prove their usefulness. But his test of usefulness is supplied by the very consideration which Dewey in the above quotation treats with scorn, "concern with security." To be sure, Dewey was talking about the security already attained of an "economic régime," a plutocracy, whereas Merriam is talking about the security still to be obtained of *the common man*. "Freedom," says Merriam, "is the great aim of the state," and this he defines in the words of the late President

Roosevelt's message to Congress of January 11, 1944, and repeated in his campaign speech in Chicago that same autumn:

We have come to a clear realization of the fact that true individual freedom cannot exist without economic security and independence. "Necessitous men are not free men." People who are hungry and out of a job are the stuff of which dictatorships are made.

In our day these economic truths have become accepted as self-evident. We have accepted, so to speak, a second bill of rights, under which a new basis of security and prosperity can be established for all—regardless of station, race, or creed.

Among these are:

The right to a useful and remunerative job in the industries, or shops, or farms, or mines of the nation;

The right to earn enough to provide adequate food and clothing and recreation;

The right of every farmer to raise and sell his products at a return which will give him and his family a decent living;

The right of every businessman, large and small, to trade in an atmosphere of freedom from unfair competition and domination by monopolies at home or abroad;

The right of every family to a decent home;

The right to adequate medical care and the opportunity to achieve and enjoy good health;

The right to adequate protection from the economic fears of old age, sickness, accident, and unemployment;

The right to a good education.

All of these rights spell security. And after this war is won we must be prepared to move forward, in the implementation of these rights, to new goals of human happiness and well-being.

America's own rightful place in the world depends in large part upon how fully these and similar rights have been carried into practice for our citizens. For unless there is security here at home, there cannot be lasting peace in the world.[11]

In short, pragmatism, instrumentalism, experimentalism are merged with and go to swell the current of democratic reformism, in support of which the Darwinian hypothesis had begun to be invoked from the early eighties by Ward, Ritchie, Ely, Patten, and others.[12]

I wish now to turn for a moment to the Marxian doctrine of class struggle. The historical connection between Marxism and Darwinism seems to have been very slight. The Marxian doctrine is the older, but there appears to be no evidence at all that Darwin owed anything to it, or was even aware of it. Indeed such indebtedness as existed appears to have been on the other side. For in 1860 we find Marx writing Engels regarding the *Origin of Species,* which had appeared the year before: It "is very important and serves me as a basis in natural science for the class struggle in history." [13] Darwin had furnished Marx a new propaganda weapon, but that was all.

That, nevertheless, certain logical affinities exist between Marxism on the one hand and each of the variants of evolutionism which we have been considering is apparent. Thus Spencerism, with its exaltation of a rigorously competitive society and the notion of the survival of the fittest, is a sort of inverted Marxism, in which the Marxian proletariate is replaced by the leaders of industry. Moreover, both Marx and Spencer looked forward to a time when the particular struggle which each depicted would *terminate in a more or less perfect society.* In the last analysis *they were utopians.* Between Marxism and Social Darwinism there is the affinity, first, of a common sympathy for the plight of the masses, but whereas Marx looked forward to violent revolution as the way out, Darwinism put its money at first on "the inevitability of gradualness," to use the graphic expression coined by those great exponents of social reform, the Webbs. Latterly, to be sure, the recognition that de Vries, Vernon Kellogg, and others have accorded the unheralded "sport" as a source of biological variation, tends to minimize this difference, while at the same time creating another. Chance mutations and quantum jumps are headed for no predictable destination; Marxism is very confident that it is.

But the principal affinity between Darwinism and Marxism appears when we turn to the philosophy of instrumentalism or experimentalism and its conception of thought as planning. Such a conception simply passes by as obsolete the idea of thought as the fine fruit of a cognitive, reasoning faculty which, just because of its detachment from the daily concerns of men, is able to arrive at abstract and permanent truths. Marxism, however, carries its rejection of the same idea even further. For according to Marx all institutions, all approved beliefs, even all the procedures of education and learning are conditioned by interest and situation and constitute "ideologies," the purpose of which is not the apprehension and the dissemination of truth but the defense of the established economic order, at least, its "mystification." [14] The autonomous reason of the eighteenth-century Enlightenment, the power to see things *sub specie aeternitatis,* is demoted by instrumentalism to a planning device for meeting the shifting demands of an ever changing environment, and is then further reduced to the ignoble role of a tool of propagandists. The eternal verities become, first, relative truths, then half-truths, or less than half-truths, even deliberate falsehoods.

To sum up the argument to this point: the two principal efforts to give evolutionary concepts a social or political application are associated respectively with the names of Spencer and Darwin. Spencer emphasized the notion of the struggle for existence among individuals, and optimistically assuming that the survivors from the struggle were the "fittest" in a social sense, next proceeded to identify them with the economically successful, "the wise and the wealthy." His theory thus joined hands with other intellectual forces of contemporary laissez faire-ism, and in that company materially influenced the interpretation of the Constitution of the United States for more than a generation. Today its importance is negligible.

Darwinian social theory stands at the opposite pole to the theory just reviewed. *From the first it was an elaboration by advocates of economic reform in the interest of the masses.* Their initial step was to replace the idea of the struggle for existence among creatures with the idea of the struggle with environment, thus transforming the relatively inert, or only cataclysmically active environment of the Darwinian biology, into a *primary efficient agent of social improvement.* In the second place, the Darwinian social theorists laid down the proposition that the struggle with environment must take place under the active supervision of government if its beneficial results were to be equitably distributed throughout society. For Spencerian laissez faire-ism, the Darwinians substituted the gospel of governmental intervention in the economic sphere in the interest of the common man.

A derivative from Darwinian social theory via Jamesian pragmatism is the instrumentalism or experimentalism of John Dewey and his group. This too is democratic, reformist, socialistic. At the same time its extension of certain implications of evolutionary thought challenges some of the more fundamental elements of classical American political thought. The cornerstone of the latter at its inception was the notion of a natural law of final moral and political values which were the discovery of reason. The natural law of experimentalism, on the other hand, is the natural law of the sciences, which exists independent of and indifferent to moral values. So there are no final truths, and reason as such is left without any reason for being. In its place is that continuous mental activity which we term planning, man's capacity for which is the explanation of his survival in the struggle for existence, and his only ground for hope for the future. Truth, in short, is a plan of action which is operationally successful. It is therefore relative and variable, the pliable instrument of an ever shifting problem of adjustment to "specific situations." [15]

And if instrumentalism demotes truth from the dignity of a discovery of the autonomous reason to the menial role of a tool in the struggle for satisfaction, Marxism carries the denigrating process still further, presenting "truth" (in quotation marks) as a weapon in the class struggle of a self-serving established economic order—as propaganda, in short.

One thing remains—to translate these results, or some of them, into the traditional categories of American political and constitutional thought. In view of what has been said already the subject does not require elaborate treatment. Social Darwinism—as I have redefined the term—has been a definite influence working with those who have within recent years sought to replace our original passive conception of governmental function with a positive, active conception. From the point of view of the former the *liberty* of the individual was the single most valuable asset of society, as on the frontier it undoubtedly was. In the activist conception, on the other hand, as illustrated in the late President's speech which was quoted a few pages back, the duty rests squarely on the shoulders of a democratic government to guarantee "the economic security and independence" of its constituents.

The efforts which have been made to date to realize the latter conception in terms of legislation have resulted in what is nothing less than a revolution in our constitutional law, one which has undone completely the work of Spencerian laissez faire-ism in that field. The principle of the "federal equilibrium," which was especially dear to lawyers and judges of the laissez faire school, the doctrine of "freedom of contract," which was their own creation, and the doctrine of the separation of powers, have all today gone by the board as limitations on Congress' power. The Supreme Court's power to pass upon the constitutionality of legislation remains, to be sure; but bereft of the support once given it by the above-mentioned doctrines, is today, in the national theater, little more than a superfluous pageant, a fact which, nevertheless, has not sufficed to save it from heavy attack as still being incompatible with the majority's right to rule.[16]

The latter right, indeed, charged with the duty to spread the control of government over an ever widening circle of human relationships and activities in the interest of "the common man," promises to become, if it has not become already, the be-all and end-all of constitutional government in the United States. In the field of economic endeavor especially, "liberty," which once stood at the head of the column of constitutional values, has been supplanted by "equality." In terms of evolutionary theory, "survival of the fittest" has given way to the right of all to survive in comfort so far as this can be contrived by governmental action.

Finally, although the doctrine of evolution as a natural science construct is professedly indifferent to the quality of the changes which it purports to explain, yet when it has been brought into contact with the utopian presuppositions of the American political tradition it has strengthened these by lending to the naïve faith of the frontier the vocabulary of philosophy. Also it has taught us to accept the fact that all improvement means change; and even if the further inference that all change means improvement is today regarded with increasing skepticism, the fault at any rate does not lie at the door of the doctrine of evolution.

NOTES

1. George Washington listed in his will as one of the advantages to be anticipated from a national university the acquiring by those who studied there of "knowledge in the principles of Politics and government." See also my *Court over Constitution* (Princeton University Press, 1938), pp. 220-225, for other similar statements of the period.

2. Some of my readers may recall Tenniel's famous cartoon in *Punch* which was suggested by Disraeli's declaration when the controversy was at its height that he "took his stand with the angels." "Dizzy" as an angel was no very ingratiating spectacle. A later reminder of the same controversy occurred in connection with the late William Jennings Bryan's visit to Princeton in the early twenties. Seeing the eminent biologist Professor Edwin Grant Conklin in his audience, Mr. Bryan proclaimed with emphasis, "Professor Conklin can't make a monkey out of me," to which Professor Conklin replied *sotto voce* to a companion, "It's either monkey or mud!"

3. The story is well told in Benjamin R. Twiss's *Lawyers and the Constitution, How Laissez Faire Came to the Supreme Court* (Princeton University Press, 1942). At about the time the Supreme Court was beginning its work of "translation," Sir Henry Maine was writing in his *Popular Government* (New York, Holt, 1886): "There has hardly ever before been a community in which the weak have been pushed so pitilessly to the wall, in which those who have succeeded have so uniformly been the strong, and in which in

so short a time there has arisen so great an inequality of private fortune and domestic luxury. And at the same time, there has never been a country in which, on the whole, the persons distanced in the race have suffered so little from their ill-success." *Popular Government,* p. 51.

4. The theological tinge appears, for example, in Woodrow Wilson's Denver address of Sunday, May 7, 1911, where the idea that progress was inevitable and had the backing of God was proclaimed. *Public Papers* (New York and London, Harper, 1925–27), II, 291–302.

5. President McCosh of Princeton, although he is said not to have relished Professor Macloskie's *tour de force,* contemporaneously revived in evolution's defense St. Thomas Aquinas' axiom that "truth is one." But whereas St. Thomas applied the axiom to subordinate reason to revelation, Dr. McCosh put revelation on the defensive vis-à-vis the truths of science.

6. *Glimpses of the Cosmos,* p. 352, quoted by Richard Hofstadter, *Social Darwinism in American Thought* (University of Pennsylvania Press, 1944), p. 57. It should be observed that Professor Hofstadter uses the expression Social Darwinism to cover Spencerian evolutionism, whereas I distinguish the two.

7. *Ibid.,* p. 125. The notion that man's shortcomings are not grounded in his own nature but arise from external and remediable conditions stems, of course, from Rousseau.

8. Merle Curti, *The Growth of American Thought* (New York and London, Harper, 1943), p. 578.

9. Hofstadter, *op. cit.,* p. 115. My italics. Quoted with the approval of the publishers, the University of Pennsylvania Press.

10. *Ibid.,* p. 103. On the origin of pragmatism, see Philip P. Wiener's excellent article, "Peirce's Metaphysical Club and the Genesis of Pragmatism," *Jour. of the History of Ideas,* VII (April, 1946), 218–233. Professor Lovejoy is there cited for the statement that "pragmatism" had acquired thirteen or more meanings by 1908.

11. *New York Times,* Jan. 12, 1944. It ought to be added that Professor Merriam yielded no whit to the late President in optimistic outlook. The following passage from *Systematic Politics* is in point in this connection:

"The year 1945 may seem an unfortunately chosen moment to declare that violence is on the decline—in the midst of the world's greatest sweep of war. But war is likely to be curbed as a result of this titanic struggle. Internal violence is on its way out—as seen at many points. The father's power of life and death over his family, the master's right to brutality over his slaves, the officer's right to kick and beat his subordinates, the institution of the duel, private war and violent feuds, flogging in schools, disfigurements, torture—all tend to disappear as instruments of government or of society. In the broad field of criminology prevention tends to take the place of punishment in many instances.

"This does not mean, however, that there will not be an organization of violence for various purposes in future society. But war as an instrument of national policy and violence as the staple of internal order and justice are on the decline in modern civilization and, as far as the eye can see, will continue on their downward way. It is thinkable and possible that there may be yet more dreadful and destructive wars than the world has yet seen, raging over long periods of time and over the whole earth, and such an alternative must always be borne in mind. Yet, in dealing broadly, as here, with the tools of government and their trends, it is clear that we move in the direction of peaceful rather than violent methods of settling disputes between individuals and associations." *Op. cit.* (University of Chicago Press, 1945), p. 301. It will be noticed how belief in a beneficent trend which has been operating for centuries colors this passage. Presumably the passage was written before Hiroshima. In the light of that event the notion of possibly bigger and better wars, leading ultimately to peace, somehow fails to appeal.

12. Important in this general connection is Professor Dewey's position on the question whether adjustment to environment can be effected through changes in environment. Dealing with this question Professor Sidney Ratner writes: ". . . Dewey laid down the doctrine that human thinking arises out of specific needs and frustrations. When it is

successful, it leads to a control of the environment, which is achieved through acts based upon previous analysis or resolution of the original complex situation into its composite elements and upon a projection of a plan of action or experiment." "John Dewey and Charles Darwin, a Study in Some Unexplored Relationships" (MS.) citing John Dewey, *Essays in Experimental Logic* (University of Chicago Press, 1916), pp. 1–74. Professor Ratner also brings to my attention the following pertinent statements in Dewey's own words: "The entire significance of the evolutionary method in biology and social history is that every distinct organ, structure, or formation, every grouping of cells or elements, has to be treated as an instrument of adjustment or adaptation to a particular environing situation. Its meaning, its character, its value, is known when, and only when, it is considered as an arrangement for meeting the conditions involved in some specific situation." *Studies in Logical Theory,* (University of Chicago Press, 1903), p. 15. Idealistic logic "ignored the temporarily intermediate and instrumental place of reflection; and . . . overlooked its essential feature: control of the environment in behalf of human progress and well-being, the efforts at control being stimulated by the needs, the defects, the troubles which accrue when the environment coerces and suppresses man or when man endeavors in ignorance to override the enviroment." *Essays in Experimental Logic,* p. 22. "Ideas that are plans of operations to be performed are integral factors in actions which change the face of the world." Dewey, *Quest for Certainty* (New York, Minton, 1929), p. 138. I wish to take this opportunity to acknowledge Professor Ratner's valuable counsel and aid on this phase of my paper.

13. *Marx-Engels Correspondence* (New York, International Publishers, 1935), pp. 125–126. I am again indebted to Professor Ratner who writes: "The connection between the influence of Marxism in the U.S. and that of Darwinism is not close. Darwinism and Marxism, as you know, were both conceived and developed independently. I know of no scientist or philosopher or popular reader who was won over to Darwinism by first being converted to Marxism, or vice versa, at least in the U.S."

14. "Upon the several forms of property, upon the social conditions of existence, a whole superstructure is reared of various and peculiarly shaped feelings, illusions, habits of thought, and conceptions of life. The whole class produces and shapes these out of its material foundation and out of the corresponding social conditions. The individual unit to whom they flow through tradition and education may fancy that they constitute the true reasons for and premises of his conduct." Quoted by George H. Sabine, *A History of Political Theory* (New York, Holt, 1937), p. 693.

15. "A distinctive feature of Dewey's *Ethics* was the Darwinian approach. He stressed the biological basis of human life and conduct: 'Moral conceptions and processes grow naturally out of the very conditions of human life.' He also broke new ground by demonstrating that moral principles, properly understood, were not commands to act or to forbear acting in a given way, but were 'tools or methods which enable each individual to make for himself an analysis of the elements of good and evil in the particular situation in which he finds himself.' " Ratner, article referred to in n. 12, citing John Dewey and James H. Tufts, *Ethics* (New York, Holt, 1908, revised ed. 1932), pp. 34 ff., 343–344.

16. See especially Henry S. Commager, *Majority Rule and Minority Rights* (Oxford University Press, 1943).

INTRODUCTION TO CHAPTER VI

EVOLUTIONISM IN AMERICAN ECONOMICS,
1800–1946

SINCE the formulation of the Darwinian theory of natural selection owed much to the Malthusian political economy it was only appropriate that the circuit of ideas should close in the nineteenth century with the return of evolutionary concepts to upset the static assumptions which had dominated nineteenth-century laissez faire economics in America.

While it appeared at first that evolution verified the competitive economics of Social Darwinism, further consideration made it clear by the end of the century that man's social environment was superimposed upon his natural environment, not merged with it; while the variability of man's social behavior could be conceived at best as but loosely analogous to genetic variations at the organic level. Consequently there emerged a new economics prepared to use its own conceptions of economic variation and selection in the analysis of the dynamics of social change. In his appraisal of recent economic thought Professor Spengler, adopting the point of view of the genetic evolutionist, finds within the tolerant limits of social selection place for a considerable variety of variations in economic behavior. He shares with the biologists the desire for more intensive investigation of the origins of these variations; and he is willing for the present to leave open the question as to whether such tolerance of variations will contribute to long-run economic progress.

S. P.

VI

EVOLUTIONISM IN AMERICAN ECONOMICS, 1800–1946[1]

JOSEPH J. SPENGLER

All things flow; nothing abides. . . . Opposition brings men together, and out of discord comes the fairest harmony, and all things have their birth in strife.

Heraclitus

IT HAS sometimes been said that between economics and evolutionism there has been and there is little affinity. Such statements, of course, are quite wide of the truth. For, as will be shown, what long was the most important brick in the evolutionary edifice was taken over from English classical economics; while the favorableness of the weather of opinion to the growth and spread of the theory of evolution was traceable in part to the earlier diffusion of the ways of thinking common to economists. Economics, on the other hand, drew on biology for analogies, and long made use of a canon of natural history that Darwin found applicable: "Natura non facit saltum." But to the real influence of evolutionism upon economics we shall come presently.

This chapter relates chiefly to the less significant direct and to the far more significant indirect influences of evolution theory— in particular the theories of Charles Darwin and Herbert Spencer, and those of students of the development of culture—upon American economics. The views of pre-Civil War economists are, therefore, little more than noticed. The post-1865 period is divided, for convenience of treatment, into three subperiods: (a) the interregnum, 1865–85, when a moribund derivative of laissez faire economics was ascendant; (b) 1885–1930, when American neoclassical economics took form and crystallized only to begin to give place to an economics that was more realistic and more suited to facilitate collective economic action; and (c) 1930 to the present, a period marked by economic and social distress and an intensified search for new directions.

Evolution, together with its mechanisms must be defined broadly and loosely if it is to accommodate the heterogeneous views of those American economists who were sensible, in their writings, of the fact and the theory of evolution at the organic and the social levels. The evolution theory to whose direct and indirect influences post-Civil War economists were exposed issued principally from three sources. From Spencer came finally his law of progressive evolution, based upon his supposition that "the homogeneous" is unstable and that there is everywhere a persistent tendency to equilibrium; his corollary observation that if, as is almost invariably the case, a final stable state is not reached, the evolutionary process is reversed, matter disintegrates and motion is absorbed; and his many illustrations of the supposed operation of this law and its corollary. From Darwin came two principles: (a) since, despite the tendency of all organisms to progressive increase, their respective numbers remain relatively constant, there must be a continual struggle for existence; (b) since (for reasons that long remained obscure) considerable variation, much of it hereditary, characterizes all organisms subject to the struggle for existence, relatively more of those with favorable variations than of those with unfavorable variations survive the struggle—whence there is natural selection, what Spencer called the "survival of the fittest," and an accumulation of favorable variations. While Spencer's somewhat philosophic theory was intended to account for variation, favorable and unfavorable, Darwin's theory failed to provide a satisfactory explanation of the origin of variation and of the contribution of heredity to the combination of variations; for this and other reasons, therefore, evolution came to be identified by many with natural selection and the "survival of the fittest." Finally, from students of culture came increasing knowledge of the extent and the causes of the growth and the diffusion of subjective and objective culture—knowledge which at times was translated into Darwinian terms. From these several types of evolution theory economists gradually inferred that (as Heraclitus had said) nothing abides, that man and his institutions are plastic and susceptible of great variation and modification, and that continual change (usually for the better rather than for the worse) must be taken for granted.

With these earlier notions may be contrasted the recent conceptions of evolution formulated, respectively, by Needham and by Lotka. According to Needham, "the world is compounded of Organization and Energy; . . . the world is a series of levels of organization, integration, and complexity; . . . these levels occur both in time (evolutionary succession) and in space (morphological envelopes)"; and, "as the time-process goes on," less wasteful "higher forms of aggregation, . . . higher patterns and levels of organization, become possible." Lotka, after noting that "fundamental to the concept of evolution is the idea that it is in some sense a directed process," states that

the direction of evolution is such as to make the flux of energy *through the system of organic nature* a maximum. . . . Natural selection will so operate as to increase the total mass of the organic system, to increase the rate of circulation of matter through the system, and to increase the total energy flux through the system, so long as there is presented an unutilized residue of matter and available energy.

Man has largely substituted, in respect to his own species, *"exosomatic* evolution" for that "slow adaptation of anatomical structure and physiological function in successive generations by selective survival" which has characterized other species. For man, through the development of an efficient "receptor-effector apparatus," has greatly increased the quantity of captured energy at his disposal, and, up to now, has utilized it to elevate his plane of living and to increase his numbers.[2]

The extent to which American economists have taken notice of evolution theory and its mechanisms has depended in part upon the length of the time periods covered by their studies. For the data with which the economist deals may be divided into those which are substantially invariant, and those which are substantially variant, the degree of variability being a function of (among other things) time. If the period covered by an economist's study is short, there will be little or no essentially evolutionary variation with which he needs to concern himself; but if the period covered is sufficiently long, there will be variation evolutionary in character of which he may want to take account.

The measure of attention which American economists have given to evolution theory has depended also upon their conceptions of the scope of economics. The content of economics may be included under three heads: (a) that relating to the pricing and the allocation of economically scarce resources; (b) that relating to the determinants of the levels of economic activity; and (c) that relating to long-run trends in economic aggregates and in the individual and the collective economic behavior of the persons composing such aggregates. The scope of each of these categories, and of economics in general, may be narrowly circumscribed, or it may be broadly defined. If the scope of categories (a) and (b) is narrowly defined, while little or no significance is attached to category (c), economics cannot deal with evolution and its mechanisms; it can concern itself with little more than equilibration under essentially static conditions. If, on the contrary, categories (a) and (b) are broadly defined, and if weight is given to category (c), economics may take evolution theory into account.

In one respect the thought ways of American economists were more suited than were those of their fellow social scientists to render them hospitable to theories, such as those of Spencer and Darwin, that seemingly found in the progressive selection of favorable variations a source of melioration and improvement. For economists had made much of that which they called competition. Adam Smith, whose great work had served as a textbook to several generations of Americans, described "free and universal competition" as the most powerful impetus to "good management" and economic progress.[3] His British and French followers, Ricardo, Malthus, Say, McCulloch, the Mills, and others, all of whom were known in America, had reasoned in like manner. In America, both before and after the Civil War, the salutary influence of competition was emphasized by many writers on economics. By the capacity of an economic act to stand the test of competition they measured that act's efficacy. Upon the supposedly meliorative effects of competition they built their case for laissez faire. As long as competition persisted, industry and skill would prevail over indolence and ignorance. So testified McVickar, Cooper, Tucker, Cardozo, Wayland, and others before the Civil War; and so, in effect, testified many post-Civil War writers. In support of this view were marshaled the teachings of that commonsense philosophy which continued dominant in American colleges until the closing decades of the nineteenth century.

Despite their thought ways, American economists did not, as we shall see, embrace evolution theory at once. Among the reasons for this cool reception must be included their conception of the nature of the competitive process. Presumably they conceived of competition in terms of cooperation much more than in terms of struggle, and as an essentially static rather than as a dynamic process. The failure of mid-nineteenth-century evolution theory to include a satisfactory account of the sources of favorable variations probably did not greatly affect its reception at the hands of writers on economic matters; for most of these, despite their emphasis upon the civilizing effects of commerce and industry, did not dwell upon the implications for economic analysis of history and of the already current stage theories of cultural development.[4]

I. THE PERIOD OF PROTO-EVOLUTION: 1800–1865

Developmental views were not unknown to American writers upon economic matters in the period that preceded the introduction of the theories of Spencer and Darwin. While these views usually had to do with change at the cultural level—with change that was assumed to be *progressive* in character, they sometimes related to change at the organic level, or to organic restraints upon change at higher levels. These views may be examined in terms of the Godwin-Malthus controversy which subsequently facilitated the deduction, by Darwin, Spencer, and A. R. Wallace, of the struggle for existence and natural selection through the elimination of the unfit and the survival of the fit; for this controversy continued to give focus to developmental views in England and France whence American writers long drew much both of their inspiration and of their thought-directing animus.

The Godwin-Malthus controversy, in its most elemental terms, had to do with the reciprocal relations between man's supposed proclivity to multiply and his sociomaterial condition and environment. Godwin asserted that, given an appropriate modification of the institutional structure of society, man's cultural and physical progress would always more than suffice to prevent a misery-producing pressure of numbers upon resources. This Malthus denied, saying that the existing institutional structure was better suited than any alternative institutional structure to contain man's propensity to multiply, and that the limited improvement of which the common man's lot was susceptible could be won only through the acquisition of suitable and proper habits. Malthus' *Essay,* therefore, tended to emphasize, particularly for the superficial reader, the supposedly constant elements in the institutional complex and in the psychological make-up of men, and to play up the obstacles that stood in the way of the improvement of man's mundane lot. The works of Godwin and of certain of Malthus' critics, on the contrary, tended to emphasize the supposedly variable elements in the cultural complex and in man's psychological make-up, and to play up the forces making for the rationalization of individual behavior and for progress in its various guises.

The question at issue was not wholly new. It had been touched upon in the mid-eighteenth century, by Cantillon and the physiocrats, and it had been clearly posed a little later by Robert Wallace and Condorcet. It had permeated Smith's notion of a stationary state, in which technological knowledge was no longer growing, and in which manufactures and commerce were no longer expanding because, in consequence of the augmentation of population and capital, wages and profits had fallen to levels at which they just sufficed to maintain population and capital constant.[5] Smith thus recognized that a population, which increases by transforming part of its environment into itself, can no longer grow when environmental elements directly or indirectly essential to its augmentation are supporting as large a population as they are then capable of supporting. Subsequent writers, e.g., Ricardo, Malthus, Mill, followed Smith in conceiving of the possibility of a stationary state, or equilibrium of forces (or flows), issuing primarily out of the inability of the environment to support a larger population. But they conceived of a stationary state which, while not necessarily happy, was free of the terrors of the Smithian structure; for whereas Smith's discussion suggested that population growth would continue until wages had been pushed to a very low level, the discussions of later writers suggested the possibility and even the probability of higher standards of life, smaller populations, and higher real wages.[6]

It is not surprising, therefore, that classical economics contributed to the formulation of the theory of evolution and prepared a climate of opinion congenial to its acceptance. For, as the late Lord Keynes remarked after the manner of Engels, "The principle of the Survival of the Fittest could be regarded as a vast generalisation of the Ricardian economics." When Darwin and Spencer applied this principle to man as an organism they but showed that free competition, which, according to the economists, had created the wealth of nations, had also "built Man";[7] and they re-enforced the entrepreneur's plea for laissez faire and his belief in its creativity.

All or nearly all such discussions of evolution theory as are to be found in American writings on economics in the pre-Civil War period issued out of the Godwin-Malthus controversy, or had to do with demographic selection. For these writings were based upon the principles of English-French classical economics, or they were designed to repeat or to formulate an opposing set of principles. Both the adherents and the critics of English classical economics, however, found themselves in an environment that was different from the English and the French environments. They found themselves in an underpopulated country rich in employment and investment opportunities, in a socioeconomic situation favorable to all types of social mobility, and (sometimes) in a religious milieu that emphasized beneficent Providential design. Whence the adherents of the classical school tended to subordinate when they did not attempt to reformulate the seemingly pessimistic portions of classical economic theory; and its critics developed principles optimistic in tenor and sometimes evolutionary in character.

That interracial competition might affect the demographic and possibly the institutional structure of American society was suggested by a number of pre-Civil War writers, some of whom were primarily economists. It was said, for example, that since the Negro, like the Indian, was inferior to the white man, he would gradually disappear along with the Indian, if he were removed from the shelter of slavery and subjected to unrestricted competition from the whites. It was predicted by George Tucker and other American Malthusians, furthermore, that the growth of the free-labor population and the consequent depression of the price of free labor below the cost of slave labor would bring the slave system to term, probably in the early twentieth century, and cause the more economical free-labor system to be substituted in its place. Some writers contended that the institution of slavery was inimical to the growth of the white population, while others declared that it checked the increase of both whites and Negroes. Subsequently, however, so desperate were the defenders of the slave system to justify it, that they converted this contention into a defense of the slave system: Only in an economy founded, as was the Southern, upon slavery, would the growth of both the slave and the nonslave population be under sufficient restraint to permit the aversion of Malthusian misery.[8] Economists apparently did not take much part in the pre-Civil War controversy over the alleged superiority of the Anglo-Saxon and the Protestant and its implications for immigration policy.[9]

The dynamic idea of progress—"that civilization has moved, is moving, and will move in a desirable direction"—apparently was at the bottom of most of the social evolutionism that permeated pre-Civil War economics. The proponents of this idea, so important in modern history,[10] founded it, not upon Lamarckian principles, but upon the belief that culture is cumulative—a belief of which they discovered support in the advancements underway in science, technology, industry, and education.[11] While this theory was viewed by some—the propertied, the clergy, the defenders of the slave system—as a possible threat to the status quo,[12] it was employed in practice, even as was subsequent evolution theory, to support such diverse and opposed causes as those of peace and expansionism.[13] It is significant for the purposes of the present discussion because it tempered the impact of pessimistic foreign interpretations of the principle of population, because it made continual change a part of the American pattern of expectations, and because it prepared the way for the acceptance of the theories of Spencer, Darwin, and the social evolutionists.[14]

The theory of progressive economic evolution received its most complete statement in pre-Civil War America at the hands of Henry C. Carey, critic of the doctrines of Malthus and Ricardo, principal formulator of American nationalist political economy, and exponent of the view that the unrestrained operation of natural law which governs both the physical and the social world must produce interindividual and international harmony. Carey's views differed in many respects from those of late nineteenth-century economists under the influence of evolution theories; yet his basic outlook was quite similar: within rather wide limits man is plastic, his social organization is elastic, and his several environments are continually susceptible of modification by himself and his fellows; whence his material and social condition is always susceptible of change, change which is bound to be progressive in character so long as men conduct themselves, individually and collectively, in an appropriate manner.[15]

The economy of man is susceptible of progressive evolution, Carey's argument suggests, because man is morally responsible and physiologically and psychically variable, because in consequence he is capable of "individuality" and of "association" (or collective life), because his culture is cumulative in character, and because competition for the services of man and nature accelerates "societary circulation." While man cannot "alter the existing quantity of force," he can "affect its distribution and its mode of manifestation"; and while he cannot modify the quantity of matter, he can assist it to take on "new and higher forms." Specifically, Carey reasoned, much as did Spencer by whom he was influenced in his later years, that man progresses through the growth of occupational and other forms of differentiation and the correlated development of such forms of association (or interhuman cooperation) as advancing differentiation makes possible and necessary. "The greater the variety of employment—the greater the demand for intellectual effort—the more dissimilar become the parts, and the more perfect becomes the whole." In general, Carey's philosophy ran in terms of lower and higher forms of organization of matter, with matter tending to take on more advanced forms, of which man is the highest; and with "every increase in the extent to which matter [takes] upon itself the form of man," his "power to guide and direct the forces provided for his use" tends to increase. For the principle of the survival of the fittest he had no place in his system, since it was but a form of Malthusianism.[16]

Carey's recommendations respecting social policy and his anticipations regarding man's mundane future reveal the dynamic and optimistic qualities of his economic philosophy. He was alive to the supposedly beneficent effects of competition which he believed to be essentially cooperative in character, yet he rejected a laissez faire system that was completely unrestricted; for he believed that protectionism and certain other forms of governmental intervention would accelerate man's progressive economic evolution by stimulating industrial and occupational differentiation and thus making for the perfection of economic organization. Instead of Malthusian misery he foresaw a steady improvement in man's lot. For progress in the powers of association, stimulated where necessary by the growth and concentration of population and aided in agriculture by the tendency of settlement and cultivation to proceed from less fertile to more fertile soils, would make for an increasing economy of human force, for falling reproduction costs, for the steady diminution of economic inequality, and for the simultaneous expansion of property's absolute share and of labor's absolute and relative shares in the national dividend.

These economic tendencies in turn would operate, psychically and physiologically, to adjust man's population growth to the requirements of his welfare. For man's disposition to procreate is not invariant as is that of brutes or that of Ricardo's economic man;

it varies with time and circumstance and passes more and more under rational control as man's economic and cultural situation advances. Furthermore—and here Carey again reasoned in terms of the disposition of energy just as had Spencer[17]—as man's power to maintain life grows, his mental activity increases and his energy is partly diverted from reproduction to other functions, with the result that his natural fecundity tends to fall to a level consistent with the maintenance of equilibrium between "the power to maintain life and that of procreation." [18] Carey pleaded for no fundamental modification of the politico-economic structure of the country; for harmony pervaded the universe, and changes would come as they were needed so long as men obeyed the laws of harmonious and beneficent nature to which man and matter alike were subject. The realization of the welfare of men, therefore, called neither for the extensive governmental intervention proposed by the Fourierist, Brisbane,[19] nor for the midwifely assistance of the class struggle urged by Marx.

Some of Carey's views remained alive until the latter part of the nineteenth century when they were either discarded or reformulated by the nation's first generation of professional economists; but they exercised little direct and persisting influence upon the response of American economists to evolution theory.

II. INTERREGNUM: 1865–1885

The twenty-year interval that separates Appomattox and the founding of the American Economic Association was marked by both agricultural discontent and economic expansion. Economic analysis, together with descriptions of economic practice, continued to run in terms of the atomistic rather than in those of the organic, in terms of self-locomoting human pellets rather than in terms of conditioning social patterns and fields. For Spencer's evolutionism, which in the eyes of many only confirmed belief in the beneficent theory of progress inherited from the eighteenth century, there developed a veritable vogue. To the essentials of Darwinism acceptance was extended. Emphasis was upon the fact and the mode of selection, however, the theory of natural selection being treated as the virtual equivalent of the theory of evolution; the theory of the origin of favorable variations was not played up despite the fact that Darwin's theory of blending inheritance called for enormously higher mutation rates than does particulate inheritance.[20]

This interval also saw the transfer to the social world of man of the law of struggle which Darwin had found to be descriptive of the plant and animal world—an application that, while invalid, was in keeping with a pellet theory of interhuman economic relations. For evolutionism, when transmuted into Social Darwinism, well suited the climate of opinion of a burgeoning Age of Gilt and Mammon that was witnessing the integration of the economy and the rise of the captain of industry. An outstandingly successful business man was hard put to find a philosophical basis for his *apologia pro vita mea* more satisfactory than this essentially perverted form of Darwinism.[21] Social Darwinism, of course, stressed the theory of selection; for its exponents took favorable variations in the economic and social sphere for granted.

What passed for political economy at this time was not affected, directly and substantially, by the theories of Spencer and Darwin, only four economists (Sturtevant, Newcomb, Sumner, and Walker) referring thereto favorably. Nonetheless, a number of economists who favored the status quo wrote as if they subscribed to Spencer's views on individualism, competition, and survival even though they made no favorable mention of his doctrines.

A number of circumstances appear to have been responsible for this initial failure of American economics to assimilate the new evolutionary philosophy. Economists and economics had not yet become professionalized, much of the teaching being carried on, as before the Civil War, by clerics and individuals of a clerical turn of mind, for whom evolution could not be, as it was for some, a substitute for religion.[22] There existed no professional associations and journals to facilitate the interchange and development of economic views.[23] Economics was viewed as "a finished product" which one could master "by reading a single volume," the only prerequisites being "Common Sense and a good knowledge of the English language"; and critical study of economic phenomena was "unpopular."[24] The "guardians of the true faith" in fact considered no one an economist who was not an exponent and defender of laissez faire,[25] presumably a laissez faire pervaded by cooperativeness and harmony rather than by bitter struggle and practices worthy of Reynard the Fox. Felicity could be maximized only if men observed those natural economic laws which held for all times and in all places, and which, many economists supposed, expressed the will of Divine Providence.[26] It would have been surprising if economists, who were imbued with this spirit of social finality and theological certitude, had at once sought to merge economics with Spencer's godless theory of purposive adaptation, or with Darwin's even less palatable theory of the purposeless selection of favorable variations accidental in origin. How could a theory of struggle be transmuted into a theory of voluntary and harmonious cooperation? How could Chance draw out of Chaos and Old Night all things material and social, and many of remarkable design, which theretofore had always been looked upon as the handiwork of the divine Watchmaker? [27]

Some of the influential laissez faire economists of this period simply ignored evolution theory. For example, Amasa Walker, critic of Malthus, was content to observe that "if human laws and institutions do not interfere to prevent, the natural order of things will be sure to bring out the best physical condition of mankind"; but he did not connect this opinion with evolution theory.[28] Of similar opinion was David A. Wells, who, like Walker, was an exponent both of laissez faire and of equity in the distribution of wealth. If "life among the masses" is not "somewhat more than a struggle for existence," then "artificial" conditions are responsible; and these may be ameliorated.[29] A. L. Chapin, who recast Wayland's manual which had been in use for half a century, expounded the "determinate laws" to which, it was "obvious upon the slightest reflection, that the Creator had subjected the accumulation of the blessings of this life." While he apparently was confident that self-interest, tempered by the golden rule, would improve the human lot, he laid down no evolutionary principles.[30] A. L. Perry, who came to view "political economy as the science of sales," described "society" as "God's handiwork" and as displaying "those peculiar laws that mark a divine hand." Hence he was of an optimistic turn of mind, and counted upon the Creator to prevent such evils as overpopulation; but he did not make use of evolution theory.[31]

Other exponents of laissez faire referred to evolution theory only to condemn it. For example, John Bascom looked upon Darwinism, with its exclusive emphasis upon "physical causation," as irreligious;[32] presumably it was inconsistent with his conception of a world regulated by "laws of trade" which expressed "God's government," and to which economic man must conform. Yet, he believed, much as did later exponents of Social Darwinism, that "unpitying poverty" and "war and pestilence must winnow the feeble races" and eliminate worthless human material.[33] Years later, still both a Malthusian and a critic of the environmentalist philosophy of socialism, he expressed himself somewhat after the manner of a Spencerian: Man was developing. Society was progressing through integration. At both the physical and the rational level, life was "slowly rising to a more perfect equilibrium." [34]

Much more vigorous than Bascom in his criticism of Darwin was Francis Bowen who "managed to be wrong about almost every important nineteenth-century intellectual issue." [35] A common-sense philosopher and a critic of Comte,[36] Bowen condemned both the environmentalism of Buckle and the developmentalism of Darwin on the ground that they were materialistic, fatalistic, agnostic, and pessimistic.[37] Neither on moral nor on religious grounds could Bowen stomach a theory that seemed to postulate a mechanical and behavioristic man.[38] In 1860 he merely described Darwin's theory as quite inadequate and improbable.[39] But in 1879, having observed that Darwin had revived Malthus' invalid and "gloomy doctrine of 'a battle for life,'" he declared that Darwinism rested upon and must fall with Malthusianism, which had been completely refuted as a principle of political economy. Yet he seemed to question that divinely authored "laissez faire principle" in the beneficence of whose workings he had expressed faith in his earlier economic writings.[40] For he found negative demographic selection in operation. The lower and inferior classes were outbreeding the upper; the "unfittest" were outstripping the "fittest." Civilization would not continue if the "educated classes" failed to reproduce themselves.

"If they do not fill the vacant places on the earth's surface, these will soon be occupied by the progeny of the ignorant and the debased, who, in this respect, are the dangerous classes of society." [41]

Post-Civil War critics of contemporary capitalism and socio-economic theory were under compulsion both to condemn Social Darwinism and to develop a theory of social evolution in terms of which the reform or the replacement of capitalism might be anticipated and accelerated. Henry George, the most influential of these critics, gave expression to this compulsion; but his analysis, like that of other American critics, was economically and historically immature. While he criticized Malthus rather effectively, he simply dismissed Darwin's views, neglecting to demonstrate the sociological untenability of Social Darwinism; and he expressed great but not unqualified faith in the efficacy of the competitive process. He looked upon Spencer's evolutionism as conducing to fatalism and as failing to "account for an original purpose and fundamental will behind the manifestations of 'matter in motion'"; but he accepted the Spencerian view that "civilization is an evolution . . . a progress from an indefinite incoherent homogeneity to a definite, coherent heterogeneity."

George did not suppose, however, with Spencer and others, that progress was inevitable and continuous. Quite the contrary. Like some of the founding fathers he was pessimistic regarding the future. "Every civilization that the world has yet seen," he declared, has declined and fallen, following the arrest and stagnation of its growth. For progress is achieved through that association and that communal (or collective) activity which augment the *creative* power of men. Yet, because the fruits of this power are finally channeled, by the institution of private landownership, into the hands of the few, pronounced inequality always comes into being, and, after braking the progress of civilization, finally brings about its downfall.

George was more optimistic than would be Henry and Brooks Adams several decades later; for he believed that his theory of economic evolution placed in the hands of men the power to prevent that growth in inequality which in the past had always put an end to progress and brought poverty and retrogression in its wake. It was but necessary that land rent be socialized and used for the benefit of the community which had created it; if this were done, progress would continue and provide for man an ever improving material and cultural environment. George did not observe, as others would do later, that strategically situated members of the community might and could seize other social surpluses than rent; and that, therefore, if the growth of inequality were to be prevented, arrangements must also be made to capture and use these surpluses for the benefit of the community to whose activities they were supposedly imputable.[42]

Simon Newcomb, astronomer-economist, and J. M. Sturtevant, midwestern college president, wrote of economic matters much as did most of the orthodox economists who rejected or ignored evolution theory; but they incorporated evolution theory into their economics and implicitly supposed that harmony rather than strife dominates the economic affairs of men. Newcomb, who drew upon Spencer while ignoring Darwin, conceived of man as a being who is impelled by "an unlimited series of desires" to employ his "faculties" and to adapt "means to ends" so "as to secure the maximum gratification of desires with the minimum of inconvenience." Economic exchange binds men together, thus making of them a kind of social organism which is kept in equilibrium by exchange. This organism is capable of progress, which is achieved on the one hand, through continuous economic specialization, or differentiation, and, on the other, through a consequent and "increasing adaptation of the parts," or integration. Newcomb, a defender of the captain of industry, believed that too few "men of the higher orders" and too many "of the lower orders" were being born; but he did not trace out the economic implications of this supposedly dysgenic reproductive selection.[43]

Sturtevant, who claimed that he had applied the principle of the struggle for existence and the survival of the fittest "years before" he had "had any knowledge of Mr. Darwin's observations,"[44] made extensive use of this principle; but, like his contemporaries, he neglected the circumstances that make for favorable variations. He believed that the cultural and the biological progress of advanced peoples is assured so long as the "law of competition" is allowed to operate freely and, in respect to the human species, to assume the form of a "struggle for existence" which only "the strongest" survive. It becomes the business of the economist, therefore, "to show how the laws of human nature, when not viciously counteracted, would regulate . . . the economics of all peoples." The questions with which economists "have to do are not ethical, but purely economic. The laws which determine the several results are not moral, but natural laws, as far removed from the control of human wills as cohesion or electricity." The price of violation of these laws is "confusion and disaster." The reward of their observance is progress and escape from misery.

If the law of competition is allowed free play, the supply of men will always adjust itself nicely to the productive power of the earth, there will be no "melancholy" Malthusian denouement, and the quality of man and his civilization will continue to improve. First, competition will spread civilized communities over all parts of the earth where "there are natural resources to sustain them." It will carry both men and capital from places where they are superabundant to places where they are in short supply and able to obtain a better return.

Second, application of the law of competition "will always de-

rive each succeeding generation from the soundest and the health-
iest part of the generation that precedes it." For any civilized society "under the influence of competition" consists of four classes
of persons. The "two lower strata of society" include those "who
are not able to perform a sufficient amount of labor for their own
support" and those who, "though able to labor for self-support, are
not able to support families." Because of their condition, which
may be the result of disease, vice, misfortune, or inferior natural
endowment, the members of these two inferior classes "can contribute nothing to the capital of the future" and they will not "be
to any considerable extent parents of the coming generation." The
topmost of these four classes consists of the wealthy minority "who
are able to command an income that surpasses all that is needful
for the sustenance and substantial support of a family," but who,
in consequence of the self-indulgent spirit "which is apt to prevail
in the homes of the rich," rear few children and do not "contribute
to the population of the future in proportion to [their] numbers."
The "ranks of population for coming generations are therefore
chiefly filled from the third class" which includes "the great majority of the people," namely, those "who by a life of labor and
frugality are able to support a family in plenty and substantial
comfort." In sum, competition at the biological level operates to
eliminate family strains not well suited to survive and advance the
species at the same time that it favors the comparatively rapid
increase of those with "physical and mental vigor, a sound body
and an active and instructed mind."

In general the principle of competition, which for Sturtevant
was equivalent, at both the biological and the cultural level, to
Darwin's struggle for existence, operated, if unimpeded, to improve the biological composition and to advance the cultural level
of a population. While the principle of competition tends to override all obstacles in the end, interference with its operation—for
example, through the exclusion of a substratum, e.g., Negro slaves,
of the population from the benefits of civilization and the impact
of the struggle for existence—gives rise to evils, e.g., disease, which
"it will be exceedingly difficult to eradicate, when society has
reached its maturity." The possible sources of favorable variations
at the cultural and the biological levels Sturtevant did not analyze.
Nor, in his treatment of the "stimuli to labor," did he give attention to man's plasticity, or to his manner of habit formation; he

remained content instead to discuss the role of man's "rational soul" and to report the tendency of his standard of living to rise with the advance of civilization.

Of the economic writings which appeared in the period under survey only those of William Graham Sumner, first of the sociologist-economists, and Francis A. Walker, most prominent of the post-Civil War economists, seem to have sluiced some evolutionism into American economic thought. For the evolutionism of Sturtevant and Newcomb exercised little influence. Since some of Walker's work and much of Sumner's appeared after 1885, they contributed, both before and after 1885, to the assimilation of evolution theory into economics. Each man in his own way drew attention to the significance for economics of the plasticity of human nature and man's institutions; and both helped to free political economy from the paralyzing grip of natural theology. Both contributed to the understanding of the competitive process and the economic role of the state. Concerning the scope of economics they differed. The greatest contribution to evolutionism was made by Sumner who substituted the Darwinian for the Spencerian conception of the theory of social change, undermined that teleology which theretofore had permeated American economic philosophy, and prepared the way for the approaches of Veblen and the institutionalists.

Walker is a transitional figure in the history of American economics. While he lacked Sumner's grasp of evolution theory and its significance for economic analysis, he did not ignore it as did his most prominent economist contemporary, C. F. Dunbar,[45] but touched upon it in two ways. First, as a student of demography, he analyzed the circumstances making for change in the ethnic composition of the American population. He denied the commonly held view that the supposed decline in the rate of increase of the native population was attributable to climatic conditions or to physiological changes. It was attributable, rather, to changes produced in the psychology of the older population stocks by industrialization and by the coming of the newer immigrant types. Immigration, Walker argued, much as had Franklin a century earlier, was not serving to increase the population; it was merely substituting later immigrant strains for the potential descendants of those stocks which had originally settled this country.[46] Walker's unfavorable appraisal of some of the economic and demographic effects of immigration was reflected in the controversy over the advisability of restricting immigration which continued until after World War I when immigration was finally subjected to effective control.[47]

Second, Walker rejected the then dominant arid and doctrinaire laissez faire economics, and presented instead a body of doctrine scientific in temper and founded upon the premise that, within fairly wide limits, man's nature is elastic and his institutions are susceptible of change. Walker condemned as unreal and misleading that hypothetical economic man of whose supposed behavior economists discoursed, and he urged that adequate attention be given to man as he is and to those institutions and customs by which his behavior in relation to wealth is affected. He asserted, furthermore, that political economy had nothing to do with natural theology.

Walker was alert to the forces making for change. Formerly, he noted, laissez faire philosophy had been in the saddle, and the members of the employing class had looked upon themselves as "the natural trustees of the laboring class." But these views had been undermined by two new and powerful forces. One was the study of human nature which had followed the announcement of "the great law of natural selection." The other was the growth in awareness of the great improvements that had been taking place in the economic, social, political, and material conditions of the common man. Walker himself, probably because he was impressed by these changes, pleaded for a study of the effects of consumption upon civilization, saying that consumption, through its effects upon man, gave direction to his culture.[48] This plea Patten and Veblen later undertook to satisfy.

Walker dwelt upon the salutary influence of competition when free, particularly in his criticism of Bellamy, and he advocated close scrutiny of all proposals, socialistic or otherwise, to extend the power of the state. Yet, although he was a Malthusian, he denied that population pressure operated as among plants and animals, to eliminate the unfit and to raise the "standard of size and strength and functional vigor among men." For among men "the solidarity of the family" served to defeat "the effort of nature" and to convert the struggle between individuals into one "between families as units." [49] Walker also rejected both that doctrinal bulwark of the class in power, the theory of the harmony of interests, and its corollary, that the members of functional groups are always rewarded according to their individual contributions. He thus recognized that force, or power, may play a part in the distribution of the product, and prepared the way for the bargaining theory of wages; but he did not trace out the implications of his observation. He was content to say that if competition is not free and equal for all and consequently the worker does not automatically get what is rightfully his, he must struggle both to get it and to realize his highest advantage;[50] and that this struggle is eased when competition among businessmen is intense, and incompetent entrepreneurs are speedily eliminated.[51]

Walker's theory of profits reflects the spirit of an age which made a virtue of struggle and conflict, and which looked upon the captain of industry much as the medieval world had looked upon the knight. Profits constituted the measure of efficiency. Profits were enjoyed only by supramarginal entrepreneurs. To the efforts of the more successful of these entrepreneurs, the captains of industry, society owed much of its industrial progress.[52] Strangely, not many years later the drive against monopoly would start, and economists would begin to lay the groundwork for tollgate theories of profit.

William Graham Sumner, more than any American economist, effected an integration, however unsatisfactory to the present generation, of the principles of variation, natural selection, and classical economics. Yet in so doing he lost his identity as an economist, becoming a sociologist as did Giddings, Cooley, and Ross later; and, through his influence upon Veblen and others, he helped to undermine the very Social Darwinism he was so instrumental in formulating. Because Sumner's influence upon economics has been pervasive rather than specific in character, and because his contributions lie primarily in the field of sociology, his work will receive only passing mention here. From Malthus, whose principle of population he always upheld, Sumner got his notion of the great importance of the man : land ratio; while from Spencer he took a theory of social evolution which he recast along Darwinian and nonteleological lines. From his anthropological, and (possibly) from his economic studies, he drew his conception of the societal universe as a kind of self-equilibrating social organism composed of interconnected folkways, mores, and institutions; from these studies he also derived his economic determinism which made the form and content of the ideals, thought ways, customs, social relations, and noneconomic institutions of a society depend in a large measure upon its industrial and economic organization, or maintenance substratum. Out of these several analytical elements Sumner built his defense of economic competition, his argument that social change is snail-like, and his case against the isms of his day, imperialism, protectionism, reformism, statism, and socialism.

Sumner took no stock in the rational psychological theory in terms of which the economists of his day were wont to treat economic behavior. He played up the role of the viscous and the quasi-constant elements in the cultural complex and he played down that of projective and creative thinking. An objectivist, skeptical of motives and instincts, Sumner was content to collect behavior tendencies and group them under four heads, or interests: hunger, love, vanity, and ghost fear. The societal process he found to be logical, irrational, and fatalistic. It was absurd to suppose that man could make the world over; for each individual is but a child of his own age, a minuscular part of a social organism that changes slowly in response to invention, discovery, telluric alterations, war, and so on. Even when a great change in the interclass distribution of economic power permits a successful revolution, only some of the mores prove susceptible of change; the others persist, concluded Sumner, the moral relativist, largely because they are useful or expedient under the circumstances.

Economic competition, in Sumner's social theory, is but one form of the more general struggle which men wage with nature and with each other for the products of nature. He distinguished, furthermore, between the struggle of the classes for dominance and the struggle of men for existence; and he noted that the latter form of struggle itself underwent evolution, changing from a sheer struggle for life and existence in a poverty-ridden society to a struggle for improved living standards in a more comfortable society. The effects of this struggle at the several levels of life were generally beneficial. It eliminated the unfit and it rewarded the fit. It served to distribute among men, according to their differing merits, the variously valued places which society had to offer. It tended to carry the superior classes to the top of the social structure where, although they now could somewhat influence the selective operation of the mores in their own favor, they could continue to remain only if they maintained their superiority. In general, therefore, Sumner's analysis suggested that this struggle made for salutary selection, appropriate change, and minimization of the need for governmental regulation.

Sumner was not convinced, however, that socioeconomic evolution would always of necessity proceed along a progressive course. In fact there was real danger that the middle class, the class of the Forgotten Man which, Sumner believed, must above all others be preserved, would be crushed between plutocracy from above and collectivism from below. And it was obligatory upon the state to preserve this class just as it was obligatory for the state to repress selfish interests that sought to impair the rights of others.[53]

III. THE FORMATIVE AND CRYSTALLIZING PERIOD, 1885–1930

With the establishment of the American Economic Association in 1885 and the professionalization of economics, its subject matter began to undergo expansion and differentiation and to develop a scope and form that persisted through the 1920's, only to give way finally under the double burden of international contraction and domestic collapse in the economic sphere. Throughout this period, of course, there occurred in the real world of affairs economic events whose cumulative effect was to undermine the body of economic doctrine generally accepted at its inception. This period saw, among other things, the infiltration of Deweyistic and behavioristic psychology, the diffusion of Veblenianism and the rise of institutionalism, the recognition of the importance and the cumulative character of economic change, the development of the theory of the creative state, some refinement of the concept of an economic system that tends both to evolve and to move toward equilibrium, the elaboration of the theory of fluctuations, with its emphasis on periodicities and trends, and an increase in the stress upon empiricism and induction. It also witnessed the rejection of Social Darwinism and laissez faire and their corollaries despite the support that this social philosophy temporarily received from the nation's entry into the late nineteenth-century struggle of the Great Powers for world empire. The developments which we have enumerated both reflected and shaped the influence of evolutionism upon American economics.

Although economists of this period paid more attention to evolutionism, they no longer used it to defend the status quo and a "root, hog, or die" social philosophy. Evolution theory acted directly and indirectly to make some economists aware of the plasticity and creativity of man, of the dynamic character of environment and of the reciprocal relation obtaining between it and man, and of the never-endingness of change; it helped to undermine the pellet theory of interhuman relations and to direct attention to the fundamental importance of activities and process. Economists differed widely, of course, in the extent to which they assimilated evolutionism into their economic philosophy.

In a textbook that supplanted Walker's even as Walker's had supplanted Wayland's, A. T. Hadley, subsequently president of Yale, explicitly recognized "the principle of natural selection" and "recent psychological study" as somewhat outmoding the economics of John Stuart Mill. Hadley found in Darwinism what he could not find in preconceived and varying ethical codes, namely, a standard acceptable to all and suited to bridge the gap between economics and ethics, a standard in terms of which the socially good could be clearly distinguished from the socially bad. This standard was the standard of survival. That is good which in the long run prevails. That has the right to remain, and most probably will remain, which has long survived. That is bad which, because it lacks survival qualities such as the capacity to adapt itself, is eliminated. This test of survival, Hadley believed, held for laws and institutions, for customs and feelings, for individuals and groups.[54]

Although Hadley described some of the selective processes that were essentially economic in character, he made only indirect and guarded application of the survival standard; and he neglected entirely the reciprocal effect of the standard of value upon the conditions of survival. The struggle for existence, he declared, was probably as severe among men as among lower forms of life; but it was "between groups more than between individuals" and "for domination more than for annihilation"; and it affected the habits and institutions of men rather than their physical structure. While communities with stronger forms of organization tend to displace those with weaker organizations, the victories achieved prove Pyrrhic ones when the circumstances making for strong organization also make for the preservation of weaker and degenerate individuals and thus weaken the victorious communities in the longer run. Those institutions are best, consequently, which, besides having survival power in themselves, give "the best individuals the chance to set the pace for the whole community and force it up to their level" and thus conduce to race improvement and survival. It was not of interclass conflict, therefore, that the champion of competition approved; rather it was of competition among individuals within given classes, since this form of struggle prevented man from taking undue advantage of his fellow men. Free competition and free enterprise, Hadley's argument runs, are superior, on grounds of performance and survival power, to their opposites. So also is the institution of private property superior to its opposite, in part because it generates prudence in respect to marriage and procreation and thus prevents excessive population growth.[55]

Hadley's opinions regarding evolutionism were supported with slight elaboration by W. G. L. Taylor. Evolution will not produce "physical degeneracy" in man. For with progress, "subjective evolution" is replacing objective evolution; and individuals, by means of internal adjustments, are "rectifying unhealthy physical symptoms in order that the mind may be supported in higher psychic struggles."[56] Elsewhere he noted that a rising standard of consumption favors the common man indirectly in that it removes the need for low-grade, cheap-labor occupations.[57]

S. Sherwood, who considered Spencer's theory but a generalization of Smith's division of labor, protested against the application of physical laws of matter to society, since social causation is psychical in character. "To make society intelligible we must accept the principle of economic selection, or utility, as the universal law of social causation." For this law—"the greatest utility with the least sacrifice"—describes both that human activity "directed to preserve status and that which aims at social evolution."[58]

Some of the founders of the American Economic Association, all of whom were essentially conservative in temper and some of whom had studied with the German historical economists, broke with the Social Darwinian and laissez faire tradition of American academic economics even more completely than did Walker and "Old School" Hadley. They described the state as an agency whose assistance is indispensable to progress and they declared against unregulated competition.[59] Where competition is unrestrained and public powers are narrowly limited, declared H. C. Adams in a classic statement of the new view, the business morals of the worst men prevail, government is rendered weak and corrupt, and beneficent monopolies are not established in those lines to which the monopolistic form of organization alone is well suited. Therefore Adams opposed the Spencer-Sumner conception of laissez faire, and declared that the state must determine "the plane of competitive action," "realize for society the benefits of monopoly," and restore "social harmony." [60] L. M. Keasbey went further, declaring the "sovereign national state" to be the "determining factor in economic advance" since, without the help of this "politico-economic organism," man cannot "unite with his fellows in the joint fulfillment of their wants and in harmony" with life.[61] In subsequent years, economists rejected the laissez faire philosophy of the Social Darwinians, approving in increasing measure of enlargement of the state's restrictive role, and in somewhat lesser measure of enlargement of its creative role, almost always on the implied ground that such changes would improve the efficiency and the survival power of the free enterprise system. Improved economic and political analysis, together with changes in economic organization and in the material conditions of existence, and a growing awareness of these changes and their implications, contributed to this revision of the role of the state in theory and practice.[62]

Richard T. Ely, a leading founder of the new economic association who did much to interest organized religion in economic affairs, devoted a not too critical book[63]—in his review of the literature there is no reference to Closson and Lapouge—to evolution, in which he declared "a general human retrogression" to be inconceivable. He inferred that the "social organism" had been evolving in accordance with the Spencerian principles of differentiation and integration; but he did distinguish clearly between the Darwinian and the Spencerian mechanisms of change. While he allowed adequate scope for governmental intervention, he played down the principles of struggle and selection and played up competition as a not unkindly process.

Ely preferred, as had List, a stage theory of economic evolution based upon the ways people get a living, since these ways profoundly influence the "whole social life" of a people. The stages through which an economy evolves he listed as follows: (1) the hunting and fishing; (2) the pastoral; (3) the agricultural; (4) the handicraft; and (5) the industrial, which develops from a purely competitive phase through one of concentration into one of integration. The class structure, the social organization, and the thought ways of a people depend largely upon its stage of economic development. Ely did not attempt to account for the movement from lower to higher stages, but he pointed to several evolutionary tendencies then under way: that free goods, public property, and accentuation of the social aspects of private property were increasing; and that cooperation was growing, with unconscious social cooperation gradually giving place to conscious social cooperation. He was not pessimistic concerning the future; yet he declared that it would not be easy to "retain the advantages of associated effort with freedom of movement and a socially desirable distribution of products." [64]

At the same time he observed that competition itself was undergoing evolution. It was being subjected to control by law, custom, religion, benevolence, public authority, and association for mutual aid. Moreover, because of improved conditions (e.g., establishment of civil service) and because of man's increasing power over the forces of nature, competition was serving more effectively than ever both to select competent individuals and to establish environments suited to serve individual and collective purposes.

Competition in the large economic sense may be formally defined as *the struggle of conflicting economic interests on the basis of the existing legal and social order for the sake of economic advantage of one sort or another*. Competition, then, undergoes a process of evolution and is capable of unlimited regulation, provided the element of rivalry is not removed. Modern competition rests upon a basis of property both public and private, and of contract, and certain laws and customs which regulate personal conditions, giving us servitude or freedom in their various forms. Property and contract themselves are regulated, and change with economic development. Competition, then, takes for granted the fundamental institutions of economic society, and these qualify and limit the struggle for existence.[65]

He denied, much as had T. H. Green, that "industrial liberty" is an absolute value. It is but one of a number of goals (among them equality and, most important, fraternity) with all of which it must be harmonized.[66]

Unlike Marshall, Hadley, and others, Ely was not apprehensive lest the "amelioration of man's social and physical environment" reduce the intensity of the struggle for survival and thus foster dysgenic selection; for he apparently supposed, much as had John Fiske and J. M. Baldwin, that selection by nature would give place to selection by man.[67] The great force in society, Baldwin had declared, was not, as eighteenth-century philosophers believed, a nature or an environment extraneous to society. On the contrary, "the chief forces working in society are truly social forces, . . . immanent in society itself. . . . Man as man comes into being and

unfolds his powers through society." [68] With this type of philosophy, to which John Dewey and G. H. Mead were also to give
expression, Ely was in sympathy. In light of its principles, Ely
believed, the defects of the existing socioeconomic order could be
remedied through reformist measures, and socialism could be
avoided.

From a number of economists who flourished in this period
evolutionism received virtually no attention. Typical of this group
—it is impossible within a short essay to consider more cases—are
F. M. Taylor, C. J. Bullock, Irving Fisher, H. J. Davenport, and
E. R. A. Seligman. Taylor concerned himself with price theory,
whereas Bullock dealt with change in his historical writings but
enunciated no laws. Fisher, though a student of invention and of
demographic selection, did not include evolution as such within
the scope of economics. In his later and more important works
Davenport centered his economics around "the competitive order"
which, however, he found to be neither beneficent nor immune
to change.[69] Seligman observed that specialization was developing
along Spencerian lines; that man, through his advances in civilization, was partly emancipating himself from the bondage of nature; and that emphasis upon the changing and historical character of economic institutions had done much for economics; but he
rated the contribution of Marx much above that which Darwin
and Spencer had made to economics.[70]

Some attention was given to evolutionism by J. B. Clark and
F. W. Taussig. In his *Philosophy of Wealth*[71] Clark reflects the
evolutionary influence of Spencer and Knics, expresses marked
optimism, and points to the inadequacy of the anthropological
assumptions of economics. He declares society to be an organism
which, together with its members, is evolving. Social differentiation and interdependence are increasing, as is altruism, which
along with self-interest, governs man. The expansion of man's
wants is making for individual improvement and social progress.[72]
But the continuation of this progress is contingent upon the maintenance of "true competition," or "rivalry for public favor," and
upon the prevention of both "strife" and rivalry-suppressing combination; for only where there is true competition do the most
useful individuals succeed, and the fittest organizations and systems survive. Clark believed, however, that true competition could
be preserved through moral force.[73] In his subsequent works Clark
did not further consider the question of evolution except to outline

the conditions of technical progress, indicate the obstacles thereto, note the relation of dynamic change to profits, and show that state intervention is prerequisite to the maintenance of salutary rivalry.[74]

Had Professor Taussig's major research interest lain in the field of social economics, he would certainly have written much of evolution and selection. For he looked upon social development as probably unending, and he concerned himself with invention, with human motivation, with vertical social mobility, and with other forms of social selection. In his *Inventors and Money-Makers,*[75] he claimed that the prospect of gain is essential to the stimulation of an inventor's "instinct of contrivance" and to the multiplication of variations in technology; and he indicated that an invention has a better chance of success when both its inventor and its businessman sponsor are cool and calculating.[76] In a later joint study he reasoned that, as a rule, a business leader's success is the result of his superior native endowment rather than of his superior environment or access to opportunity.[77] In his treatment of social stratification Taussig showed that the cumulative cultural and institutional forces at work in the upper and in the lower reaches of the income pyramid made the poor poorer and the rich richer than they would have been had the distribution of income been governed primarily by the distribution of native endowment.[78] In his last as in his earlier writings he questioned whether socialism would spread widely, and he observed that all that we know "tells against the possibility of securing that sort of millennium which the enthusiastic proponents" of new social systems expect.[79]

The writers on economics who lay most stress upon evolutionism in the interval under consideration constitute a heterogeneous group. The sociologist-economists, men who (like Sumner) abandoned economics to found sociology, in part because of their interest in evolutionism, include L. F. Ward, F. H. Giddings, C. H. Cooley, E. A. Ross, and A. W. Small. Anthroposociological evolutionism was defended by C. C. Closson and criticized by John Cummings and W. Z. Ripley, all economists. Evolutionism pervaded the writings of S. N. Patten and T. N. Carver, two of the most influential economists of this period, and it dominated the unorthodox economics of Thorstein Veblen, the spiritual progenitor of the essentially evolutionary institutionalist school of economics. Evolutionism also permeates the work of the latter-day institutionalist, John R. Commons. Finally, evolution theory usually had a place in the Cassandra literature (e.g., of the Adamses) and in the essentially socialistic works of this period. These several contributions we shall now examine.

To the evolutionary aspects of the sociologist-economists who founded American sociology we can give only passing attention, despite the influence which they seem to have exerted upon the place of evolutionism in American economics. They dwelt upon the role of social and physical environment, itself in part the product of the past behavior and history of men, in the economic affairs of man. They opposed unrestricted laissez faire, pointed to the shortcomings of the competitive system, criticized the eugenic and hereditarian philosophy of Galton, smothered Social Darwinism, stressed the functional importance of the middle class, and treated the state as an agency whose task it is both to compose conflict and to execute positive programs. They noted that cooperation as well as conflict characterizes the economic affairs of men. They emphasized the dynamic social rather than the static biological nature of man, the importance of mass education as an instrument of social reform and as a source of favorable social variation, and the need to rest policy formation and societal engineering upon valid social principles. Thus they contributed to the replacement of static social theory and blind economic evolutionism by dynamic social theory and an evolutionism that comprehends human purpose.[80]

Although Ward condemned competition as wasteful and unsuited to accomplish the purposes it was supposed to serve,[81] he indicated that the struggle for existence had declined in intensity with cultural progress, and would largely disappear with the adequate application of science to social questions.

Whenever society becomes sufficiently intelligent to grapple with the social forces as it has with the physical forces they will yield as readily and come as fully under its control. The world sustains now the same relation to the social forces that it did to the physical before there was any form of art whatever . . .[82]

He added that since progressive change issues out of the fact that man's desires grow in number and content, consumption and desire must play an important role in social progress.[83]

Cooley stressed the social character of economic evolution and the fact that natural selection is not an important source of social change. Man progresses in consequence of his power of communication; because he is plastic, sympathetic, and cooperative; because he causes his own environment to evolve.

The process of change . . . comes about through the competition of influences and the propagation of opportune innovations in thought and action. The selective principle, the arbiter of competition, is ever human nature—but human nature conditioned in its choices by the state of communication, which determines what influences are accessible, as well as by the constraining momentum of its own past.[84]

Economic competition, as described in theory and practiced in reality, was unfavorable to social progress because it emphasized the wrong values, suppressed the energies of society, produced discontent, inefficiency, and revolt, and made for the elimination of biologically superior strains. "We shall never have an efficient system until we have one that appeals to the imagination, the loyalty, and the self-expression of the men who serve it." [85]

Ross concentrated, even more than Cooley, upon social process, criticized current European and American selectionist doctrines, and outlined the possibilities of social control. The economic struggle was not a struggle for survival, nor did it eliminate the unfit. "Starvation takes ever thinner shavings from the under side of society, while overfeeding is beginning to plane down the upper side. . . . It is hardly a struggle to exist, still less a struggle to reproduce, but chiefly a struggle to rise; and the winners are liable to be out-multiplied by the losers, and displaced by their progeny." [86]

At best the struggle promoted the capable; at worst it partly suspended natural selection among the rich. In general, social selection eliminated those whom society considered misfit rather than those whom society deemed unfit. He described the competitive form of social organization, itself the product of evolution, as the type apparently best suited to assign tasks and stations and to release energy, effort, and creativeness.[87]

Although Giddings, admirer of Darwin and Sumner, built his theoretical system around the evolutionism of Spencer, he emphasized the psychic as well as the subjective factors, and gave due weight to cooperative tendencies. A liberal individualist, he looked upon competition as stimulative of effort and quickening of thought, and as persisting despite efforts to restrict it; but, because the competitive process was "inherently defective," he pointed to the need of its regulation.[88] He characterized as "pre-Darwinian" those economists who looked upon man (as did Cairnes) as a kind of unchanging molecule. For human nature, social institutions, and the organic economic aggregate were undergoing "incessant modifications" of which economists needed to take account.[89] Subsequently, Giddings, whose theory of social evolution reflected Spencer's influence, sought to show that an economy becomes ever more rational in organization.[90] In society at large environmental pressure was giving place to environmental stimulus, with the result that social evolution was becoming progressive.[91] In the economic sector of society the "marvelous differentiation and development of the division of labor" on the side of production, was being accompanied, on the side of consumption, by "an equally marvelous standardization and assimilation." [92] These and other changes presumably would continue. Comparison of the social theory of Giddings with that of Spencer furnishes a conservative measure of the decline of Social Darwinism.

In Europe in the latter part of the nineteenth century and the early twentieth century the study of Darwinian selection converged with that of differential natural increase and of cityward migration to stimulate interest in interclass and interracial selection and in the social factors by which it was influenced, and to give rise to the work of Ammon, Lapouge, and others. In the United States concern over problems issuing out of immigration intensified this interest which also was fed, here and abroad in vulgar circles, by the ideological requirements of the new imperialism. Of this "racism" there is but limited evidence in American economic literature. Veblen's comments on race[93] are completely overshadowed by his other views. C. C. Closson, alone among the economists, developed and defended the principles of the new anthroposociology of Ammon and Lapouge. Closson's views were attacked by John Cummings, a critic also of Veblen, who reasoned in effect that there was no significant correlation between ethnic and social composition, and that ethnic differences were too small to influence human affairs appreciably. He described the new race theory as "racial phrenology," and the ethnic factor as a badly defined "Holy Grail." [94] W. Z. Ripley, author of what was long the standard work on race, agreed with much that Cummings had said, declaring that anthroposociology did not give enough weight to environment and that mental and physical traits were not highly correlated.[95] Closson, in his reply, asserted that the data bore out Lapouge and Ammon; that Cummings' views were at variance with the facts which "show that the economic standard of worth is not indifferent to the ethnic factor"; and that demographic, military, and economic eclipse might be the lot of an ethnic group if it conducted itself according to Cummings' pre-Darwinian racial egalitarianism.[96]

Closson concerned himself primarily with interracial selection and its social causes and consequences, and only secondarily with the cognate problem of interclass selection. Demographic selection was important because social attainment and social progress on the part of a population depended primarily upon its quality which in turn was largely the product of hereditary factors. Because individuals and ethnic groups differed widely with respect to hereditary qualities, the qualitative composition of populations tended to change for the worse or for the better according as social conditions favored dysgenic or eugenic demographic selection. Of any given large and comparatively unselected population, a small fraction falls below the social tolerance limit, a larger fraction falls below the socially useful level, while a still larger fraction falls below the level of competence prerequisite for contributing to social progress.[97] Racial groups also differed in accordance with the so-called laws of anthroposociology, to which Closson subscribed. Relatively dolichocephalic Homo Europaeus was wealthier, more active industrially, more migratory, more disposed to inhabit lower altitudes, and more frequent in upper and urban classes than was relatively non-dolichocephalic Homo Alpinus.[98] The ensemble of (chiefly social) conditions that regulated demographic selection and evolution were producing dysgenic effects. Homo Europaeus, being subject in greater measure than was Homo Alpinus to ambition, industrial competition, and the stresses of cities which "are great consumers of population," was losing out in his reproductive struggle with the latter.[99] Superior family strains within given groups were also losing out in their reproductive struggle with inferior family strains. For under the impact of "the subsidiary struggle for comfort, wealth, power, and social position" populations became stratified and superior individuals and families moved into the upper classes where conditions were less favorable to natural increase. "For the most part . . . selection means the increase or decrease of certain family stocks, not so much from different degrees of hardship as from different standards of living, habits, ideals, etc." Closson therefore approved Lapouge's observation that the "hope for permanent human betterment lies in systematic selection." [100]

In view of past and prevailing selectionist tendencies, Closson believed, the proper course of action for the Nordic or Anglo-Saxon ethnic groups was clearly indicated. The Chinese were destined to be the colonizers of the tropics,[101] where the Nordics were unable to thrive. For rigorous social and natural selection among the Chinese had eliminated both weaklings and innovating spirits and had converted that people into a race of industrious, routine-minded, and hardy mediocrities capable of multiplying rapidly on a low standard of life in the tropics and elsewhere. It was essential, therefore, that the Nordic race reserve the as yet unoccupied temperate regions for itself and against both the brachycephalic peoples and the Chinese; and that less densely populated Nordic countries like the United States admit as immigrants only superior dolichocephalic Nordics who readily assimilated the social standards of the immigrant-receiving country. For were inferior stocks allowed to form the racial substratum of the United States and other Nordic countries these inferior stocks would in time biologically displace the superior Nordic stocks as they already were doing in Massachusetts and in France. Closson suggested also that America was in need of new standards of social value, inasmuch as the dysgenic trends prevalent in the United States were finally traceable to the prevalence of those pecuniary and honorific conceptions of success which Veblen had so effectively described. If, on the contrary,

family stability and increase were fully recognized as an essential factor of the standard of success, our ambitious classes would, perhaps, compete therefor almost as strenuously as they now do for professional distinction, economic mastery, or social conspicuousness. Instead of the usure, we should have the increase of the abler elements in the community.[102]

Energy and its use constitute the basis of the economic philosophy of both T. N. Carver and German-trained Simon Nelson Patten,[103] who was second only to Veblen in his stress upon evolutionism. A planner and an optimist who believed that man, particularly modern man, is the product of an environment that he has helped, and is helping, to create, Patten took little stock in economic statics, or in the principles of the Maltho-Ricardian school. Instead he emphasized economic dynamics and man's capacity to contribute to the shaping of his destiny. Man, Patten believed, is essentially a creature of habit, much of whose behavior is involuntary, and a being whose culture and behavior patterns are largely shaped by his objective (i.e., physical) and subjective (i.e., traditions, customs, habits, etc.) environments and by changes in these environments. Notwithstanding, Patten urged men to establish conditions conducive to favorable variation inasmuch as it rather than selection is the primary source of progress. And he observed that since the environments of men are much more susceptible of change and prone to change than are their characters, men never become fully adjusted to their environments; and that out of the efforts of men to bring their activities into harmony with the requirements of their changing environments, come modification of motor reactions, further environmental changes, changes in thought and ideals, alterations in societal class composition, and, as a rule, socioeconomic progress.

Energy surpluses make for favorable variations which tend to persist, whereas energy deficits generate struggle and emotion rather than strength, irrationality rather than intelligence, and dormancy rather than growth and development. Moreover, energy surpluses, which are essentially economic in character and origin, give rise to progress and civilization; for they produce new types of behavior which, as a rule, yield a surplus of pleasure over pain, and, therefore, tend to be repeated until they become imbedded in the habit structure of the individual and in the social heritage of man. At the same time forms of behavior which, because of environmental or other changes, yield a surplus of pain over pleasure, tend to be selectively eliminated. Furthermore, as energy surpluses develop, selective forces remove individuals who refuse to adapt their consumption habits to the new surplus situation and who, in consequence, overconsume, overindulge, and otherwise behave in a manner destructive of health or unfavorable to reproduction. In times of energy deficits, of course, selective agents remove those who cannot obtain adequate nutrition.[104]

Fundamental to Patten's analysis of socioeconomic evolution are his distinction between a pain or deficit economy and a pleasure or surplus economy and his account of the transformation of the former into the latter. Among the pain economies he included "all civilizations before the nineteenth century, . . . primitive societies . . . and the backward despotisms of the East." A pain economy develops when the environment from which men wrest subsistence is local and dominated by nature, when life is biologic rather than social, and when undernutrition is an important selective agent; and as it develops it shapes the religious, ethical, and social theories and beliefs of those who are dependent upon it.

Beings in a pain economy have vigorous motor powers but a low development of the sensory powers. As they pass from one environment to another the requisites for survival are determined by the enemies and pains to be avoided. Food and pleasure are . . . necessary, but they are not the main objects of conscious thought. When such beings have developed their sensory powers far enough so that forms of thought and ideals are created which aid them in their activities, there is formed for them a pain society, the end of which is protection from enemies. There is a pain morality, the purpose of which is to keep persons from committing acts and putting themselves in situations which lead to destruction. There is also a pain religion, the purpose of which is to invoke the aid of higher beings in the ever recurring contests with enemies and pain.[105]

A pleasure economy may be said to exist when life depends upon many rather than upon few conditions; when men have established some mastery over nature and have begun to draw support from a general rather than from a local environment; when there is an absence of "fear"; when nice sensory discriminations make for survival; and when, in consequence, an economic, or energy, surplus arises. Such economies began to flourish in the nineteenth century and, because they were of recent origin, to give rise to new social and ideological requirements. For as men move out of a pain into a pleasure economy it becomes necessary for them to give up many of the ideals and customs and ways of thought they developed and found useful in their pain economy stage of existence and to adopt those prerequisite to harmonious social life in a surplus economy. For example, aggression and conflict must give place to cooperation. Men must unite against the internal evils of the pleasure economy even as they formerly united against the external enemies of the pain economy. In particular, men must adjust their patterns of consumption to the new condition of surplus and to the "primary law of social progress, . . . that society progresses from a simple, costly, and inharmonious consumption to a varied, cheap and harmonious consumption." [106] For only if such adjustments are made will the increase in energy supply be properly distributed and converted into an expanding source of goods and services; while if they are not made, economic progress will be retarded and the new pleasure economy itself may be undermined just as past pleasure economies were undermined by luxurious, unhealthful, and vicious consumption.

In his earlier works Patten suggested that "a social commonwealth" would come into being as men became adjusted to life conditions in a pleasure economy. In a later essay,[107] however, he declared that the pleasure economy proper would be succeeded by a creative economy in which pleasure would be sought in creative action rather than in consumption as such; and he indicated that in Anglo-American parts of the world a creative economy was already beginning to manifest itself. The full emergence of a creative economy was contingent, he observed, upon development of noncoercive associations, together with appropriate ideals, social theories, and ethical principles. He contrasted the thought ways and institutions of this new stage of economic progress with the corresponding elements of the two preceding stages as follows:

Stage of Progress	Form of Struggle	Form of Control	Character of the Social Bonds
1. A pain economy	Race struggle	Ancestral control	Blood bonds
2. A pleasure economy	Class struggle	Wealth control	Interest bonds
3. A creative economy	Self direction	Character control	Social beliefs

Type of Thought	Thought Limitations	Kind of Philosophy	Type of Morality
1. Theological	Substance	Anthropomorphic	Traditional
2. Rational	Space	Material	Utilitarian
3. Pragmatic	Time	Ideal	Telic

From his study of the intellectual history of England[108] Patten inferred that changes in the material conditions of a community are accompanied by changes in its class and psychic composition which, in turn, may react upon these material conditions. So long as local conditions are hard, the timid, conservative, hero-worshiping, stay-at-home *clingers* predominate. But with the improvement of conditions the *sensualists*—originally warriors and priests— come into their own. Eager to satisfy some dominant passion, and avid for adventure, the sensualists break away from local conditions, become conquerors, and collect tribute from the clingers. When, because of the advent of modern conditions, the sensualists could no longer proceed as in olden times, they became captains of industry and sought to collect tribute in this guise. The *stalwarts,* who represent a reaction from sensualism toward asceticism and of whom Calvinists and skilled workmen are representatives, constitute a class peculiar to the modern world. They love dogmas and creeds, subordinate policy to principle, and prefer clearness and simplicity; in thought and action they are independent, while in politics they are utopists and democrats. With the growth of wealth in modern times still another class, the *mugwumps,* has developed. Its members (e.g., rentiers and salaried and professional people) enjoy leisure and freedom from the struggle for existence. Cosmopolitan in their sympathies, compromisers in politics, and agnostics in religion, the mugwumps have well-developed analytical and critical faculties but a weak capacity for individual or concerted action. Because of the changes still under way in the material conditions of life, the clingers and the sensualists were giving place to the mugwumps and to the stalwarts. Patten concluded, however, that the stalwarts would eventually triumph over the mugwumps and make stalwart values rather than mugwump values dominant.

In the world of thought also, Patten believed, change rules; but it is more cyclical than secular in character. With economic development is associated aesthetic, moral, and religious development. When men find themselves in a new environment, they at first formulate a body of economic doctrine, since the objects of economic thought are easily compared. In the wake of this economic doctrine comes a body of aesthetic ideas, then a moral philosophy, and finally a body of religious doctrine. In ancient nations, ideological decay succeeded this final religious stage. In modern nations, however, power merely reverts temporarily to more primitive and mobile individuals, some classes gain at the expense of others, and economic conditions undergo further modification until finally a new body of economic doctrine is constructed out of reassembled ideas of the past and such new ideas as appear to give meaning to recently acquired factual information. Thereafter aesthetic, moral, and religious doctrines develop in order.

Patten believed the direction of social change to be upward, and the conditions of life and the characters of men to be such as are conducive to the realization of ever higher ideals. The overfed and the underfed were being eliminated, together with those who lacked the qualities—activity, hopefulness, altruism, and confidence in the unseen—necessary for the development of a higher level of life. Those possessing these qualities were winning the race for survival, while stalwartism, with its stress upon character, was triumphing over sensualism and mugwumpism. Meanwhile the environments of men were continuing and would continue to change and to impose upon men the necessity of making the very adjustments out of which progressive evolution flows.

Carver formulated his discussion of evolutionism in terms of the transformation of energy, and found in evolutionism support for his thesis that the competitive form of economic organization is superior to all others. The *summum bonum* consists, for Carver, in transforming the maximum of solar energy into human energy, in storing appropriate amounts of energy and thereby advancing civilization, and in increasing productive power through the proper use of energy. Group and individual forms of existence which conduce to this *summum bonum* tend to survive the never ending struggle for existence.[109]

Among the questions to which Carver sought answer, therefore, were these: What system of social organization is most suited to generate and utilize energy and thus insure that the group will successfully meet the tests of the struggle for existence? What behavior practices make for individual and family survival? What is the role of economic competition and selection in that many-formed human conflict which issues out of scarcity and self-interest? And he sought his answers in the evolutionary history of the economic practices and organizations of man.[110]

Individualism and self-centered individual behavior occupy a prominent place in Carver's system of thought; but this place is subordinated to that of the sovereign national state. For the sovereign state imposes restraints upon the struggle of its individual members to survive, in part, at least, because it is subject to the as yet unrestricted primordial struggle of national groups for existence. A nation's strength is conditioned by the productivity and the adaptability of its members; but their capacity to release energy, and to make effective use of it, is governed by the extent to which appropriate laws and rules exist and are enforced.

"In the age-long struggle for existence, those groups or human types have survived whose mental and moral qualities have enabled them to utilize their energy most economically and effectively."[111] Individuals and the state can utilize energy effectively only if the state reduces the antagonism of individual interests, mitigates the "severities of the struggle for existence," prohibits harmful or nonserviceable methods of struggling for individual advantage, and guards production against predation.[112] The state, therefore, must punish monopolists, curb inheritance when it makes for idleness, maintain a satisfactory tax system, and take steps consistent with individualism to prevent poverty.[113]

State-imposed restraints will not suffice by themselves, however, to make individualism work; for competitive consumption, which makes for waste, and which "always works badly,"[114] may become ascendant. It is highly desirable, if not essential for group survival, therefore, that men subscribe to the "work-bench" rather than to the "pig-trough" philosophy of life; for then they will consume in order to produce rather than produce in order to consume.[115]

The competitive system, when subject to very careful and strict governmental supervision and interference, "is the best and most workable scheme of economic organization that has ever been invented." It is "the result of a gradual adjustment to circumstances," in the light of the "best wisdom available"; and it has outstripped all other participants in the struggle of systems for existence. It has done this because under it men are rewarded according to their worth, and the ascent of worthy individuals and efficient practices is favored by the selective forces peculiar to the system; and it will continue to do this so long as the government suppresses all "uneconomic ways of getting wealth" and thus forces everyone "to act in his own self-interest precisely as he would if he were animated by the most completely altruistic motives and patriotic sentiments."[116]

That sovereign group will be strongest, other things being equal, therefore, whose economy, while competitive and individualistic, makes acquisition depend upon production, and proscribes conflict among individuals.[117] For economic competition is the highest form of human conflict, and the most satisfactory means of composing those rivalries which grow out of the desire to possess wealth. It stresses production and service rather than destruction and deception; hence it is superior to political competition, to military competition, and to other forms of conflict, all of which are more wasteful, less democratic, and less conducive to the ascent of talent.

Yet, in proportion as the state absorbs private enterprise and as economic competition is done away with, its place is taken by political competition, which is an inferior method of composing the rivalries that originate in scarcity, and which sometimes gives way to a yet more inferior form, military conflict. If an inferior form of competition is substituted for economic competition, the condition of most individuals becomes worse than it would have been under economic competition, and the capacity of the sovereign group to meet the tests of the struggle for existence at the international level is greatly reduced.[118]

Carver failed, as did nearly all the American economists who discussed evolution, to note that it is dependent both upon favorable variations and upon the natural selection which chooses among the variations and thus conditions the manner in which they are combined in time. For he stressed the selective rather than the creative (or mutational) aspect of economic evolution, and, despite his great emphasis upon the role of energy, he failed to give due weight to what Lotka has called the "receptor-effector apparatus."

Veblen, more than any other economist, is responsible for the introduction of evolutionism, together with an understanding of its psychological and sociological implications, into American economics. But, since his evolution theories have been much written about,[119] I shall merely indicate the salient features of his system of thought and note some of its influences.

Economics, Veblen believed, was too narrow in scope; it was taxonomic, teleological, and unequal to the task of explaining economic reality. What was needed was an economics broader in content and evolutionary in approach: an economics with a theory of the "process of cultural growth as determined by economic interest, a theory of a cumulative sequence of economic institutions stated in terms of the process itself."[120] Received economics was not, and could not be, an evolutionary science, so long as it derived its psychological and its anthropological preconceptions from natural law, hedonistic psychology, and the prevailing "common-sense apprehension of human nature." Yet, Veblen reasoned (consistently with his theory of social evolution), these unsatisfactory preconceptions in time would lose credibility; and an evolutionary economics would develop. For under the pressure of industrial, as distinguished from pecuniary employments, and "under the stress of modern technological exigencies, man's everyday habits of thought are falling into lines that in the sciences constitute the evolutionary method. . . . The social and political sciences must follow the drift, for they are already caught in it." [121] This development would follow, as had other developments, the Darwinian pattern of change, not the untenable telic pattern outlined by Spencer; and it would be carried out, not by the inert, hedonic man of received economics, but by the active man of modern psychology who responds selectively that he may survive.[122]

While Veblen's theory of social change is frequently couched in the language of Darwin, and while it is nonrational and non-teleological as is Darwin's, it is also pervaded by the spirit of Marxism, of which Veblen was a careful student. The life of man in society is a struggle for existence, or for standards of life; and social man and his institutions, under the pressure of changing circumstances, continually undergo selective adaptation, while the changing institutions themselves select individuals with the fittest temperaments and adapt them to the changing environment.[123] Reasoning from the supposed effects of the growth and spread of the machine process Veblen inferred that differences in occupational discipline make for differences in habit and outlook, just as changes in occupational discipline make for changes in habit and outlook.[124] Yet at times, much in the manner of Marx, Veblen implied the struggle for existence to be a struggle for standards and status, that is, for income, instead of the consequence of occupational differences and change;[125] but unlike Marx, he did not consider the triumph of socialism to be fore-ordained, and he even suggested the possible rise of the militarized state.[126]

Veblen conceived of man as possessed both of the complement of instincts usually reported by his psychologist contemporaries, and of a trio of far more important value-oriented behavior dispositions: the production-favoring instinct of workmanship, the altruistic parental bent, and a knowledge-seeking idle curiosity. Habit patterns grow out of man's responding to his environment; they are cumulative, giving rise to institutions which are "habitual methods of carrying on the life of the community in contact with the material environment on which it lives," and which, while subject to modification as the environment changes, help give shape to environment. Social change, therefore, is genetic in character, and unfit institutions tend eventually to be eliminated. But their elimination is not wholly assured. Thus "predatory" institutions, e.g., church, state, and private property, have long persisted despite the fact that they make for waste and the restriction of output. Their eventual disappearance is not improbable, however, Veblen implied.[127]

Veblen's theories, although defective as economics and as sociology, did much to weaken the repute of received economics and to make necessary a restatement of the psychological preconceptions of economics. It drew attention to the role of change, to its cumulative character, and to its significance for business cycle analysis. And while it won no homogeneous school of disciples, it did give rise to a number of interrelated approaches whose employers are sometimes described as members of the institutional school of economics.

Out of the late nineteenth- and early twentieth-century attack upon the hedonistic presuppositions of economics, which was inspired by Veblen, there developed a larger controversy over the relation of psychology to economics. Much of this controversy is traceable, directly or indirectly, to Darwinian and institutional evolutionism which rejected hedonism. A half century ago H. W. Stuart was proposing the banishment of revised hedonistic theory from political economy on the ground that it had already been discarded by psychology because of its unsoundness.[128] Patten's economic psychology was being criticized because it postulated a passive mental mechanism.[129] And Veblen was calling for a conception of human nature that adequately recognized habit formation and its cumulative effect upon the whole of man's cultural matrix;[130] yet more than a decade later Downey was criticizing prevailing economic psychology because of its neglect of the role of habit and its exaggeration of the role of "reasoned choice."[131] Some economists (e.g., I. Fisher, H. J. Davenport) attempted to avoid these criticisms by dispensing with psychology altogether and concerning themselves with problems of price. Others, of whom Professor F. A. Fetter was a leader, restated the theory of value in accord with the then prevailing volitional psychology.[132] J. M. Clark indicated that since economics is a science of human behavior, the economist must make use of a conception of human behavior that psychology substantiates and that accounts for the development of wants, behavior patterns, and so on.[133] W. C. Mitchell, who had already analyzed man's economic motivation and stressed the importance for purposes of reform of the changeable part of human nature,[134] agreed with Clark's view; but he added that the economist, in his study of human behavior, "must go beyond the contributions that professed psychologists make to the general science of human behavior."[135] This controversy over the role of psychology in economics continued through the 1920's and into the 1930's, becoming merged in part with the larger controversy over the significance of institutional economics.[136] While the period since 1930 has been marked by occasional efforts to avoid explicit psychological assumptions, these efforts have not been attended with great success; for the Keynesian psychological postulates and the prevailing emphasis upon expectations have combined with a persisting interest in the development of economic institutions to keep modern psychology in the foreground.[137]

Veblen's Darwino-Marxian method of handling economic questions gave rise also to what was called the institutional approach to economic theory, an approach which emphasized the evolutionary character of man's economic institutions and behavior and the need for intelligent economic controls. Economic theory, declared W. H. Hamilton in 1918, must concern itself with economic institutions and processes; it must be founded upon an acceptable theory of human nature; and it must be relevant to the modern problem of economic control.[138] To the content of this new approach a number of economists made important contributions. For example, Clark highlighted the economic aspects of social control and the relations of psychology to economics. W. C. Mitchell dealt with the place of intelligence in economic evolution, the influence of money in economic affairs, the economic significance of the plasticity of man's nature, and the role of cumulative change in business activity, economic institutions, and man's way of thinking about these institutions.[139] A. B. Wolfe dwelt upon the ethical implications of economics, while M. A. Copeland suggested the adoption of a natural science point of view.[140] In general the scope of economics was enlarged. Yet, probably because institutionalism lacked a coordinating body of theory, it did not give rise to a school.[141] But it helped to satisfy what Edie called the "need for a broadening philosophy of economics which shall evaluate the multitudinous controls of specific institutions in terms of their bearing upon the decay or creation of human progress." [142] It has made economists aware of the highly plastic quality of human nature and of the possibilities of social control in economic affairs; and it is making economists sensible of the fact of continuous and unending economic change. The influence of "institutional economics" will be greatly increased if, as it is not improbable, it is merged effectively with Keynesian economics and the economics of resource allocation and combination.

Evolutionism also pervades the economic philosophy of John R. Commons, like Veblen a great institutionalist, albeit of a different genre. Commons' approach has not yet caught on, partly because his final formulation is relatively recent and appeared in a period of great unemployment, partly because it is difficult, and partly because Commons has lacked skillful proponents of his views.

Commons noted the influence of environment in his earliest works;[143] yet his economic philosophy, which grew out of his continuing experience with legislating and arbitrating, was slow to mature. Not until 1924 were his final views foreshadowed in *The Legal Foundations of Capitalism,* a work in which he built his economics around the bargaining transaction and showed how the conditions surrounding this transaction have evolved, especially the concepts of the courts.[144] His final views appeared a decade later in *Institutional Economics,* a study of "collective action in control of individual action." [145]

Scarcity, according to Commons, gives rise both to a conflict of interests that stands out in transactions and to corrective collective action. For since men are mutually dependent upon one another, this conflict cannot be permitted to persist unabated; it must be subjected to the governance of rules designed to create a harmony of interests through persuasion, coercion, and duress. These rules are maintained by collective action. Institutional economics has to do primarily with this collective control of individual transactions, and with those elements of the bargaining transaction which determine the legal bases of economic relations and action. Institutional economics is concerned, therefore, with futurity, with a futurity of which man is capable only because he is "institutionalism," and his "institutionalized mind" extends into remote time and space and makes possible the giving of orders "around the world and to generations unborn." [146] Commons' institutional, or "going concern," theories are built upon both automatic equilibrium theory à la Newton and process theory à la Darwin, with its emphasis upon "infinitesimal but *unintended or accidental* changes"; their "attention, however, is directed towards *intended* or *purposeful* changes, and to a *managed* equilibrium instead of an *automatic* equilibrium." They presuppose, not men who are the pawns of evolutionary fate, but men who, "by individual or collective action, control evolution itself according to their own ideas of fitness." [147]

Social evolution at the economic level is accomplished, Commons declares, through changes in custom which are subject to "purposeful" rather than to "blind" natural selection. Custom is "the mere repetition, duplication, and variability of practices and transactions"; it is "analogous to heredity," giving rise to, and facilitating the transmission of, individual habit. Customs are continually undergoing variation which brings into being new customs that compete with old customs and replace them when circumstances are appropriate.

There is a continual selection of customs going on, and consequently there is a survival of customs fitted to the changing economic conditions and the changing political and economic dominance. Since this occurs by operation of the human will, it is much like the artificial selection of Darwin's evolution, applicable, however, to practices and transactions suited to changing social conditions . . . [148]

Commons did not believe that customs can be changed radically or suddenly, since they issue out of "Instinct and Habit, which are the mere repetition of acts found by experience to be preservative of life, or enjoyment, and of survival in the struggles of competition." [149] Yet he emphasized the importance of human purpose and "Willingness" in the evolution and selection of customs. [150] And he showed how, when scarcity gives place to relative abundance, individual liberty, governmental control, and the nature of restraint undergo modification. [151] He thus laid the groundwork for realistic analysis of economic change and stabilization. Commons' approach is not likely to become really effective, however, until it is clarified and integrated with the Veblenian type of institutionalism, Keynesianism, and neoclassical allocation and pricing theory.

The period under review was marked by the ascent of urbanism to predominance, by a growing awareness of the failure of man (despite the vast increase in the mechanical power at his disposal) to solve old and new social problems, and by the breakdown of the older systems of religious and politico-economic thought. These conditions gave rise, on the one hand, to the skepticism of Henry and Brooks Adams, and, on the other hand, to a literature critical of capitalism that ranged from questioning liberalism to revolutionary variants of Marxism. The skepticism and despair of the Adamses produced works calculated to undermine the easy optimism which pervaded Spencer's philosophy and which had been founded upon Darwinian principles, and to re-enforce the differently based pessimism (which the Adamses shared in part) of racist and eugenist writers who believed that the supposedly superior races and individuals were losing out in their reproductive struggle with the supposedly inferior races and individuals. The literature critical of capitalism, on the other hand, contributed to the dissipation of Social Darwinism and the associated defense of laissez faire. It weakened the repute in which the competitive form of economic organization was held; for while some critics called only for the governmental regulation of economic competition, others called for its rejection as a method of marshaling the economic resources of the community. Finally, it emphasized the social character of the evolutionary forces that were shaping economic society, drew from the persistence of the evolutionary process the conclusion that the existing form of economic organization would eventually give place to a superior form, and indicated that man could, e.g., through participation in the class struggle, accelerate the advent of a better and more equitable set of arrangements for getting the economic work of society done.[152]

We touch upon the work of the Adamses in this chapter, not because they were economists or exercised much influence upon economists, but because their conclusions were formulated in categories significant for economics.[153] Henry Adams announced what amount to two laws of evolution. Impressed with the fact that a law of social acceleration was at work, he applied to history what he called the rule of phase, and he expressed it in terms of a law of inverse squares. Accordingly, on the supposition that the "mechanical phase" just about ending in 1900 had lasted from three to four centuries, Adams inferred that the preceding "religious phase" had lasted about 90,000 years, whereas the coming "electric" and "ethereal" phases would last less than 20 and 5 years respectively. That such a rate of growth could not persist Adams did not consider in terms of alternative growth curves; but he did state that "a new social mind" would be required, a mind that, his prophecies of the future suggest, he did not expect men to develop.[154] According to Adams' second law, the supposedly unending progressive tendencies of both Darwinian organic and cultural evolution would eventually be swamped, in accordance with the second law of thermodynamics, by the increase of entropy or the "degradation of energy." [155] Adams thus put in universal terms what some economists, e.g., Stanley Jevons, had stated more restrictedly when they predicted that economic growth would be checked by the exhaustion of the accessible supply of fuel and minerals. Although Adams apparently put the fatal terminal date in the too near future—Lotka[156] reports that the conditions requisite for life may persist another million years, during which time organic evolution will continue as presumably will social evolution—he drew attention to a neglected limit on progress.

Brooks Adams' theory of the rise and decay of civilizations ran in terms of economics, geography, demographic and societal selection, and the disposition of energy. Civilization develops as a society's endowment of energy increases and as physical dispersion gives way to physical concentration and consolidation. With the progress of concentration, however, other changes take place which finally bring both concentration and civilization to term. Economic values supersede other values; the emotional, martial, and artistic types give place to men of greed, to capitalists and usurers, and the condition of the peasant deteriorates. The functional importance of woman declines, and with it the rate of natural increase. Eventually, because of war or exhaustion, disintegration sets in and continues until once again the forces favoring concentration become ascendant. Adams' theory ran counter to both the orthodox belief in indefinite progress and the belief of the socialists that they and their program would finally triumph. In subsequent works, in which Adams developed aspects of his "law of civilization," he emphasized in greater measure the role of struggle in human affairs.[157]

The non-Marxian and quasi-Marxian critics of capitalism and the competitive system, e.g., Bellamy, Lloyd, Gronlund, the Christian socialists, attacked laissez faire and Social Darwinism, described competition as a wasteful struggle and pointed to its defects as a principle of social organization, noted how economic motivation would change as society was appropriately reorganized, stressed the possibility and the efficacy of interventionism, and explicitly or implicitly formulated theories of evolution that gave promise of a better society.[158] Orthodox Marxians, with the example of Engels before them, condemned Social Darwinism, together with its corollaries, as an invalid application of a subhuman law to human society, attacked laissez faire and competition, and emphasized the Marxian theory of social change and the class struggle. Weismannism and the mutation theory they found especially to their liking; for if, as Weismann held, the germ plasm was not adversely and permanently affected by bad environment, an improvement of environment would soon produce beneficial effects; while if organic nature made use of mutational spurts, society might also do so and thus avoid gradualism.[159]

Of the developments of this period a summary will not be attempted. One gets the impression, however, that economists, e.g., Carver, had become somewhat aware of effects analogous to those now being noted by biologists. First, those characteristics which make for success in intraspecific competition—which tends to become more intense as a species wins out in its struggle with environment and becomes common—frequently weaken the species in its struggle with other species for survival. Competition, economic and otherwise, within nonprimitive human societies, being essentially between individuals, is intraspecific. Second, since interindividual competition at the human level is for success measured in social rather than in biological terms, and since what makes for social success may be and at present frequently is opposed to what makes for biological success, human competition and selection affect the species adversely. Third, thoroughgoing competition at the biological level not only does not insure progressive evolution; it is not even the best mechanism for accomplishing this purpose.[160] Biology therefore does not constitute a foundation on which to erect a defense of unrestricted competition. In so far as generalization from the biological to the social level is permissible, it is to the effect that competition must be subjected to a social control animated by explicit and avowed purpose; for environment, which within limits is subject to control and modification, conditions both the frequency of favorable variation (however defined) and the selection and survival of favorable variations.

Between economics, conceived as a theory of equilibration and equilibrium, and economics conceived in Darwinian evolutionary terms there exist several seeming theoretical contradictions which can, however, be overcome. First, equilibrium economics postulates a state of balance whereas evolution at the biological level is the product of imbalance[161] even as is evolution at the social level. Second, equilibrium economics supposes that the movement of its variables into equilibrium does not change the character of its variables or the initial conditions of equilibrium. The equilibrium approach therefore is most suited to the study of adjustment in periods of time sufficiently short to permit both man and his institutions to remain qualitatively constant. It is not unqualifiedly suited to longer-time analyses. For with the passage of time both man and his institutions undergo qualitative change either because of movements intended to restore equilibrium, or because of developments in man and his institutions already under way at the time of the equilibrium-seeking adjustments, or because of independent changes in the remainder of the economy or the societal system. The economist who would take economic evolution into account must, therefore, modify the equilibrium approach to allow for continually occurring variations and qualitative changes in man and his relevant institutions.

IV. NEW DIRECTIONS: 1930–1946

Evolutionism as such has not played a prominent part in American economic thought since 1930, despite the occasional appearance of works dealing with economic development; for the problems of this period, to which economists have had to give attention, have been immediate and persistent: unemployment, war, and stabilization. This period witnessed the formulation and the acceptance of the essentials of Keynesianism and its prescription for unemployment, together with the development of such corollaries to Keynesianism as planning in terms of all-inclusive national budgets and analysis in terms of manipulable macroscopic systems. This period also saw the development of various aspects of the theory of imperfect competition, the growing use of indifference conditions, and the employment of the theory of games to elucidate economic and political problems. The new approaches to economic problems do not involve evolution theory as such; yet some of them are sensible of the predominantly social and dynamic character of man and his heritage, and some are providing a groundwork for developmental analysis. In a sense, therefore, the economics of the 1930's and early 1940's was as evolutionary in spirit as that of preceding decades; but it did not concentrate upon supposedly longer-run evolutionary tendencies as did Marxian economics which, being concerned above all else with economic and social change in the capitalistic world, has exercised most influence upon the theory of economic evolution.

The failure of American economists to give greater weight to evolutionism is attributable to (among other circumstances) their stress upon the one-at-a-time approach and their implicit recognition of the prognostic shortcomings[162] of contemporary economic science. For example, industrial development has been treated largely in terms of static comparative advantage, with the result that the ecological interrelatedness of the elements that determine industrial growth has been ignored. Consequently, industrial location theory, together with the application of such variation-forming stimuli as subsidies and tariffs, has not been well developed; and it has commonly been assumed that individuals acting as individuals can and should carry out industrialization programs which could be accomplished much more expeditiously through collective efforts. Again, it is often assumed that the persistence of competitiveness in the American economy is attributable to the continuing validity of the postulates underlying the theory of pure competition rather than to the frequent appearance of innovations (or variations) which undermine or offset those restrictions upon competition which continually tend to develop.

Although Marxism *per se* is no better suited than contemporary economic science to prognosticate the future, the Marxian theory of social change has won comparatively wide acceptance since 1930. For Marxian theory, having always stressed social change, was readily adapted by its proponents to "explain" the post-1930 sequence of events and to meet the growing demand for a broadened synthesis of economics and the related social sciences. This adaptability is attributable in some measure, of course, to the extensive support which the Russian state gives Marxian social science. It is attributable in greater measure, however, to the broadened scope of Marxian social science; to its extension of dialectical theory to embrace much more than forecasts of the doom of capitalism, and to its incorporation into itself of much of social psychology and the functional theory of mind, of sociology and history, and of ethics. Only the articulate representatives of one or two religious faiths have followed suit. Neither the spokesmen for conservatism nor the spokesmen for liberalism have integrated and restated their philosophies in terms that are in keeping with the requirements of the social situation and the present state of knowledge. *Faute de mieux,* therefore, students of socioeconomic change will continue to adopt the Marxian theory in much greater degree than in the 1920's, despite its great inferiority to marginalism as a managerial instrument and its inherent defectiveness as a predictive instrument.

While Schumpeter's dynamic economics, with its emphasis upon a changing and change-producing innovator,[163] has not as yet stimulated an evolutionary approach, Keynesian economics, which was static in its pristine form, has been, and is, re-enforcing the spirit of evolution in American economics. For example, Keynesianism emphasizes the importance of expanding consumption. But since the obstacles which stand in the way of such expansion are in part economic, and in part cultural and institutional, an approach to the consumption problem that recognizes its evolutionary institutional aspects is essential to its full solution. Again, because Keynesianism has stressed the process of transition rather than the condition of equilibrium, it has stimulated period analysis, from which it is not many steps to long-run analysis. Yet again, the growing importance now being attached to expectations in dynamic analysis should dissolve some of the murk surrounding the subject of economic motivation and causation and enkindle interest in economic evolution proper. Finally, efforts to apply Keynesian principles at the action level are making it clear that administrative economics must embrace other social sciences and must take account of the pseudo-orthogenetic drifts in the economy.

Although contemporary economics is dynamic rather than static in character, it is much less dynamic than it needs to be, or than it should be in light of contemporary social theory with its emphasis upon the predominantly man-made nature of Western man's environment and upon the essentially social character of man's mind and activity. It has not itself been subject to enough selection and evolution. For example, present-day sophisticated analyses of the maximizing and minimizing behavior of the individual seem to consist little better with psychological theory than does the subjective marginalism of yesteryear.

Economics tends to be too static in its approach, partly because its content is not periodically subjected to a selective winnowing. For one thing, the skill with which new theories are sold to the economist public has much to do with their reception and speed of acceptance. For another, economics is not periodically submitted to the test of a rigorously selective mathematical logic designed to eliminate irrelevant matter and to make for the retention only of materials and methods that are pertinent. It is not surprising, therefore, that the handling of various economic questions is defective; that dynamic aspects of wages, interest, and rent are not being subjected to a sufficiently close-up and detailed analysis; that careful and detailed accounts have not been provided of the growth and the institutionalization of wage patterns and of expectations regarding wage differentials; and that the dynamic implications of the development of bilateral monopoly in employer-employee relationships, or of the prospective professionalization of business, have not received much attention.

Economists have tended to overlook the significance of the decline in the intensity of competition for their own theories and findings. For example, in recent years it has been observed that entrepreneurs are much less sensitive to changes in wage and interest rates than marginal economics presupposes, or than can be accounted for on grounds of expectations. Those who have made these discoveries have not gone on to demonstrate, however, that entrepreneurs can behave in this "unmarginal-like" manner and still survive only because competition has been stifled and rigorous selection has been averted. If competition were fairly intense, and if some entrepreneurs behaved in accordance with the rules of marginalism, while others behaved in accordance with such rules of "averageism" as are embodied in present accounting methods and business practices, the former group of entrepreneurs would eventually displace the latter. In short, entrepreneurs can violate the principles of marginalism and survive, not because there is something wrong with the principles of objective marginalism, but because competition and selection are so unrigorous.

We do not live in an economy whose component elements are so snugly and tightly interconnected that a change in an element in any one sector is necessarily and promptly communicated to elements in other sectors. Rather, we live in a loosely knit and roomy economy in which there is a great deal of play and in which, as a rule, a change in any one component of the economic system must be of critical magnitude before it can appreciably influence other components of the system. Selection is less intense, therefore, than it would be if the system were more tightly knit. There are those, however, who would deny that this loose-knitness is necessarily undesirable. They would argue that a loose-knit system may be more conducive than a tight-knit system to favorable variations—enough more favorable to override the difference in selective rigor—and therefore more congenial to long-run progress.

Economists, as we have indicated, have not given much attention to the origin and development of favorable social and economic variations, presumably because they have considered this question to lie outside the scope of economics. They have therefore neglected the factor to which must be imputed in much greater measure than to selection as such those great improvements in human welfare which are essentially economic in character. Consideration of socioeconomic variation would make apparent also that while analytical distinction is prerequisite to the refinement and solution of specific economic problems, it can make its greatest contribution only if the scope of the economist's approach is broadened.

The theory of economic causation and change has not been sufficiently subjected to acute analysis and empirical tests. Both Sumner and Commons, it will be remembered, thought of economic change as proceeding very slowly because customs and habits supposedly change very slowly. This view overlooks the important role of education. It also underemphasizes the fact that since power is highly concentrated in modern societies, relatively small changes in the composition of the groups possessing this power probably can greatly modify the manner in which an economic system works. Economists have failed also to analyze adequately the effects of power, or force, upon the distribution of income and the employment of factors, for they have always supposed competition to be intense enough to swamp force. They have failed, furthermore, to study the influence which social and economic structures per se exercise upon the distributive pattern and upon the income receiver's configuration of expectations.

In their discussions of the circumstances making for the survival of sovereign groups and economies, American economists have placed major stress upon the individual, presumably because they have postulated a strong tendency to full employment. Make acquisition depend upon production, they have said, and competitive individualism will inevitably give the best results attainable. These authors, probably under the influence of positivism, have overlooked or underestimated the role of ethical values in social interaction and in the functioning of economic systems. These economists have also overlooked the fact that the functioning of an economic system is independent, in important respects, of the actions and desires of individuals *qua* individuals. The effective operation of an economic system calls for the observance of certain rules and procedures. If these are violated, the system functions ineffectively; its material and moral supports are weakened; and it tends to give place to other systems more suited to survive under the circumstances. It is evident, therefore, that collective action, consistent both with the normative structure of a people and with the enforcement of the operational principles inherent in its economy, is prerequisite to the long-run survival of this group's economic system.

Concern with the operation of systems as systems does not, however, permit the overlooking of selective principles at work within systems. For example, economic and political selection is in need of far more study than it has received. To what extent is economic selection superior to political? Does Gresham's law operate in the political field? May economic and political selection be considered apart from one another as Carver supposes? If so, how may political selection be contained? How does economic selection affect reproductive and biological selection, and, through this medium, the long-run efficiency of economic systems? And so on.

Economics must be somewhat evolutionary in its approach, both because it is concerned with data in flux, and because it must help man to give direction to this flux. The assisting of change that is salutary in character calls for knowledge of the essentially constant and the essentially variable elements in the economico-cultural matrix. It calls also for a greater emphasis upon activity as such, and for a lesser emphasis upon those consummatory end-products after which individuals are supposedly striving.

CONCLUSION

At the time when the evolution theories of Spencer and Darwin were first introduced into the United States most Americans probably subscribed both to the spirit of the eighteenth-century doctrine of continuing progress and to the main tenets of laissez faire, in part because American conditions seemed to offer material evidence of the long-run validity of these views. Writers on economics, moreover, probably would have understood Keynes's observation that the "Principle of Survival of the Fittest" was one "vast generalization of Ricardian economics." Nonetheless, even though the new evolutionism stood ready, as the later transient triumph of Social Darwinism demonstrated, to give temporary support to the doctrine of laissez faire, evolutionism was not promptly assimilated into American economics. In fact, not until the closing decades of the nineteenth century did the new doctrines really begin to make themselves felt, directly and indirectly, in American political economy; and never did they produce a work of the order of Bagehot's *Physics and Politics.*

Their effects were cumulative, however. Evolutionism made, directly and indirectly, for a new conception of human nature, a conception that emphasized its plasticity. This new conception influenced economics both immediately and through the medium of the new psychology. Evolutionism also made easier the formulation of those theories of cultural change and functional mind which subsequently undermined pre-Darwinian economic statics. Finally, evolutionism made for a complete change in the climate of philosophical opinion, and introduced a new frame of reference in terms of which order was discoverable in movement and change. Eventually, therefore, the new evolution theories—at least the Spencerian variants—partly destroyed themselves and their initial effects even as they had destroyed their static predecessors; for they gave birth to theories of mind and nature that facilitated the substitution of social control for the very dogma of laissez faire which evolutionism originally had been supposed to sanction. Today the direct and indirect effects of evolutionism—Darwinian, Spencerian, historical, and cultural—are so much a part of our economic thought ways that we are no longer aware of their existence. Could ideological triumph be greater?

NOTES

1. I am indebted to Professor Clark L. Allen for critically reading this chapter.

2. Spencer's theory of evolution, which pervaded his later writings, received its first complete expression in his *First Principles* (1862) where he further developed the thesis set forth in "Progress, Its Law and Cause," *Westminster Review,* N.S., XI (April, 1857), 445–485. In *Social Statics* (1850) the evolutionary process is looked upon as real but progressive and teleological. As early as 1852 he observed, following Malthus in part, that those who survive the struggle for existence are the more fit ("A Theory of Population, Deduced from the General Law of Animal Fertility," *Westminster Review,* N.S., I [April, 1852], 499–500). Spencer attached more weight than did Darwin to Lamarckism. On the introduction of the views of Spencer and Darwin into America see R. Hofstadter,

Social Darwinism in American Thought, 1860–1915 (Philadelphia, University of Pennsylvania, 1944), chaps. i–ii. On cultural evolution theory in mid-nineteenth-century America see B. J. Stern, *Lewis Henry Morgan: Social Evolutionist* (Chicago, University of Chicago, 1931).

For Joseph Needham's views see his review of "Levels of Integration in Biological and Social Systems," *Science & Society,* VII (Spring, 1943), 190; "Evolution and Thermodynamics," *Science & Society,* VI (Fall, 1942), 356, 374–375; "On Science and Social Change," *Science & Society,* X (Summer, 1946), 225–229, 244; also his presentation of Herbert Spencer's evolution theory in terms of successively higher stages of integration and organization, *Integrative Levels: a Revaluation of the Idea of Progress* (Oxford, Clarendon, 1937). Lotka's theory is stated in "The Law of Evolution as a Maximal Principle," *Human Biology,* XVII (Sept., 1945), 167, 186, 188, 192–194; "Evolution and Thermodynamics," *Science & Society,* VIII (Spring, 1944), 168; *Elements of Physical Biology* (Baltimore, Williams & Wilkins, 1925), especially Part IV. Author's italics.

3. *The Wealth of Nations* (Cannan ed. New York, Modern Library), pp. 147 ff.

4. For example, the stage theory of the associationist Albert Brisbane (*Social Destiny of Man* [Philadelphia, Stollmeyer, 1840], pp. 269 ff.) appears not to have influenced American political economy much if at all. See L. L. Bernard and J. Bernard, *Origins of American Sociology* (New York, Crowell, 1943), and J. Dorfman, *The Economic Mind in American Civilization, 1606–1865* (New York, Viking, 1946). Lewis Morgan's theory (*Ancient Society,* 1877) somewhat resembled Brisbane's. See B. J. Stern, *op. cit.,* chap. vi.

5. *The Wealth of Nations,* Book I, chaps. viii–ix, and Book III. In a melancholy declining state the condition of the common man was even worse than in a stationary state.

6. See my "Malthus's Total Population Theory: a Restatement and Reappraisal," *Canadian Jour. of Economics and Political Science,* XI (Feb., May, 1945), 83 ff., 234 ff.; also L. Robbins, "On a Certain Ambiguity in the Conception of Stationary Equilibrium," *Economic Jour.,* XL (June, 1930), 194–214. Malthus' views were not very evolutionary.

7. J. M. Keynes, *Laissez-faire and Communism* (New York, New Republic, 1926), cf. Frederick Engels, *Dialectics of Nature* (London, New York, International, 1940), pp. 19, 208–210, 235.

8. On the contents of this paragraph see my essays, "Malthusianism and the Debate on Slavery," *South Atlantic Quarterly,* XXXIV (April, 1935), 170–189; "Population Theory in the Ante-Bellum South," *Jour. of Southern History,* II (Aug., 1936), 360–389; "Malthusianism in Eighteenth Century America," *Amer. Economic Review,* XXV (Dec., 1935), 691–707; and "Population Prediction in Nineteenth Century America," *Amer. Sociological Review,* I (Dec., 1936), 905–921. See also W. S. Jenkins, *Pro-Slavery Thought in the Old South* (Chapel Hill, N. C., 1935); A. A. Ekirch, *The Idea of Progress in America, 1815–1860* (New York, Columbia, 1944), pp. 43–45, 70, 130, 235–237, 250–251; J. Dorfman, *The Economic Mind,* I, 243, II, 535, 538, 571, 865, 958–959. B. Franklin anticipated later writers who declared slave labor to be more expensive than free labor; O. Ellsworth and T. Cooper, those who believed that population growth would destroy the slave system; and B. Franklin and D. Raymond, those who found in the growth of slavery a check to the growth of the white population; Ezra Stiles, those who believed that the free Negroes would disappear.

9. Ekirch, *op. cit.,* pp. 93–96, 100–104; R. A. Billington, *The Protestant Crusade, 1800–1860* (New York, Macmillan, 1938).

10. See J. B. Bury, *The Idea of Progress* (London, Macmillan, 1920); Ekirch, *op. cit.*

11. Its late eighteenth-century formulators, Condorcet and Godwin, especially the latter, did anticipate organic change. Lamarck's principle was sometimes made use of by American writers.

12. See Ekirch, *op. cit.,* chaps. v, vi, viii, pp. 122–125.

13. *Ibid.,* pp. 36, 41–42, 49–50, 57, 60–61, 63, 66, 105. Lewis Morgan's evolutionary scheme has afforded a prop to imperialism. See B. J. Stern, *op. cit.,* p. 176.

14. Although the views of Auguste Comte exercised influence upon American social science in general, they do not appear to have had much direct effect upon American economic thinking. See L. L. Bernard and J. Bernard, *Origins of American Sociology,* Part III.

15. For Carey an appropriate manner meant in accordance with the natural laws which operate with equal force in the physical and in the social universe.

16. *Principles of Social Science* (1858–59) (Philadelphia, Baird, 1871), I, chaps. i–iii, 53, 88–89, 91; *The Unity of Law* (Philadelphia, Baird, 1872), pp. xvii–xviii, 295–296, 370. A. D. H. Kaplan summarizes Carey's system in his *Henry Charles Carey: a Study in American Economic Thought* (Baltimore, Johns Hopkins, 1931). Carey is one of the small number of American economists who, like Mill, were influenced by Comte. Comparison of Carey's *The Past, the Present, and the Future* (Philadelphia, Carey & Hart, 1848) with his *Principles of Social Science* suggests that Carey, who always believed in progress, drew upon Spencer's theory of progress first announced in 1857.

17. Cf. Lotka's treatment of the distribution of energy among activities and evolution, *Science & Society,* VIII (Spring, 1944), 169.

18. This and the preceding paragraphs are based upon Carey's *Social Science,* especially chaps. iii–iv, vi, viii, x, xv, xx, xxx, xxxviii, xli–xlii, xlv–xlix, li, lii. For a shorter and final statement see *The Unity of Law.* Carey comments favorably on Spencer's "A Theory of Population" (see n. 2, above), which also influenced later American writers (see my "Notes on Abortion, Birth Control, and Medical and Sociological Interpretations of the Decline of the Birth Rate in Nineteenth Century America," *Marriage Hygiene,* II (1935–36), pp. 43, 158, 288). See *Social Science,* III, 296–308, 312 n.

19. See Brisbane, *op. cit.,* pp. 331 ff. Brisbane, a believer in progressive cultural evolution, observed that intelligent intervention would accelerate the rate of social progress and convert the "commercial and financial vassalage" in the offing into an ideal association.

20. See R. A. Fisher, *The Genetical Theory of Natural Selection* (Oxford, Clarendon, 1930), chap. i; Julian Huxley, *Evolution: the Modern Synthesis* (New York, Harper, 1943), chaps. i, viii.

21. Hofstadter, *op. cit.,* especially chaps. i–ii; also E. Grace, M. F. Ashley Montagu, and B. J. Stern, "More on Social Darwinism," *Science & Society,* VI (Winter, 1942), 71–78. See also Andrew Carnegie's account of the biological basis of competition in his "Wealth," *North Amer. Review, 148* (June, 1889), 655 ff.; T. C. Cochran and W. Miller, *The Age of Enterprise* (New York, Macmillan, 1942), chap. vi.

22. See M. J. L. O'Connor, *Origins of Academic Economics in the United States* (New York, Columbia, 1944), especially chaps. v–vi. Francis Lieber's comment in 1871 is not too unrepresentative. "Darwinism is . . . repulsive dogmatism, and unintelligible besides. What does the Darwinian think selection is? An agent without an agent?" See T. S. Perry, *Life and Letters of Francis Lieber* (Boston, Osgood, 1882), p. 409. For an opposite opinion see Henry Adams, *The Education of Henry Adams* (New York, Modern Library), pp. 225, 231.

23. The American Social Science Association (1865–1909) and its organ, the *Jour. of Social Science,* did not adequately meet this need. The *New York Social Science Review,* established in 1865 for the discussion of political economy and statistics, ran only a few numbers. Its contributors were disciples of Spencer, Mill, and Bastiat; advocates of laissez faire; and believers in beneficent natural laws that governed all creation and impelled man "irresistibly forward in his march of progress." See *ibid.,* I (1865), 65, 97 ff.; Bernard, *op. cit.,* chap. xxxiii and Part VIII.

24. See Joseph Dorfman, *Thorstein Veblen and His America* (New York, Viking, 1934), p. 22; Richard T. Ely, *Ground under Our Feet* (New York, Macmillan, 1938), p. 125; W. F. Folwell, in letter cited by Ely in his "American Economic Association, 1885–1909," *Proceedings,* XI (1910), 65. Economics was taught "as an integral part of the common-sense philosophy," which A. T. Hadley later characterized as follows: "You are to believe what common sense tells you as *we* see it—'we' representing the respectable body of thinking men in the nineteenth century. You are at perfect liberty to believe

otherwise; but if you do 'we' shall perceive that you have no sense, and we shall treat you accordingly." See his *Some Influence in Modern Philosophic Thought* (New Haven, Yale, 1913), pp. 16–17.

25. F. A. Walker, *Discussions in Economics and Statistics* (New York, Holt, 1899), I, 328. W. D. Howells (e.g., in *The Traveler from Altruria*) looked upon academic economists as apologists for the existing order (see V. L. Parrington, *Main Currents in American Thought* [New York, Harcourt, Brace, 1930], III, 247). E. R. A. Seligman attributed the great popularity of laissez faire at this period to the unprecedentedly favorable economic conditions. See "Economics and Social Progress," *Publications of the American Economic Association*, 3d ser., IV (Feb., 1903), 58.

26. See Ely, *Ground*, pp. 123–140; J. Dorfman, *Veblen*, chap. ii.

27. Keynes, *op. cit.*, pp. 16-17.

28. *The Science of Wealth* (Boston, Little, Brown, 1866), pp. 469–470. Walker thought well of the works of Bastiat, Mill, and Perry.

29. *Practical Economics* (New York, Putnam, 1885), pp. 257–259; this was written in 1875.

30. *Elements of Political Economy* (New York, Sheldon, 1878; new ed. New York, Sheldon, 1886), chap. i; see also chaps. xii–xiv. The first edition appeared in 1837.

31. *Political Economy* (New York, Scribner, 1873, 1883), pp. 96, 109–110, 238–239; his *Elements of Political Economy* appeared in 1865–66.

32. "Buckle's History of Civilization," *New Englander*, XXI (April, 1862), 175.

33. *Political Economy* (Andover, Draper, 1859), pp. 9–12; "The Natural Theology of Social Science," *Bibliotheca Sacra* (1867–69), XXV (Oct., 1868), 659–662, XXVI (Jan., 1869), 140 ff.

34. *Social Theory* (New York, Crowell, 1895), pp. 129, 178, 527–545. See also his discussion of the function of competition and its limits, *ibid.*, pp. 144–165. "Competition gives play to individual powers. It begets motion, and settles the leadership when confusion arises. It keeps in the foreground the efficient forces of the world. . . . It will more and more pass by quiet diffusion into those higher phases of development in which natural laws are taken up into reason and ruled by it." *Ibid.*, p. 164. Cf. his "Competition, Actual and Theoretical," *Quarterly Jour. of Economics*, XIV (Aug., 1900), 537–542.

35. Bernard, *op. cit.*, pp. 129, 820.

36. "Martineau's Translation of Comte's Philosophy," *North Amer. Review*, 79 (July, 1854), 200–229.

37. See *Gleanings from a Literary Life, 1838–1880* (New York, Scribner, 1880), preface, and the essays included under "philosophy."

38. See e.g., "Buckle's History of Civilization" (1861), *ibid.*, pp. 247 ff.; "The Idea of Cause" (1879), *ibid.*, pp. 164–198.

39. "The Latest Form of the Development Theory," *ibid.*, pp. 199 ff. See also "Dualism, Materialism, or Idealism," in *ibid.*, especially pp. 162–163.

40. See his *American Political Economy* (New York, Scribner, 1870), chaps. i, ii, viii. This work had appeared in substantially the same form in 1856 as *The Principles of Political Economy*. See also "The Utility and the Limitations of the Science of Political Economy" (1838), in *Gleanings*, pp. 118 ff.

41. "Malthusianism, Darwinism, and Pessimism," in *Gleanings*, pp. 361–362, 367–368, 379–380.

42. George's theory of progress is developed most effectively in *Progress and Poverty* (1879). See also *The Science of Political Economy* (1897) and *A Perplexed Philosopher* (1892) in which he criticizes Spencer for giving up his view, expressed in *Social Statics*, that "equity . . . does not permit property in land." George's views have been carefully summarized by G. R. Geiger, in his *The Philosophy of Henry George* (New York, Macmillan, 1933). On George's social philosophy see *ibid.*, pp. 273–284, 322–333, 518–536, 548–559; on George's controversy with Spencer see *ibid.*, chap. vi.

43. *Principles of Political Economy* (New York, Harper, 1886), pp. 5–9, 23, 112, 141–142.

44. *Economics, or the Science of Wealth* (New York, Putnam, 1877), p. 272. Our discussion is based principally upon chap. xi and pp. 9, 147–148, and 271–272 of this work. Sturtevant first developed his population doctrine in 1863 before he knew of Darwin's work, saying that the "welfare of society" depends upon propagation by "the strong, the sound, the healthy" classes, and not upon that by "the diseased, the weak, the vicious, the degraded, and the broken-down classes"; and he predicted that the Negro, because now free and unprotected against the competition of the white, would be unable to earn enough to support a family and hence "must melt away and disappear forever . . . like his brother, the Indian." See "The Destiny of the African Race in the United States," *Continental Monthly*, III (May, 1863), 608 ff.

45. Apparently, Dunbar, Harvard's first full-time professor of political economy, supposed evolution theory to lie outside the scope of economics. See his *Economic Essays*, ed. by O. M. W. Sprague (New York, Macmillan, 1904). Dunbar considered Carey's work unimportant; declared laissez faire to be "no part of the logical structure of the old economic doctrine"; believed ethics to lie outside the scope of political economy; and attached no great importance to the historical approach to economics. See *ibid.*, pp. 14–16, 39 ff., 46, 50.

46. The main papers are found in *Discussions*, II. I have discussed aspects of this question and Walker's relation thereto in papers already referred to: *Jour. of Political Economy, 51* (Oct., 1933), 654–661; *Amer. Sociological Review*, I (Dec., 1936), 916–921; *Marriage Hygiene*, II (1935–36). Documentation will be found in these articles.

47. R. M. Smith in 1888 stated what became a standard argument for control, namely, that immigration would depress the standard of living of the American working classes. See "Control of Immigration, III," *Political Science Quarterly*, III (Sept., 1888), 414–417. For a later criticism of the economic arguments being advanced against immigration see I. A. Hourwich, "The Economic Aspects of Immigration," *Political Science Quarterly*, XXVI (Dec., 1911), 615–642.

48. *Discussions*, I, 308–314, 326–338; *Political Economy* (New York, Holt, 1883, 1886), pp. 17–18, 21–22, 24–25, 27, 298–299.

49. "Undoubtedly, as between weak families and strong ones, between weak tribes and strong ones, the principle of selection has worked with tremendous power, to secure the survival of the most prudent, the most frugal, the most brave, temperate and subordinate, and thus to advance the race in physical, economical and social power." *Ibid.*, p. 307 n.

50. *The Wages Question* (New York, Holt, 1876), pp. 411, 413; *Discussions*, I, 111, 303, 345, 418–421, II, 270, 293, 297, 375–376; "The Manual Laboring Class," *Publications of the American Economic Association*, III (March, 1888), 9, 11. See also Walker's critical analysis of the egalitarian military system of economic organization advocated by E. Bellamy, *Discussions*, II, 351–378.

51. *Discussions*, I, 372–374. *Political Economy*, p. 256.

52. *Political Economy*, Part IV. For incompetent entrepreneurs Walker had no sympathy; they were cost-increasing wastrels (*ibid.*, pp. 256–257). He was not so extreme as some in his praise of the entrepreneur. The captain of industry, declared C. R. Henderson, for example, "has risen from the ranks largely because he was a better fighter than most of us. Competitive commercial life is not a flowery bed of ease, but a battle field where the 'struggle for existence' is defining the industrially 'fittest to survive.' In this country the great prizes are . . . found . . . in industry. . . . In this fierce, though voiceless contest, a peculiar type of manhood is developed. . . ." See C. R. Henderson, "Business Men and Social Theorists," *Amer. Jour. of Sociology*, I (Jan., 1896), 385–386.

53. Sumner's early economic views are to be found in his *Problems in Political Economy* (New York, Holt, 1884), in his many essays, in his *Folkways* (Boston, Ginn, 1907), and in his (and A. G. Keller's) *The Science of Society* (New Haven, Yale, 1927). The formulation of the above paragraphs has been helped very much by two excellent studies of Sumner's work, that of Hofstadter, *op. cit.*, chap. iii, and that of Donald W. Calhoun, "William Graham Sumner," *Social Forces*, XXIV (Oct., 1945), 15–32. See also

L. L. Bernard, "The Social Science Theories of William Graham Sumner," *ibid.*, XIX (Dec., 1940), 153–175; E. M. Lemert, "Folkways and Social Control," *Amer. Sociological Review,* VII (June, 1942), 394–399; C. H. Page, *Class and American* Sociology (New York, Dial, 1940), chap. iii.

54. *Economics, an Account of the Relations between Private Property and Public Welfare* (New York, Putnam, 1896), pp. 18–19. Hadley developed this thesis more fully in a paper on "The Influence of Charles Darwin on Historical and Political Science," in *Some Influences in Modern Philosophic Thought,* pp. 121–142. See also *Publications of the American Economic Association,* 3d ser., XI (April, 1910), 96–97. Cf. Woodrow Wilson's views as reported by W. Diamond, *The Economic Thought of Woodrow Wilson* (Baltimore, Johns Hopkins, 1943), pp. 26–27, 43, 45, 85–86, 93.

55. Some comfortable nations had "possibly" overdone this prudence, he noted, however. See *Economics,* pp. 15, 17–25, 30 ff., 46, 49, 390 ff., and chap. iii; "Population and Capital," *Publications of the American Economic Association,* IX (Oct.–Dec., 1894), 557–566; "Economic Theory and Political Morality," *Publications of the American Economic Association,* 3d ser., I (Feb., 1900), 53.

56. "Hadley's 'Economics,' " *Jour. of Political Economy,* IV (Sept., 1896), 474–475.

57. *Ibid.,* pp. 488–489. Taylor approved (*ibid.,* p. 493) Hadley's observation that tariffs affect consumption adversely by restraining its diversification (see Hadley, *Economics,* par. 496).

58. "The Philosophical Basis of Economics," *Annals of the American Academy of Political and Social Science,* X (Sept., 1897), 206, 218–221, 235–236, 240.

59. Ely, *Ground,* pp. 132–149; *Publications of the American Economic Association,* I (March, 1886), 5–46, 3d ser., XI (April, 1910), 47–93. Hadley, Taussig, Sumner, and Laughlin were among those—the "Old School"—who at first refused to join the new association because of its alleged leftish tendencies. Walker, on the contrary, became its first president.

60. "Relation of the State to Industrial Action," *Publications of the American Economic Association,* I (Jan., 1887), 7, 11, 26, 36–38, 39, 47, 64. Cf. the somewhat similar views of E. J. James in *ibid.,* I (March, 1886), 26, and I (May–July, 1886) ("The Relation of the Modern Municipality to the Gas Supply"), pp. 9, 73–76.

61. "The Economic State," *Political Science Quarterly,* VIII (Dec., 1893), 604–606, 619–620, 621, 623–624. Darwin is quoted on p. 606.

62. Wagner's formulation of the so-called law of increasing functions of the state also exercised some influence. The trend may be traced in the textbooks. See J. W. Jenks, "The Principles of Government Control of Business," *Publications of the American Economic Association,* 3d ser., IX (April, 1908), 1–20. See also M. A. Copeland's article on the community of interests in *The Trend of Economics,* ed. by R. G. Tugwell (New York, Knopf, 1924), pp. 105–152.

63. *Studies in the Evolution of Industrial Society* (New York, Macmillan, 1903, 1906). The opinions which Ely expressed in previous writings touching upon evolution appear in this work; hence our references are limited to it. His bibliography through 1937 appears in *Ground under Our Feet,* pp. 309 ff. On the religious aspects of his work see J. Dombrowski, *The Early Days of Christian Socialism in America* (New York, Columbia, 1936), chap. iv.

64. This paragraph is based on *Studies,* Part I, chaps. iii–v; the preceding paragraph, on chaps. i–ii.

65. *Ibid.,* p. 156, also pp. 128–163. See also his *Property and Contract in Their Relations to the Distribution of Wealth* (New York, Macmillan, 1914).

66. *Studies,* pp. 423–424.

67. *Ibid.,* pp. 137–139, 160, 163–181.

68. *Ibid.,* pp. 456–457.

69. See *The Economics of Enterprise* (New York, Macmillan, 1913); *Value and Distribution* (Chicago, University of Chicago, 1908). In his *Outlines of Economic Theory*

(New York, Macmillan, 1896), pp. 326 ff., Davenport criticized Spencer's population theory. In his *The Economics of Alfred Marshall* (Ithaca, Cornell, 1935), Davenport refers critically to institutional economics (pp. 258–259).

70. "Economics and Social Progress," *Publications of the American Economic Association*, 3d ser., IV (Feb., 1903), 52–70; *Principles of Economics* (New York, Longmans, Green, 1905), chaps. iii, xix, xxxix; *The Economic Interpretation of History* (New York, Columbia, 1902, 1907), Part II, chaps. i–ii, v–vi. Seligman, of course, stressed the importance of economic factors and relations. Seligman criticized Giddings' "economic ages" (*ibid.*, p. 147).

71. Boston, Ginn, 1886. Much of this book appeared in article form in the *New Englander*, 1877–83.

72. *Op. cit.*, chap. iii, also pp. 99 ff., 149 ff.

73. *Ibid.*, pp. 64–67, 110, 120–122, 149–151, 173, 188–189, 203–206, 218–220. Clark describes the "want of a true teleology" as lessening the practical value of political economy (*ibid.*, pp. 205–206).

74. *Essentials of Economic Theory* (New York, Macmillan, 1907), preface, chaps. xii, xix–xxii. In *The Distribution of Wealth* (New York, Macmillan, 1899), he sought to show how in a frictionless universe "a natural law . . . would give to every agent of production the amount of wealth that agent creates." See *ibid.*, preface. Earlier he had concluded that the prevailing form of society was the product of evolution; and that the spirit of rivalry which pervaded it was well suited to release its productive energies. See "The Modern Appeal to Legal Forces in Economic Life," *Publications of the American Economic Association*, IX (Oct.–Dec., 1894), 501.

75. New York, Macmillan, 1915. This work has to do chiefly with the relations between economics and psychology.

76. *Ibid.*, pp. 33, 50–54, 96 ff. The psychological doctrine of this work was taken over from instinct psychology.

77. "Our results strongly suggest, even if they do not prove, that inequality of earnings between the several occupational classes has its origins in a fundamental inequality of native endowments, rather than in an inequality of opportunities." See F. W. Taussig and C. J. Joslyn, *American Business Leaders. A Study in Social Origins and Social Stratification* (New York, Macmillan, 1932), p. 268.

78. *Principles of Economics* (New York, Macmillan, 1911, 1915, 1921, 1939), Book V and the chapters on socialism in Book VII. See T. Parsons on Taussig's sociological theory in the Taussig Festschrift, *Explorations in Economics* (New York, McGraw-Hill, 1936), pp. 359–379.

79. *Principles*, II, 1939, p. 529.

80. Class and related aspects of the theory of each of these sociologists is treated by Page, *op. cit.*

81. Hofstadter, *op. cit.*, chap. iv; S. Chugerman, *Lester F. Ward, the American Aristotle* (Durham, Duke, 1939), pp. 294, 307–315; Ward, *Glimpses of the Cosmos* (New York, Putnam, 1915), IV (1889, 1895), 153 ff., 345 ff.

82. *Applied Sociology* (Boston, Ginn, 1906), p. 320.

83. Chugerman, *op. cit.*, pp. 293, 455 ff., chaps. xvi, xxxii–xxxvii, xxxix. Consumption was outside the scope of economics and within that of sociology, according to Ward. E.g., see *Pure Sociology* (New York, Macmillan, 1903), p. 282.

84. "The Process of Social Change," *Political Science Quarterly*, XII (March, 1897), 81, also pp. 72–73, 77.

85. *Social Process* (New York, Scribner, 1918), pp. 134–135, 221; also *Human Nature and the Social Order* (New York, Scribner, 1902).

86. *Foundations of Sociology* (New York, Macmillan, 1905), pp. 340–341. His *Social Control* appeared in 1901.

87. *Principles of Sociology* (3d ed. revised, New York, Appleton-Century, 1938), pp. 214–223; *Social Control*, pp. 378–379.

88. See *The Modern Distributive Process*, by J. B. Clark and F. H. Giddings (Boston, Ginn, 1888), pp. 25 ff., 33 ff., 62–63, 68–69; and Giddings, "The Theory of Profit-Sharing," *Quarterly Jour. of Economics*, I (April, 1887), 367–376.

89. "The Sociological Character of Political Economy," *Publications of the American Economic Association*, III (March, 1888), 28–47.

90. See chap. iii, "The Economic Ages," in *Studies in the Theory of Human Society* (New York, Macmillan, 1922). This chapter first appeared in *Political Science Quarterly*, XVI (June, 1901), 193–221. The papers included in *Studies* provide a fair picture of Giddings' views on evolution and sociology.

91. *Sociology* (New York, Columbia, 1908), pp. 32–43.

92. *Studies*, p. 62.

93. On Veblen's race theory see his *The Place of Science in Modern Civilisation* (New York, Huebsch, 1919), pp. 457–496, and *Essays in Our Changing Order*, ed. by Leon Ardzrooni (New York, Viking, 1934), pp. 232 ff.; also Dorfman, *Veblen*, under "race." On racism in late nineteenth-century America see Hofstadter, *op. cit.*, chap. ix.

94. "Ethnic Factors and the Movement of Population," *Quarterly Jour. of Economics*, XIV (Feb., 1900), 171 ff. Cummings' writings indicate that he was far from being an egalitarian, as Closson charged. E.g., see *Jour. of Political Economy*, XII (Dec., 1903), 98–101; XV (March, 1907), 149–165; XVII (April, 1909), 206–219; and VII (Sept., 1899), 425–455 (where Veblen's leisure class theory is appraised).

95. See Ripley's comments on Cummings' article, *Quarterly Jour. of Economics*, XIV (May, 1900), 426–428, and his "Ethnic Influences in Vital Statistics," *Publications of the American Statistical Association*, V (March, 1896), 18–40. Ripley's views on race appear in his *The Races of Europe* (New York, Appleton, 1899). See also his "Geography as a Sociological Study," *Political Science Quarterly*, X (Dec., 1895), 636–655.

96. "The Real Opportunity of the So-Called Anglo-Saxon Race," *Jour. of Political Economy*, IX (Dec., 1900), 78–79; "A Critic of Anthropo-Sociology," *ibid.*, VIII (June, 1900), 397 ff., 410; also Closson's replies to Ripley in *Quarterly Jour. of Economics*, XI (Oct., 1896), 92–104, and XV (Nov., 1900), 143–146.

97. See Closson's note to his translation of O. Ammon's "The Doctrine of Probability," *Jour. of Political Economy*, VII (March, 1899), 219–220. This note is based upon classifications of populations by Ammon, Booth, and Giddings. For Giddings' final classification scheme see his *Studies in the Theory of Human Society*, pp. 287–289.

98. "Further Data of Anthropo-Sociology," *Jour. of Political Economy*, VII (March, 1899), 243, 245, 249, 252; "The Races of Europe," *ibid.*, VIII (Dec., 1899), 58–88. The latter paper consists largely in a comparison of the views of Ripley and Lapouge.

99. See preceding note; "Social Selection," *Jour. of Political Economy*, IV (Sept., 1896), 449–466; "Dissociation by Displacement: a Phase of Social Selection," *Quarterly Jour. of Economics*, X (Jan., 1896), 160–161, 164 ff.

100. *Ibid.*, pp. 161–163; *Jour. of Political Economy*, IX (Dec., 1900), 97 n.; *ibid.*, IV (Sept., 1896), 449. For this reason apparently he disapproved the arguments of those who would make the struggle for existence sufficiently intense to eliminate all inadequate elements. See *Jour. of Political Economy*, IV (June, 1896), 398.

101. In another paper he said that the Italians, or "more probably the Chinese," would replace indigenous races. See "The Races of Europe," *Jour. of Political Economy*, VIII (Dec., 1899), 71.

102. "The Real Opportunity . . . ," *Jour. of Political Economy*, IX (Dec., 1900), 96, also pp. 79, 84–86, 88, 91–93, 95–97.

103. For accounts of Patten's life and works see R. G. Tugwell, "Notes on the Life and Work of Simon Nelson Patten," *Jour. of Political Economy*, XXXI (April, 1923), 153–208; J. L. Boswell, *The Economics of Simon Nelson Patten* (Philadelphia, University of Pennsylvania, 1933). Patten's economic philosophy is foreshadowed in *The Premises of Political Economy* (Philadelphia, Lippincott, 1885). His views are rather well represented in a collection of his essays, ed. by R. G. Tugwell, *Essays in Economic*

Theory (New York, Knopf, 1924), and in his *The Development of English Thought* (New York, Macmillan, 1899).

104. This paragraph is based primarily upon *Heredity and Social Progress* (New York, Macmillan, 1903); *The Development of English Thought;* "Over-Nutrition and Its Social Consequences," *Annals of the American Academy of Political and Social Science,* X (July, 1897), 33–35; and *The Theory of Prosperity* (New York, Macmillan, 1902), pp. 162, 167–168, 175–178, 192–199, 205–206, 230–236.

105. *The Theory of Social Forces,* Suppl. to *Annals of the American Academy of Political and Social Science,* VII (Jan., 1896), 75. Patten treats of the pain and pleasure economies in most of his works. E.g., see *Social Forces,* pp. 47–55, 63, 66, 74–85, 96–97, 144–149, also 7–16; *The New Basis of Civilization* (New York, Macmillan, 1907), especially chaps. i–ii, ix. "The Failure of Biologic Sociology," *Annals of the American Academy of Political and Social Science,* IV (May, 1894), 919–947. The premises of classical economics and, consequently, its conclusions, Patten believed, were inferred largely from static, pain-economy conditions; they were not well suited for the analysis of more dynamic pleasure economies. See *The Premises of Political Economy, The Development of English Thought,* and *The New Basis of Civilization,* pp. 10 ff.

106. *Essays,* p. 57, also pp. 35, 183. Consumption plays an important part in the adjustment of man to his environment and in his economic evolution, Patten believed. E.g., see *The Consumption of Wealth* (2d ed. Philadelphia, University of Pennsylvania, 1901); *The Premises,* etc., pp. 14–18; "Over-Nutrition . . . ," *loc. cit.; Social Forces,* pp. 76–79.

107. *Essays,* pp. 337–340, also 219–220, 267–268; cf. *Social Forces,* chaps. iv–v.

108. This paragraph and the one following is based upon *The Development of English Thought.*

109. *The Economy of Human Energy* (New York, Macmillan, 1924), pp. 23–24, 27, 76 ff., 152, 274, 280–281; *The Religion Worth Having* (Boston, Houghton Mifflin, 1912), pp. 32, 40, 127; *The Essential Factors of Social Evolution* (Cambridge, Harvard, 1935), pp. 3, 19–20, 188, 288; *Essays in Social Justice* (Cambridge, Harvard, 1915), pp. 33, 101.

110. *Ibid.,* pp. 49, 57, 85, 93 ff.

111. *Ibid.,* p. 82; *Human Energy,* p. 281.

112. *Ibid.,* chap. xiii; *Social Justice,* pp. 93, 158.

113. *Ibid.,* chaps. x–xvii, especially pp. 173, 260–263, 264–265, 303, 322–323, 348, 368–370, 375, 382–383, 386–387, 429.

114. *Ibid.,* pp. 92, 93; *Human Energy,* pp. 155–156.

115. *Ibid.,* p. 121; *Social Justice,* pp. 126–129, 278; *Religion,* pp. 15, 33, 38, 48, 99, 138; *Quarterly Jour. of Economics,* XXXIII (Aug., 1919), 714–716.

116. *Social Justice,* pp. 106, 108–109, 130, 160–172; *Essential Factors,* pp. 13, 19–20, 86; "The Behavioristic Man," *Quarterly Jour. of Economics,* XXXIII (Nov., 1918), 195 ff.

117. *Social Justice,* pp. 99–106.

118. *Ibid.,* chaps. iv–v.

119. Dorfman summarizes all of Veblen's writings in his *Veblen.* The present discussion has been influenced by A. L. Harris' two articles, "Types of Institutionalism," *Jour. of Political Economy,* XL (Dec., 1932), 721–749, and "Economic Evolution: Dialectical and Darwinian," *ibid.,* XLII (Feb., 1934), 34–79; and A. K. Davis, "Sociological Elements in Veblen's Economic Theory," *ibid.,* XIII (June, 1945), 132–149. See also Davis' two articles, "Veblen on the Decline of the Protestant Ethic," *Social Forces,* XXII (March, 1944), 282–286, and "Veblen's Study of Modern Germany," *Amer. Sociological Review,* IX (Dec., 1944), 603–609; also W. C. Mitchell, *The Backward Art of Spending Money* (New York, McGraw-Hill, 1937), pp. 279 ff.

120. "Why Is Economics Not an Evolutionary Science?" (1898), in *The Place of Science in Modern Civilisation,* p. 77.

121. *Ibid.,* pp. 58, 78–81, 145.

122. Dorfman, *Veblen*, pp. 165, 168.

123. *Theory of the Leisure Class* (New York, Viking, 1931), pp. 188 ff.; Harris, "Types . . . ," *loc. cit.*, pp. 732, 734.

124. *Ibid.*, pp. 734–736.

125. Harris, "Economic Evolution . . . ," *loc. cit.*, pp. 76–78.

126. Davis, "Sociological Elements . . . ," *loc. cit.*, p. 146.

127. *Ibid.*, pp. 140–149.

128. "Hedonistic Interpretation of Subjective Value," *Jour. of Political Economy*, IV (Dec., 1895), 71–72, 84; also "Subjective and Exchange Value," *ibid.*, IV (June, 1896), 383–385. These articles were inspired by Veblen (see Dorfman, *Veblen*, p. 130).

129. Warner Fite, "Professor Patten's Psychological Doctrines," *Jour. of Political Economy*, VII (Aug., 1899), 384–385, 391.

130. E.g., see *The Place of Science in Modern Civilisation*, pp. 73 ff. See also *The Instinct of Workmanship* (New York, Macmillan, 1914), p. 39.

131. E. H. Downey, "The Futility of Marginal Utility," *Jour. of Political Economy*, XVIII (April, 1910), 253–268.

132. *Economic Principles* (New York, Century, 1915).

133. "Economics and Modern Psychology," in *Preface to Social Economics* (New York, Farrar & Rinehart, 1936), pp. 92–169. This paper was published in 1918. See also Clark's summary of Carlton Parker's views on psychology, *ibid.*, p. 168.

134. "Rationality of Economic Activity," *Jour. of Political Economy*, XVIII (Feb., 1910), 6, 97–113; "Human Behavior and Economics," *Quarterly Jour. of Economics*, XXIX (Nov., 1914), 1–47. Mitchell was influenced by Veblen, Dewey, and Thorndike, among others. See also Z. C. Dickinson, *Economic Motives* (Cambridge, Harvard, 1922).

135. "The Prospects of Economics," in *The Backward Art of Spending Money* (New York, McGraw-Hill, 1937), pp. 360 ff. This paper appeared in 1924.

136. See the controversy of F. H. Knight and M. A. Copeland over the place of psychology in economics, *Quarterly Jour. of Economics*, XXXIX (May, 1925), 372 ff., XL (Nov., 1925), 134 ff.; see also J. Viner's articles on utility theory, *Jour. of Political Economy*, XXXIII (Aug., Dec., 1925), 369–387, 638–659.

137. G. Katona, "Psychological Analysis of Business Decisions and Expectations," *Amer. Economic Review*, XXXVI (March, 1946), 44–62.

138. W. H. Hamilton, "The Institutional Approach to Economic Theory," *Proceedings of the American Economic Association*, IX (March, 1919), Suppl., pp. 309–318.

139. See J. M. Clark, *Preface to Social Economics*, chaps. i–vii, xiv; *Studies in the Economics of Overhead Costs* (Chicago, University of Chicago, 1923); *Social Control of Business* (Chicago, University of Chicago, 1926). See also W. C. Mitchell, *The Backward Art of Spending Money* and *Business Cycles* (New York, National Bureau of Economic Research, 1928).

140. See articles by Wolfe and Copeland in R. G. Tugwell, *The Trend of Economics* (New York, Knopf, 1924); also Copeland, "Economic Theory and the Natural-Science Point of View," *Amer. Economic Review*, XXI (March, 1931), 67–79, and "Psychology and the Natural-Science Point of View," *Psychological Review*, XXXVII (Nov., 1930), 461–487. See also C. E. Ayres, *The Theory of Economic Progress* (Chapel Hill, University of North Carolina, 1944).

141. See E. M. Burns, "Does Institutionalism Complement or Compete with 'Orthodox Economics?'" *Amer. Economic Review*, XXI (March, 1931), 80–87; P. T. Homan, "An Appraisal of Institutional Economics," *ibid.*, XXII (March, 1932), 10–18, and the controversy over the alleged theoretical shortcomings of institutional economics in *Science & Society*, II (Fall, 1938), 448–470, III (Fall, 1939), 509–517.

142. L. D. Edie, "The Institutional Concept," *Quarterly Jour. of Economics*, XLI (May, 1927), 437–438.

143. E.g., see *The Distribution of Wealth* (New York, Macmillan, 1893), chap. ii; *Myself* (New York, Macmillan, 1934).

144. *Legal Foundations* appeared in 1924. For a critical review see I. L. Sharfman, *Quarterly Jour. of Economics*, XXXIX (Feb., 1925), 300 ff.

145. *Institutional Economics* appeared in 1934. It was favorably reviewed by C. L. James in the *Amer. Economic Review*, XXVII (March, 1937), 61 ff., and by A. B. Wolfe, *The Philosophical Review*, XLV (March, 1936), 192 ff. See also M. A. Copeland, *Quarterly Jour. of Economics*, L (Feb., 1936), 333 ff.

146. *Institutional Economics*, pp. 5–8, 639. "Ownership becomes the foundation of institutional economics . . . institutional economics takes its place as the proprietary economics of rights, duties, liberties, and exposures, which . . . give to collective action its due place in economic theorizing." See *ibid.*, pp. 5, 8.

147. *Ibid.*, p. 120. Commons acknowledges indebtedness to E. A. Ross's *Social Control*.

148. *Institutional Economics*, p. 45; see also pp. 635–640, 709–711.

149. *Ibid.*, p. 45.

150. *Ibid.*, pp. 45, 95–96, 637. Under the head of "Willingness" he included ideas, meaning, valuing, choosing, transacting, governing, acting, forecasting, collective action, etc. See *ibid.*, pp. 95, 96.

151. *Ibid.*, pp. 773–789.

152. On the changes and the forces making for them in this period see M. Curti, *The Growth of American Thought* (New York, Harper, 1943); R. H. Gabriel, *The Course of American Democratic Thought* (New York, Ronald, 1940); and Parrington, *op. cit.*, III.

153. On the Adamses see *ibid.*, pp. 212–236; E. Johnson, "Henry Adams," *Science & Society*, I (Spring, 1937), 362–377; and C. A. Beard's introduction to the 1943 ed. of Brooks Adams' *The Law of Civilization and Decay*, which was originally published in 1896. Henry Adams may have been influenced by Lewis Morgan's thesis (*Ancient Society*, p. 38) that "human progress . . . has been in a ratio . . . essentially geometrical."

154. See *The Degradation of the Democratic Dogma* (New York, Macmillan, 1920). The "rule of phase" (1909) is described in *ibid.*, pp. 267 ff. and in *Education*, chap. xxxv. Hornell Hart, "Technological Acceleration and the Atomic Bomb," *Amer. Sociological Review*, XI (June, 1946), 281, writes in respect to what Adams called the phase rule: "Throughout the entire sweep of history and prehistory, the power of human beings to achieve their basic purposes has been increasing at accelerating speed with local and temporary stagnations and setbacks. This long-run acceleration has taken place through series of logistic and Gampertz curves, having higher and higher rates of increase." On Adams' prophecies see *Letters of Henry Adams*, II (1892–1918), ed. by W. C. Ford (Boston, Houghton, 1938).

155. See *Degradation*, etc., pp. 137–267, on implications of increase in entropy. Adams cites (*ibid.*, pp. 216–217) Kelvin's suggestion that life conditions may last only four to five more centuries. On mineral exhaustion see *ibid.*, pp. 216–217, and *Education*, p. 477. Adams may have got from the socialists his notion of the importance of the economy of energy (see *Letters*, II, 246).

156. See Lotka, "Evolution and Thermodynamics," *Science & Society*, VIII (Spring, 1944), 166–167; also Needham, *Science & Society*, VI (Fall, 1942), 352 ff.

157. *Law of Civilization*, preface, conclusion, chap. xi, and Beard's introduction, pp. 31–37, 43. See also *America's Economic Supremacy* (New York, Macmillan, 1900); *The New Empire* (New York, Macmillan, 1902); Hofstadter, *op. cit.*, pp. 160 ff.

158. See Dombrowski, *op. cit.*; Hofstadter, *op. cit.*; Parrington, *op. cit.*, III, 241 ff., 301 ff.; A. E. Morgan, *Edward Bellamy* (New York, Columbia, 1944); and discussions of W. D. Howells' socialism by J. W. Getzels, C. Wright, and G. W. Arms in *Science & Society*, II (Summer, Fall, 1938), 376–386, 514–517, III (Spring, 1939), 245–248.

159. See Hofstadter, *op. cit.*, pp. 95–98; Engels, *Dialectics of Nature*.

160. See Huxley, *Evolution*, pp. 478–485, also chap. x; Lotka, "The Law of Evolution," *op. cit.*, pp. 188–194; R. A. Fisher, *op. cit.*; J. B. S. Haldane, "Dialectical Account of Evolution," *Science & Society*, I (Summer, 1937), 480–486.

161. *Ibid.,* pp. 480–482.

162. See F. S. C. Northrop, "The Impossibility of a Theoretical Science of Economic Dynamics," *Quarterly Jour. of Economics, 56* (Nov., 1941), 1–17.

163. An innovation may be viewed as a variation. The literature in the field of invention, which Irving Fisher treats as synonymous with innovation, "is remarkably meager, consisting chiefly of the writings of Rae, Taussig, Snyder, Schumpeter, and myself." See Fisher, *Constructive Income Taxation* (New York, Harper, 1942), pp. 78–79. Carl Snyder's views are repeated in his *Capitalism the Creator* (New York, Macmillan, 1940). Schumpeter's theory may be found in his *The Theory of Economic Development* (Cambridge, Harvard, 1934), and in his *Business Cycles* (2 vols., New York, McGraw-Hill, 1939).

INTRODUCTION TO CHAPTER VII

THE INFLUENCE OF EVOLUTIONARY THEORY UPON AMERICAN PSYCHOLOGICAL THOUGHT

AT the end of the nineteenth century American students of psychology abandoned the age-old faculty psychology with its close theological and philosophical associations and set about the development of an independent experimental science according to the current German precedents. In fact, however, several distinct American schools of psychology emerged, each of which displayed the functional and practical characteristics which Professor Boring finds to be typical both of the evolutionary influence and of the American social environment. In psychology as in other fields the first reaction to evolution was the elaboration of comprehensive systems explicitly evolutionary in character—the psychologies of Baldwin and Hall. With the shift of attention to more practical problems in the twentieth century American psychology abandoned its somewhat artificial preoccupation with evolutionary factors. But in its choice of problems as well as in its methods of coping with them contemporary psychological thought has in a real sense become an evolutionary science.

S. P.

VII

THE INFLUENCE OF EVOLUTIONARY THEORY UPON AMERICAN PSYCHOLOGICAL THOUGHT

EDWIN G. BORING

SUPERFICIALLY regarded, the origin of American psychology presents us with a paradox. The men who got what Scripture later called "the new psychology" [1] under way in America in the 1880's and early 1890's—James, Ladd, Cattell, and Baldwin—these men and the others who came on the scene before 1900 were all looking to Germany for the pattern of the new psychology.[2] There the new psychology was called *physiologische Psychologie* or *experimentelle Psychologie* and its founders had been Fechner and Helmholtz and Wundt who set the stage for the new movement in the 1850's and 1860's.[3] Up to the end of the century America was consciously copying Germany, determined to make psychology physiological and experimental, energetically concerned with the founding of laboratories and the accumulation of psychological apparatus, crossing the ocean to get its doctor's degrees—mostly from Wundt's *psychologisches Institut* at Leipzig. Consciously America was copying Germany, but unconsciously America was doing something quite different. It was building up its own particular brand of functional psychology which, under many names and in many forms, has dominated the American scene for more than half a century and, since the first World War, has become in turn something for Europe to copy. Therein lies the paradox. In seeking to import the new German movement, America unwittingly imposed upon it the special properties of the American *Zeitgeist,* altering the German model even in the act of accepting it.

We must examine first the history of these crucial events in the psychology of the latter half of the nineteenth century. We must see how American psychology got its start, and how it was, in a sense, the child of German psychology and British biology.

(1) *The new German psychology* of the later nineteenth century, one of the parents of the still newer American psychology, was itself the offspring of a marriage between the German physiology of sensation and the British philosophy of empiricism and associationism.

Sense physiology of the first half of the nineteenth century thus furnished many of the origins of the new experimental psychology. There were first the independent discoveries by the Englishman Bell in 1811 and the Frenchman Magendie in 1822 that sensory nerves are different from motor nerves and that the nerves are not simply the passive conductors of a *vis nervosa*. There was Johannes Müller's promulgation in 1826 of the doctrine of specific nerve energies, the rule that sensory quality depends upon the particular nerves excited and not upon the transmission of the qualities of the stimuli. There was Ernst Heinrich Weber who in 1834 presented the evidence for what Fechner later named Weber's Law. There was Purkinje, the phenomenologist observer of visual phenomena, who was stimulated by Goethe in his study of color and whose name is now attached to some of the facts of night vision. There was Lotze, at heart a philosopher, who wrote a physiological psychology in 1852 and started the later controversy about the relation of space perception to learning. That, all in all, indicates the quality of the setting for the new psychology within physiology.

The philosophical setting was British *empiricism,* which later became *associationism.* It began with John Locke's insistence in 1690 that the mind is a piece of white paper on which experience writes, that understanding thus arises only by way of sensation. Bishop Berkeley came next in that tradition with his subjective idealism, his emphasis upon the idea as the immediate datum of experience. There followed the famous Hume, the less famous David Hartley, the Scottish philosophers, and then James Mill and his son, John Stuart Mill. With these men associationism grew up, the mental chemistry in which it is assumed that elementary ideas combine to form complex ideas and that perception, thought, and understanding are to be explained as due to the compounding of mental elements.[4]

The new experimental psychology was born about 1860. It was

in that year that Fechner published his psychophysics, the book that showed how sensation can be measured and that laid down the principal methods which still are used.[5] At the same time Helmholtz was interesting himself in psychological principles and in writing the basic handbooks on visual and auditory sensation.[6] Wundt was putting these results of Fechner's and Helmholtz' and other investigators' together into systematic form, naming the new field *physiological psychology,* and issuing the first general handbook and systematic text in 1874.[7]

All that is the movement which William James heard about in America. It is what turned him to physiology and psychology and made him the first medium of the introduction of the new psychology into America.

(2) Meanwhile in *England* there was Darwin. The philosophical psychologists—Bain, Spencer, Ward, and Stout—did not have much effect upon American psychology except indirectly, but Darwin did. The *Origin of Species* and the *Descent of Man* raised the problem of continuity between men and animals, and Darwin's *Expression of Emotion in Men and Animals* translated this problem to the level of mind. The brilliant and versatile Francis Galton, Darwin's cousin, took up the problem of mental inheritance in his *Hereditary Genius* of 1869, and then in his *Inquiries into Human Faculty* launched the study of individual differences in human capacity, a subject matter and an interest which affected American psychology profoundly. Galton was the originator of mental tests and of the statistical methods for dealing with the measurement of individual differences.[8]

England was also the scene of the beginnings of animal psychology. Romanes, stimulated by Darwin, undertook to study animal inheritance. He built up careful criteria for the evaluation of anecdotal material, but he was criticized by Lloyd Morgan who believed that Romanes credited the animals with too much intelligence, and who laid down his canon of parsimony, the rule that the attribution of mental capacity must be minimal for the behavior observed. It was these English beginnings that were taken over in the late 1890's by American animal psychology.

(3) American psychology really began with William James's interest in the new German movement, for it did not derive from the older American psychological interests.[9]

The year 1867 saw James in Berlin struggling with the decision as to whether to make a physiologist or a philosopher of himself.

He finally chose physiology—because he preferred philosophy. He mistrusted his own adequacy to so broad and difficult a field as philosophy. He might get, he thought, a safer corner within it if he chose the easier physiology and then cultivated physiological psychology as a scientific side door to philosophy. James had been training himself in science, aiming eventually at an M.D. The year before he had spent with Louis Agassiz on the Amazon and had learned to hate descriptive science. His mind was impatient of the isolated fact. He wanted the broader generalizations. So in 1867 in Berlin he was turning to physiology as something clearly within his intellectual means, something that could lead him through the new physiological psychology toward or even into philosophy.[10]

What actually did James know then about the new physiological psychology? Not much in 1867. He got hold of Lotze's *Medicinische Psychologie* of 1852 and read it. It is not clear that he knew Wundt's *Beiträge zur Theorie der Sinneswahrnehmung* of 1862, but he certainly knew Helmholtz' *Tonempfindungen* of 1863 and his *Physiologische Optik*, which had been coming out in parts since 1856. In the autumn of 1867 James wrote in a letter:

I have begun going to the physiological lectures [at the university of Berlin] . . . There is a bully physiological laboratory, the sight of which, inaccessible as it is to me in my present condition [his poor health], gave me a sharp pang. I have blocked out some reading in physiology and psychology which I hope to execute this winter. . . . It seems to me that perhaps the time has come for psychology to begin to be a science—some measurements have already been made in the region lying between the physical changes in the nerves and the appearance of consciousness-at (in the shape of sense perceptions), and more may come of it. Helmholtz and a man named Wundt at Heidelberg are working at it, and I hope I live through the winter to go to them in the summer.[11]

James did not, however, get to study at Heidelberg with Helmholtz and the man named Wundt. Instead he went home to nurse his health, to get his M.D. at Harvard in 1869, to be ill again, and then to accept appointment as instructor in anatomy and physiology at Harvard in 1872. He kept working the facts of physiological psychology into his lectures on physiology, and in 1875, when he first offered his course on physiological psychology, he actually had a two-room demonstrational laboratory set up, where his students performed some of the psychological experiments that were regarded as basic. James really started the new experimental movement in America, as Stanley Hall himself remarked in 1890 (although he took it back later on).[12]

All this is not to say that James was either the necessary or a sufficient cause for the appearance of the new psychology in America. He is more nearly a symptom of what was about to happen, the first measle that makes sense only later when the disease has been recognized. To find the idea of the importance of the new psychology growing in James's mind for reasons that lie deep in his own needs and personality is not to say that experimental psychology would not have come to America without James. It would. James shows merely how these infections start. The spread of interest in the 1880's was much too rapid to have been entirely dependent on promotion by James, who was by temperament anything but a promoter and who did not even get his all-important *Principles of Psychology* published until 1890. Without James the start would have been different, but it would have been made. The thesis of the present exegesis is that America took what it was ready for, that it took up with evolution and the new psychology for similar reasons and that the theory of evolution, as the more basic principle, affected American psychology.

In 1878 Stanley Hall got his Ph.D. in psychology from Harvard, the first Ph.D. in this field in America. James was, of course, on Hall's committee. The thesis work was done in the physiological laboratory of H. P. Bowditch. Hall "founded" the psychological laboratory at Johns Hopkins in 1883. Now let us see what happened in American psychology in the next decade, 1883–92.

Of books there was Dewey's *Psychology* in 1886, Ladd's *Elements of Physiological Psychology* in 1887, Baldwin's *Senses and Intellect* in 1889, James's *Principles* in 1890, and Baldwin's *Feeling and Will* in 1891.

Hall founded the *American Journal of Psychology* in 1887, the *Pedagogical Seminary* in 1891. Cattell and Baldwin started the *Psychological Review* in 1894, the *Psychological Monographs* and the *Psychological Index* a year later.

As to laboratories—there were a dozen of them by 1892: Harvard, Hopkins, Indiana, Wisconsin, Clark, Nebraska, Michigan, Iowa, Pennsylvania, Columbia, Cornell, Wellesley, in that order.[13]

What Americans had gone to Leipzig to study with Wundt? G. S. Hall, J. McK. Cattell, H. K. Wolfe, E. A. Pace, E. W. Scripture, Frank Angell, Lightner Witmer, Howard C. Warren, Harlow Gale, G. T. W. Patrick—all before 1894.[14] Titchener went from his native England to study with Wundt and then came to live in America and to influence it toward the fuller acceptance of the German model. James never studied with Wundt.

My point is that all this excitement of getting the new psychology under way in America in the 1880's and 1890's is not to be accounted for by any personal acts of James, nor by the older American tradition in psychology, nor even by the wave of interest in evolution, which helped indeed but was not alone a sufficient cause. America was ready for what the times had for it, and out of those materials, with the efforts of many men, it created something which was, in its emergent totality, unique—as unique as anything with causes and a history and a respectable number of anticipations ever is.

The adjectives that best apply to American psychology are *functional* and *practical*. James had a functional psychology. Dewey started the Chicago school of functional psychology. Columbia under Cattell went in for practical psychology, the mental tests, and what has been called a psychology of capacity. Baldwin and Stanley Hall were influenced directly by the theory of evolution, which is in itself a practical theory since it stresses individual differences and for the most part regards usefulness as a reason for development. This psychology, which had already emerged before the end of the nineteenth century, was not the psychology of Germany which the Americans had gone abroad to get.

It is almost true that American psychology was personified in the person of Cattell. His pattern was the American pattern. Cattell caught the spark of the new psychology from Lotze at Göttingen and Wundt at Leipzig in 1880–82. Then he came back to Hopkins to study psychology and had brief contact with Stanley Hall, newly arrived there to take charge. After that Cattell returned to Leipzig, brashly offering himself to Wundt as his assistant in what Wundt styled "ganz Amerikanisch" fashion. He took the Ph.D. with Wundt in 1886, presenting a thesis on reaction times in which he stressed the matter of individual differences. That is significant. Wundt did not approve of this innovation, but Cattell persisted and succeeded, as he often did later in life, in achieving a modified success in rebellion against authority. He returned to America, went to England to lecture at Cambridge where he got acquainted with Galton, coined the name *mental test* and wrote an article about the tests, sent Wundt a typewriter which may, indeed, have enhanced the already stupendous volume of his productivity, founded two psychological laboratories, the first at the University of Pennsylvania and the second, in 1891, at Columbia. At Columbia he got a testing program for the mental capacities of college students under way, and from there on his life proceeded along the same pattern of the practical hardheaded promotion of psychology with all its pedantries left out. He did not make American psychology what it is any more than James did. The forces that account for American psychology account for Cattell, as they account for James.[15]

What were these forces? That is difficult to say. The dynamics of historical causation are seldom sure. Concomitance so often looks like a cause. There can, however, be no doubt that the American character was direct, forceful, frank, democratic, and practical, assessing values in terms of usefulness. F. J. Turner suggested in 1893 that such a character has been generated by the fact that for three centuries America has had a movable western frontier with free land beyond it.[16] Every man is a king when he can own his own land, moving westward again when his domain becomes too circumscribed by the advent of other settlers. Thus democracy and equality of opportunity get themselves worked into the basic structure of the value system of the frontiersman, who, it is argued, furnished America with its creed. Equality of opportunity belongs, however, only to the strong, the resourceful, the practical, those men who can stand up in the struggle with nature for existence. The "hither edge of free land" was just disappearing, with the frontier completely gone, when American psychology was getting itself established. Is it absurd to perceive a connection? Was not Cattell really a frontiersman? Was not Stanley Hall a perpetual settler, clearing the land, building a cabin, and then moving on when the region got congested? Was not the American wave of laboratory foundings essentially a pioneer movement?[17]

John Dewey has noted that the psychology of individual differences flourishes in democracies.[18] That is right because the findings of a psychology of individual differences never support inherited class distinctions. America for seventy years has wanted a simple direct psychology, removed from the subtleties of metaphysics and epistemology and from the mystery of inner experience. It is a shirt-sleeve psychology that it has desired—and that it has, for the most part, had.[19]

Has all this anything to do with evolution? The pioneer's struggle for existence has certainly something to do with Darwinian theory. America was ready enough to fall in with the excitement about evolution in the final quarter of the nineteenth century, and psychology, developing in the American pattern, was quick to use the facts and principles of evolution. It was not merely that Baldwin and Hall could take the concept of mental evolution as a central theme in some of their most important work, for there were also more covert relations. Without evolutionary doctrine in the forefront of discussion, could James have appealed to *use* as an explanation of psychological functions? Can we possibly imagine a doctrine of special creation working just as well for him? And what would have become of Dewey's contribution, and the Chicago school, and eventually of pragmatism, without evolution? At the very least I think we can say that American psychology, in so far as it was functional and practical and pragmatic, used evolutionary principles to make itself work, and that all these values, belonging with the American character, helped conversely to make that character what it was—and is.[20]

WILLIAM JAMES

There is really not so much more to be said about James and evolution and his functional psychology. James, the physiologist, read Darwin. He admired him greatly as a pattern for a scientist. He accepted the Darwinian theory in part, as his treatment of instinct and emotion shows, but he was also critical of Darwin and did not go the whole way with him. As an evolutionist James was, nevertheless, more of a Darwinian than a Lamarckian. He thought naturally in terms of the use of mental functions as having survival value.

James was even better acquainted with Herbert Spencer. In 1875 he offered his course that was called "Physiological Psychology—Herbert Spencer's Principles of Psychology," and he continued it for many years. In 1879 and half a dozen times thereafter he offered "The Philosophy of Evolution," which used Spencer's *First Principles of Philosophy* as a text.[21]

Is James truly a functional psychologist? There is some room for argument about that matter. He thought of mind as useful to the person who owns it. Someone who analyzed his employment of the word function in his *Principles* found that he almost always meant *use* by it.[23] James was closely associated with Dewey in many ways, including the promotion of pragmatism, which is, one may say, "functional philosophy" in that it deals with truth in terms of consequences. James Angell picked up his functionalism from both James and Dewey. In any broad use of the term, James ought to count as the anticipator, or with Dewey the cofounder, of American functional psychology.

FUNCTIONAL PSYCHOLOGY

John Dewey's great influence has been due to the fact that he has been, for fifty years of effective propaganda, the philosopher of social change. Thinking men usually think about change, for the *status quo,* being already present, does not need thought. Thus Dewey has come to have great importance in the thoughts of many thinking men. He has been against laissez faire and things as they are. He has been for that progress which can be gained through the struggle of intelligence with reality. He has been against complacence, and pedantry, and formality, and for experiment, and use, and innovation. That value pattern shows clearly throughout his life. "Philosophy," he wrote, "recovers itself when it ceases to be a device for dealing with the problems of philosophers and becomes a method, cultivated by philosophers, for dealing with the problems of men." [23]

Was Dewey, we ask, influenced by the theory of evolution? Emphatically Yes. He lectured in 1909 on "The Influence of Darwin on Philosophy," showing how very great the influence had been and, in general, approving of it. There are, however, two different ways of being influenced by Darwinism. You can be impressed by the role of nature in natural selection, by the importance of chance, by the inability of acquired characteristics to effect permanent biological progress. Then you become a biological aristocrat and you are not John Dewey. Or you can see how the survival of the fittest means that use and functional practicality are basic to all progress, that struggle is fundamental in the nature of human life, that kings have no divine right because individual differences exist at random and nature rules by selection among them, and that in the end the aristocracy of chance which nature establishes can be overthrown by the effectiveness of social inheritance and social evolution. There you have a tempered Darwinism that is John Dewey.[24]

To his thinking about psychology Dewey brought the concept of functional use for the events of the mind, and thus, closely related to functional use, the notion of functional activity. The way to express this matter is to say that both consciousness and activity function *for* the organism—the use of consciousness is to produce activity which "saves" the organism. That is the essential tenet of the Chicago school of functional psychology which Dewey started, and which Angell carried on. In the doctrine of this school behavior and physiology and conscious states are mixed in with each other because they are unified, not by their essential natures, but by their common aim for the survival and use of the organism.

The Chicago school may be said to have been started by Dewey's paper, "The Reflex Arc Concept in Psychology," which he published in 1896.[25] Dewey argued that what we are interested in is coordinations, total reactions that are not properly reducible to a sum of reflex arcs, none of which in turn is properly reduced to a stimulus (as a first event), followed by a response (a later event), with perhaps a sensation intermediate between them. The stimulus immediately involves the response, and the response the stimulus, so the argument ran. A function is thus a coordination, an organism achieving an end. Purpose gives it unity, and functional psychology becomes the study of the organism in use. Functional psychology is thus practical through and through, in the way that Darwin's theory was the greatest practical theory of living that has ever been put forth.

After ten years at Chicago with Angell, Dewey went to Columbia in 1904, leaving Angell behind as the chief representative of the functional school. Angell did little more than explicate Dewey. He favored "the psychology of mental operations"—Dewey's coordinations. Thus, he said, psychology passes beyond the question "What?" (description) and finds itself answering the questions "How?" and "Why?" (function and use). For the most part, he said, functional psychology is "the psychology of the fundamental utilities of consciousness"—utilities in which mind is "primarily engaged in mediating between the environment and the needs of the organism." The function of the psychological act is "accommodatory service"; the function of consciousness is "accommodation to the novel," since consciousness tends to disappear in the presence of what is habitual.[26]

We must not, however, exaggerate the importance of evolutionary theory. It was not Darwin who discovered that the body's organs are useful to it, nor was Darwin the originator of the thought that the mind is an organ. Functional psychology has back of it, besides evolutionary theory, all of faculty psychology and also all of the specific analysis of mind into functions, faculties, capacities, and propensities by the phrenologists early in the nineteenth century.[27]

MENTAL EVOLUTION

The immediate effect of the doctrine of evolution upon psychology was in England. Galton, as we have noted, published *Hereditary Genius* in 1869, and it was followed shortly by Darwin's *Descent of Man* and *Expression of the Emotions in Man and Animals*. The doctrine of the evolution of mind was being put forward seriously and vigorously. Galton's book was impressive. He showed that men of great reputation and public distinction in Great Britain tend to be related, to come from the same families. His view that genius becomes recognized through reputation whatever the economic conditions to which it is born was not effectively criticized until much later.

Galton, as we have observed, found himself promoting the study of individual differences in human abilities, proposing to inventory the psychological capacities of the members of the British nation, inventing and advocating eugenics, and in general showing how to apply the consequences of the inheritance of mental abilities to practical affairs. Romanes' books on animal intelligence and mental evolution came out in 1882–88, and Lloyd Morgan expressed his interest in the problem in *Animal Life and Intelligence* and in other books. These were the three prominent men in England who were furthering interest in the psychological problems of evolution.[28]

Now who were the men who played the complementary role in America? Interest in evolution was spread broadly. James gave a course in the subject. Dewey founded a school that depended on it. James Mark Baldwin and Stanley Hall may, however, be singled out as the most vocal proponents of the application of the theory of evolution to mental capacities. Both men were prolific writers. Neither was a scientist in the sense that he spent his own time in the observation of natural phenomena. Each read what others had done, synthetized his reading and published the results in books. Hall was more the encylopedist, Baldwin more the egoistic theorizer.

It is difficult to estimate Baldwin's actual importance. He had a brilliant mind, a facile but not a stimulating pen, and a persistent drive. He was a very prominent man in the affairs of American psychology, and he also gained attention by his polemical vigor. Such things operated to get him considered and quoted while he was on the scene, but they did not gain for him any posthumous effect that is recognizable as important.

Baldwin published three books on evolution. The first was *Mental Development in the Child and the Race* (1895). The second appeared as *Social and Ethical Interpretations in Mental Development* (1897). Later there was *Development and Evolution* (1902). The second of these books may be regarded as an early social psychology which gave such importance to imitation as a principle of organic selection in social evolution that Baldwin is usually the standard reference for that now unpopular theory of social interaction.[29]

In general Baldwin, in common with H. F. Osborn and C. Lloyd Morgan, defended the theory which Baldwin named *organic selection*. That theory was psychological in that it brought consciousness and volition into the picture, for it held that organisms adapt themselves voluntarily to the needs that the environment lays upon them, and that these adaptive habits can be maintained through many generations until such time as chance variation gets the habits established as naturally inheritable characters, thus finally relieving the organism from responsibility for their maintenance. In this manner organic selection becomes a kind of social inheritance pro tempore, a social regenerator which preserves the Lamarckian principle through enough generations until the Darwinian principle can take over. It is clear that we are seeing here how the theory of evolution was to effect social psychology.

Baldwin advocated and expounded the theory of evolution. Stanley Hall assumed it and used it, somewhat speculatively, to give content and pattern to his broad theories. Hall sometimes said that his brand of psychology was "psychogenesis," and sometimes that it was "synthetic psychology." The synthetic method for Hall consisted of the encyclopedic marshaling of facts in the support of a single hypothesis. You see the result in Hall's books and articles and also in the papers published from his famous seminary. Hall was past master at guiding his students in ransacking the library for relevant facts that had never met each other before and in stimulating the students into the publication of their papers and also into a personal discipleship which lasted for many years. Underneath this use of the synthetic encyclopedic method there runs, however, the constant reiteration of the genetic theme. Mind comes from matter and man from his protozoic ancestors, and the life of man consists in the perpetual unfolding of his potential characteristics which turn out again and again to be the reverberations of the development of the race.[30]

Of himself Hall wrote:

As soon as I first heard it in my youth I think I must have been hypnotized by the word "evolution," which was music to my ear and seemed to fit my mouth better than any other. I cannot conceive why I seemed thus predisposed to an interest in everything that could be brought under that term. . . . I think my curiosity somehow got an early tilt toward origins, and even in college [1863–67] I brought much censure upon myself by advocating the view that man had sprung from apehood.

"I was bat-eyed," Hall added,

to the difficulties and impatient at objections, and had a blind spot in my mind for every break in the developmental order and implicit faith that if anywhere there seemed to be gaps it was only because we lacked adequate knowledge. Somehow, sometime it would be proved to the silencing of all doubters that all worlds and all in them developed very gradually and by an inner and unremitting impulsion from cosmic mist and nebulae—and perhaps even this would be resolved into something more primitive—while all religions, gods, heavens, immortalities, were made by mansoul, of which a perfect God was perhaps the noblest creation; that man sprang from primeval amoeba of which chemistry would sometime tell us the origin and perhaps be able to reproduce; that every human institution, organization, and even science itself were but the unfoldment of infantile impulses in man, the courses of which could be traced back to the very dawn of the psyche in the lowest forms of animal life; that spontaneous generation, although not proved, must somehow be true; that life had a chemical basis; and that even atoms, like Haeckel's plastidules, had souls of which the human psyche was only an aggregation.

It was that broad, bold, untechnical enthusiasm that made Hall so stimulating and that spread his influence so far. Evolution was basic in his concern, which embraced, nevertheless, many other fields. "There is a sense," he said, "in which all my active conscious life has been made up of a series of fads or crazes." The fads over-lapped one another, lapsed and recurred, but Hall's own list of them is as follows: (1) evolution, (2) experimental psychology, (3) animal life, habits, and instincts, (4) child study, (5) peda-gogy, (6) sex psychology, (7) food, appetite, and motivation, and (8) religious psychology. Only his excursion into experimental psy-chology and the founding of two laboratories took him away from his main interest in genetic psychology. It remained persistently the common bond. Someone once introduced him to an audience as "the Darwin of the mind," and he took great pleasure in a characterization which so nearly expressed his aspirations.

One gets, perhaps, the spirit of this evolutionary psychology best from Hall's seminary. There the doctrine of recapitulation, as developed by Haeckel and Spencer, was common gospel, and the psychic life of man was considered as containing constant rever-berations of his phylogenesis.[31]

Thus Quantz, writing from Hall's seminary in 1898 under the title "Dendro-psychoses," went into the matter of the effect of trees on man and the reverberations of the arboreal life of his ancestors that are still to be observed. "The climbing power of infants," he wrote,

often surpasses that of adults, and goes to show that our ancestors were tree-dwellers and that the children clung to their mother whose hands were occupied in climbing from branch to branch. Young apes, as a rule, hang beneath their mothers, holding on by the long hair of their shoulders and sides. Those that failed to do this would tumble to the ground or be left behind and fall a prey to enemies from which the mothers were fleeing. Hence, natural selection would bring about a high degree of this climbing power. . . . Even the reflex act of grasping an object which touches the palm can be of no value to the child now, except to point to a former period when life itself depended on it. . . . In the use of its hands the baby shows a kinship to tree-climbers. In grasping an object it does not put the thumb on the opposite side, but takes the object between the fingers and the palm. Arboreal ancestors in going from bough to bough would strike the branches palm first from above downward, grasping with the fingers. . . . Putting babies to sleep by rocking is probably taking advantage of a rhythm which has become ingrained through long ages of swaying in the branches of trees. . . . The fear of falling is instinctive, as it is found in children who have had no individual experience to justify it. . . . Such fears of falling (barophobia), as well as the child's "monkey-like propensity to climb everything everywhere," may be reverberations from different stages of a life in which climbing and falling were daily experiences.

And so on through many pages.[32]

Similarly F. E. Bolton from the same seminary reported on "Hydro-psychoses," showing how man recapitulates some of the aquatic phases of the evolutionary series and that there are to be found pelagic reverberations in his mental life.[33]

There is thus no question about the profound effect of the theories of evolution upon the psychology of the Clark school. How influential was the school? Hall himself made disciples who remained loyal throughout their lives. On the other hand, Hall's loose speculation, his dictum "Build the top of the mountain first," antagonized the experimentalists. He influenced pedagogy more than he influenced the new psychology. Nevertheless, both he and Baldwin were symptoms of what was new in the new psychology, and functionalism was favored by the fact that the irrepressible Hall and the irrepressible Baldwin were both for it.

INDIVIDUAL DIFFERENCES

There is no doubt that the theory of evolution furnished support and re-enforcement for a psychology of individual differences. There is also no doubt that the interest in evolution was not a necessary condition for the growth of a psychology of individual differences. One finds the roots of this development in the faculty psychology of the Scottish philosophers. They influenced the thinking of the French psychologists, and thus share some responsibility for the way in which Binet and Henri and others, like Ribot, found themselves concerned with individual capacities. The Scottish school also influenced Gall and his phrenology, which was another movement for assessing individual differences, one that originally centered in France.[34] Long before evolution was a popular theory or Darwin had written the *Origin of Species,* phrenology was spreading to England and America because of its personal appeal. If you can really know something personal about each of your fellows by merely observing his appearance, then you will have suddenly gained a certain security against the adventitious complexities of the social world which is so full of personal surprises.[35]

On the other hand, it is quite clear that it was a belief in Darwinian theory which led Galton to his interest in individual dif-

ferences in human capacity. Beginning with the inheritance of
genius, he came presently to his attempts to assess and inventory
human abilities. He invented various anthropometric tests, tests
of sensory capacity, of reaction time, of memory span, and of
imagery, and he actually arranged to have a laboratory where the
public could take these tests for threepence and learn what their
capacities were. Nine thousand three hundred thirty-seven persons took the tests, but if Galton had not thought that these individual differences are inherited, he would not have bothered with
them.[36]

Galton's concern with individual differences dates from the early
1870's. Cattell's dates from the early 1880's, for by 1886 he had
managed to recast his doctoral thesis with Wundt, the thesis on
reaction times, into a study of individual differences. In 1890
Cattell wrote an article, "Mental Tests and Measurements," the
article in which he coined the term *mental test*. Galton added an
approving note to the article, which gave the specifications for ten
tests of abilities and made suggestions for about fifty more. By
1893 Cattell was advocating the giving of these tests in schools.
By 1896 he was publishing results on the mental testing of Columbia students. Cattell more than any one other person was in this
fashion responsible for getting mental testing under way in
America, and it is plain that his motivation was similar to Galton's
and that he was also influenced, or at least re-enforced, by Galton.[37] Presumably the theory of evolution determined Cattell less
than did the spirit of hardheaded American common sense, but
all these things are wrapped up together. Later it was the existence of the tests that raised again the nature-nurture problem
which Galton had posed.

Meanwhile in France Binet and Henri were developing tests of
a more intellectual character and argued in 1896 for an individual
psychology.[38] Galton's and Cattell's tests had measured simple
sensory or motor capacities, or else other simple faculties like
memory span and imaginal type. Binet and Henri turned to the
more intellectual and verbal capacities. It was for a while a question as to which kind of test was going to differentiate people better in respect of scholastic capacities and the achievements of
genius. Stella Sharp, an American, reviewed the situation in 1899
and decided in favor of the tests of the "complex" or "higher"
capacities, and she was right.[39] We all know how after 1900 the
Binet tests supplanted Galton's and Cattell's tests, how the Binet

scale came into use as a measure of what Binet called "intelligence." [40]

The choice of the intellectual and verbal skills over the sensory and motor capacities was in no conscious sense related to beliefs about evolution. The choice was made because it worked better, but, once made, it was found that the Binet scale of "intelligence" had significance for the problem of mental inheritance. Thus the question came back into association with the interest in evolution. The nature-nurture problem is, however, a matter which we must defer for later consideration.

Although Cattell did not establish intelligence tests, he did put firmly into the American scene a psychology of capacity, at it may be called. The tests tested human *faculties, capacities, abilities.* Nowadays we say they test *abilities* and *aptitudes.* A capacity, as tested, turns out to be pretty much the ability to compete in the civilized struggle for existence—the kind of personal characteristics which Americans seemed to find especially interesting. There is thus, via Cattell, a Columbia tradition which can not be separated from the main American faith.

ANIMAL PSYCHOLOGY

It was the Darwinian theory that gave animal psychology its start. Before Darwin common sense tended to accept a view that was not unlike Descartes' and that actually owed a great deal to him. Descartes had held that the animals are automata, that their bodies are machines, whereas man has a rational soul which interacts with his body at a specified point in his brain. That is the Cartesian dualism of mind and body. Body is extended substance, but mind is unextended, not occupying space. The two are discrete and there are no intermediates between them, no substances that are as much like mind as they are like matter.

Actually this dualism represents the influence of seventeenth-century theology upon Descartes, an influence abetted by language. *L'âme* in French means both *mind* and *soul,* as does *Seele* in German. That confusion and the Cartesian dictum together made it impossible clearly to distinguish the properties of the mind from the properties of the soul. When people thought of the soul as immortal, they thought actually of mind or consciousness which continued after death without a body. Theology, asserting the truth of immortality for man and denying it for animals, was declaring that men have souls and that animals have none. We have to go only one step farther and identify man's soul with his conscious mind, in order to follow Descartes in denying a conscious mind to animals.

The Darwinian theory, on the contrary, asserted the existence of continuity between man and animals, continuity in all respects, mental as well as physical, since man is believed to be derived from animals by continuous change. We have already noted how Darwin and Romanes and Lloyd Morgan attacked the problem of the mental evolution of animals to man.[41]

G. J. Romanes wrote three important books, intended to support the thesis that intelligence is continuous between the animals and man. The first, which displayed the data, he called a *comparative psychology,* using that term for the first time. For collecting evidence, he adopted a carefully safeguarded anecdotal method, protecting himself against the exaggerations of anecdote by an application of rigorous criteria of evidence. He was anxious, of course, to find as much manlike intelligence in animals as possible, and he had to beware of his own bias. Romanes lacked for his descriptions, however, a good classification of mental states, but he concluded that all animals and man can have "simple ideas," that "complex ideas" are limited to the higher animals and man, and that abstract or "notional ideas" are "the unique prerogative of man." This was a conclusion that furthered the concept of continuity while leaving man the foremost of God's creatures.[42]

It was Lloyd Morgan who in 1894 applied to Romanes' interpretations a principle of parsimony, which afterward came to be called Lloyd Morgan's Canon. "In no case," he said, "may we interpret an action as the outcome of a higher psychical faculty, if it can be interpreted as the exercise of one which stands lower in the psychological scale." Romanes, anxious to prove the Darwinian theory, attributed to animals as much intelligence as their acts would justify. Lloyd Morgan was holding that one should, in such a situation, attribute as little intelligence as their acts would justify.[43] After Lloyd Morgan, caution in anthropomorphizing the animal consciousness became standard in comparative psychology.

Lloyd Morgan's caution was re-enforced by Loeb's theory of the tropism, which was offered to the world at the same time. Loeb had little difficulty in convincing the readers of his paper that plants and protozoa are virtually Cartesian automata in their responses to stimulation. If tropistic action is determined entirely by physicochemical forces, it may therefore be supposed to be independent of volition or reason. No more than Descartes did Loeb think, however, that men are mere automata, governed only by unconscious tropisms. He sought, rather, to establish the point in the evolutionary scale at which consciousness emerges, and concluded that the existence of associative memory, the ability of an organism to profit by experience, demonstrates the emergence of mind.[44] Since the higher vertebrates obviously possess associative memory, the effect of Loeb's argument was to preserve a dualism, but to shift the critical point of separation lower down in the evolutionary scale. Men and dogs are conscious, protozoa and plants are not.[45] Such a view supports the Darwinian theory because it fills in the "missing link" between man and the animals.

About the time that Loeb's theory of tropisms was becoming well known, Jennings in America published a monograph describing the psychic life of the protozoa. Ignoring Lloyd Morgan's Canon but confining himself to the careful experimental observation of the behavior of protozoa, he was able to build up a convincing case for protozoic consciousness.[46] Later, when it was found that Paramecium could be taught to modify his behavior, it looked as if even Loeb's criterion of consciousness had been met at the very bottom of the animal scale.[47]

The result of this argument about the point of emergence of mind in the evolutionary series, an argument beginning with Romanes in 1882 and culminating with Jennings in 1904, was to make it appear that, if you start with man and work down, you will still be observing consciousness in the protozoa when you get to them, but that, if you start with the micro-organisms and work up, then you will find tropistic considerations adequate and fit, and there will be no point in the series at which there will be any such change as will lead you to assert that man himself is not governed entirely by physicochemical laws. This sort of dualism is not Cartesian. It is a Leibnitzian parallelism. You can regard everything as conscious or as unconscious, as you choose.

Now it was this controversy about Darwinian continuity that got comparative psychology started. Comparative psychology could have begun without the theory of evolution, for there have always been persons interested in animal behavior. Mere interest in animal abilities would not, however, have led to the systematic comparison that was required in the search for breaks in the continuity of the scale, nor would it easily have resulted in the cautious kind of observation that Morgan's Canon and Loeb's tropistic hypothesis entailed. It seems quite likely that, without the excitement over the theory of evolution, animal psychology would not have gotten so good a start so soon.

Once the comparative description of animal behavior was established as proper scientific procedure, it tended to perpetuate itself. Most of the comparative work in animal psychology has consisted of sampling abilities at successive levels of the evolutionary scale. Yerkes, for instance, worked on the worm, the crab, the turtle, the frog, the mouse, the rat, the crow, the dove, the pig, the monkey, the chimpanzee, and man. It was the scheme of evolution, not mere catholicity of interest, that determined him.[48]

OBJECTIVE PSYCHOLOGY

The tendency to regard the human body as a machine, affected by and affecting the external world, but independent of mind, consciousness, and will, is very old. The French psychologists liked to think in such terms. La Mettrie in 1748 wrote *L'Homme machine* to demonstrate that point of view. If Descartes could argue that animals are automata, others could certainly extend the principle to man.

Psychological objectivism was also promoted in the eighteenth century by the scientific study of reflex action. The term reflex was itself invented to indicate that action in response to stimulation may occur because the incoming animal spirits are "reflected" by the columns of the spinal cord out along certain motor paths. Robert Whytt showed in 1751 that some purposive action depends only on the functioning of a segment of the spinal cord and occurs in a decapitated animal without a brain. Since the brain has generally been supposed to be the organ of mind, reflex action is usually regarded as unconscious and therefore automatic. In the middle of the nineteenth century, however, there arose an interesting argument between the physiologist Pflüger and the philosopher-psychologist Lotze. Pflüger argued that consciousness is associated with the action of nervous tissue and that the reflexes must therefore be conscious, as indeed appears from their purposive nature. Lotze held that consciousness depends upon the brain and that the reflexes, being incapable of modification to fit special situations, are obviously unconscious. In this argument Lotze was playing the role of Loeb, and Pflüger the role of Jennings, for the reflex like the tropism can be regarded either as physiological mechanics or as evidence of conscious purposiveness.[49]

The Loeb-Jennings argument prepared the way for J. B. Watson's behaviorism of 1913. Watson, concerned primarily with the psychology of animals and of children, realized that the primary data of observation are always items of behavior—movements or secretions—and that these responses are in themselves evidences of the abilities of an organism to react discriminatively to its environment. Why bother, Watson asked, to reason out what consciousness is like, when the organism's capacity to accommodate itself to its environment is the principle point of interest? So Watson boldly proposed that psychology ignore consciousness and deal directly with human capacity as indicated by accommodatory behavior. That was behaviorism, a psychology of stimulus and response.[50]

Was Watson influenced by the theory of evolution? Not directly. He could, however, gain acceptance for his view because it was consistent with the American faith. Behaviorism (Watson to the contrary notwithstanding) was a form of Dewey's functional psychology and of Cattell's capacity psychology, the American psychology of the abilities of men as measured by their adaptive or discriminatory performances. Watson's view was essentially American, a psychology consistent with the belief in necessity of struggle for survival.

Behaviorism was itself too unsophisticated to last. It has now given place to positivism or operationism or whatever one prefers to call the newest psychological objectivism. The operationist argues that all the data of psychology, including the data of consciousness, are to be defined by the operations which are used to observe them. You can know nothing more about mind than you can find in the evidence for the existence of mind. This movement gets its sophistication from the logical positivism of the Vienna Circle and from the operational physics of P. W. Bridgman, but this is not the place for its full consideration. It is sufficient here to point out that the epistemology of operationism was already implicit in the faiths of behaviorism, functional psychology and capacity psychology, the basic American psychological faith.[51]

NATURE *VERSUS* NURTURE

Nowhere is the contrast between the once new psychology of Germany and the still newer version in America more striking than in respect of the importance assigned to the problem of mental inheritance. The Germans in the days of German greatness in psychology were attempting the complete description of the generalized normal human mind. They were concerned with its immediate physiological basis, but not at all with its biological origin. The Americans, on the other hand, were led by their interest in individual differences to consider seriously the origins of the differences, whether they lay in ancestry or in education. The theory of evolution posed for them one of their most important problems.

This interest began, as we have already seen, with Galton's *Hereditary Genius* of 1869 and his other books during the next two decades. He coined the catch phrase "nature and nurture" in 1874. He published his study of the psychological resemblances of twins in 1876. In 1877 Dugdale described the Jukes, a family in which mental deficiency predominated through several generations. By the end of the century it was pretty generally accepted that genius and imbecility are both inherited and that heredity works for mediocrity too.

At the beginning of the present century the study of biological inheritance was greatly stimulated by the finding of Mendel's laws of inheritance which had been overlooked for almost forty years. The study of genetics then became exceedingly active among the biologists, and everyone was looking for inheritable unit characters.[52] When Goddard published in 1912 his account of the Kallikak family, showing the inheritance of feeble-mindedness through six generations after it had once been introduced into a "normal" strain, it seemed for the time being as if Galton's case had been proved.[53] There were various books on eugenics in the second decade of the century, all published with the intention that the human stock should be biologically improved by selective parenthood.[54]

At the same time the intelligence tests were getting established. Binet's first scale of intelligence came out in 1905, a scale which implies the growth of intelligence with age, thus assuming that intelligence is biologically determined. It was possible to figure a mental age, and in 1911 Stern suggested that the effect of maturation be eliminated by taking the intelligence quotient, the ratio of the mental age to the chronological age. After the Stanford revision of the Binet scale in 1916, it was customary to expect the IQ to remain approximately constant during the growth of a child. That approximation was taken to mean that the IQ is unalterable, congenital, and therefore inherited.[55]

During the next two decades the role of learning in human abilities was recognized more and more. From the outside there was social pressure, for persons with a liberal political philosophy did not like a doctrine that established an aristocracy, even an aristocracy of brains. Democracy required that nurture should be able to prevail over nature. The IQ turned out to be not so constant as had been at first supposed. Intelligence continued to be indefinable, and no one succeeded in making up international and intercultural intelligence tests that would really test out national or racial differences, without dependence on cultural difference. It became increasingly clear that economic status affects intelligence as the tests test it, perhaps because it affects educational status which is in turn reflected in the types of skills required in the tests. At any rate intelligence tests were suspect of being dependent more upon verbal ability than upon a general factor common to all abilities.[56] The new methods of factor analysis favored the reduction of human abilities to many rather than a few factors. By the time of the second World War psychologists were ready to deal with learned abilities and with the aptitudes for learning the abilities. The aptitudes might be native but they too might have been learned. All in all intelligence from 1920 to 1945 might be said to have been on the way out; yet intelligence had furnished the strongest argument for native mental ability.

On the other hand, the role of nature was becoming clearer. Comparative psychology showed that instinctual behavior occurs in many animals without learning, even though practice may improve its adaptive character. The startle reflex for sudden loud sounds was analyzed in man and found to be fixed and involuntary.[57] Mental Mendelian characters did not turn up, except perhaps color blindness which is said to be inheritable and sex linked. The study of twins began to show how both nature and nurture perpetually operate concurrently. Are identical twins, when brought up in different socioeconomic circumstances, more or less alike than fraternal twins brought up under the same circumstances? Whether nature or nurture appears stronger in a given case depends on what the tests are, but no other two people are likely to be so similar as identical twins brought up under the same circumstances.[58]

The logic of the situation, moreover, required a belief in the concurrent action of nature and nurture. A child can learn to walk provided he has inherited legs to walk on. He can learn to multiply provided he has inherited the brain to do it with, as indeed some feeble-minded children have not.[59] Heredity works mostly, however, at the level of aptitudes and not at the level of finished abilities. That is because maturation is working. Aptitudes are forming as a consequence of general development of the child or young animal, and practice, while necessary, becomes more and more effective as the aptitude develops. One twin, as he develops, is given climbing apparatus, while the other is deprived of it. When the two are put together with the same opportunities to climb, the practiced twin does better at first. Soon, however, the other twin catches up. His aptitude had matured without practice and he learns quickly because he is now old enough.[60]

The nature-nurture literature is large, and the details of how much of human ability comes from heredity through the chromosomes and how much through cultural influence, education, and practice do not concern us. The fact is that the original problem which evolutionary theory set—the problem as to whether mind is inherited—is answered. In part, mind is inherited. There are few complex abilities of social importance that do not depend both upon adaptive learning and upon the inheritance of the organs or aptitudes that are essential for the learning. Mental inheritance does not, however, seem so strange as it did a hundred years ago, for nowadays everyone realizes that the mind is for the most part the way the nervous system functions, and not an unextended Cartesian substance that may prove to be immortal after it has lost its body. The growth of objectivism and the decline of mentalism in psychology has in itself been an answer to the question of biological and psychological continuity between animals and man. Evolution favors continuity and unity, just as objectivism favors the unity of the sciences.

THE CASE

We can now review the case for the importance of the influence of evolutionary thought on the development of American psychology. Such historical causation is not easy to validate or to assess.

The adult character of American psychology was formed in its youth, in the last quarter of the nineteenth century, when James and Hall and Baldwin and Cattell were building something new, based on what was going on in Germany and in England. The paternal ancestry of American psychology is German psychology, but the maternal ancestors are the biology and psychology of England. The child was, moreover, greatly influenced by the environment in which it grew up. Its nurture determined how its nature should realize itself.

The formative environment was the American temperament of the late nineteenth century. A rough, crude, frank, aggressive, practical, boastful nation America was. The Europeans found us ambitious, self-assured, direct, and unpolished. Our diplomacy had only just passed the shirt-sleeve stage. A psychologist can see in American boastfulness some ambivalence, a self-assertion based on insecurity, like whistling in the dark. Certainly the psychologists of that period had no thought that a new insight resided in them. They were looking to Germany for the best and newest, and trying to see that America did as well or better. They seemed scarcely aware of the fact that, in taking over German psychology, they were remaking it along American lines. To read Cattell's early propaganda for the mental tests, you would think that the mental tests were just a product of experimental psychology, and that America was supporting the Leipzig tradition in finding a use for its devices of mental measurement.[61] In a sense Cattell was right on this matter and Germany did contribute what America applied. There is a clear inheritance here. But America presently did much more than apply experimental psychology to human problems. It changed the whole German intent as to the purpose and significance of psychology.

This view of the American temperament is consistent with the various delineations that have been made since Turner, the historian, first undertook to explain the American character as appropriate to the pioneer, the pioneer who understands that there is ahead of him a perpetually retreating frontier beyond which there is opportunity for those strong enough to take it.[62]

The pioneer struggles to wrest from nature first his living and then his comforts. Natural selection and the survival of the fittest color his daily thoughts. It is no surprise, then, that America should have taken readily to evolutionary theory, nor that it should mold its thinking on many topics with respect to survival and success by means of the concepts of accommodation and adaptation.

When we find that American psychology has been predominantly the *functional* psychology of Dewey and the Chicago school and also the *capacity psychology* of Cattell and the mental tests, are we then to say that American psychology is founded upon the practicality of the American temperament or the adaptative principle of the theory of evolution? Plainly it is founded on both. Seemingly neither was a necessary condition. Conceivably either alone might be a sufficient reason for American psychology, but we can never tell since neither of the two occurred alone. Certainly the two forces were summative, and an American psychology of practical adjustment of the organism to the requirements of living was the necessary consequence.

The explicitly *evolutionary psychology* of Baldwin and of Stanley Hall must be regarded as contributory to the basic trend rather than essential in it. These prolific writers were constantly advertising the importance of evolution. Basic effective motivation generally lies deep, in a man or in a historical movement, but basic motivation can nevertheless be re-enforced by superficial conscious resolve. Baldwin and Hall were like the voice of consciousness, reiterating the importance of evolutionary theory for American psychology, which was already quietly taking account of the fundamental principles of biological adaptation for reasons less obvious than Baldwin and Hall brought forth.

Comparative psychology was a separate trend. It got under way definitely in an attempt to answer the question about the continuity of mind from animals to man, a question that Darwinian theory posed. Even for it, evolution can hardly be supposed to have been a necessary condition, for comparative interest in animal behavior occurs independently of concern with the theory of evolution. Nevertheless the fact is that animal psychology got its start in answering this Darwinian question, and that animal psychology got away from the question to stand on its own feet only later when the question had, in a sense, been answered.

In terms of the Hegelian dialectic the thesis had been that men have souls (hence consciousness, hence minds) and animals have not. The antithesis was that mind is continuous from animals to man. The synthesis was that mind and mechanism represent but different points of view toward the same material, that from above downward you see mind extending indefinitely into the animal scale, that from below upward you see that mechanism is essential to mind in man.[63] This solution of the evolutionary problem in comparative psychology, therefore, opened the way for the *objective psychologies* of behaviorism and operationism, which in turn found themselves re-enforced by the prevailing American psychology of function and capacity. Operationism, moreover, has turned out to be essentially a form of pragmatism,[64] which through Dewey and James is closely related to functional psychology and to the American pioneer temperament. Thus it appears that at least three different lines of development (through the tropism, through functionalism, through pragmatism) converge upon modern American objectivism, and that evolution can thus be shown to hold an important position in the development of this system, although it is not a *sine qua non* of operationism.

In brief, then, it can be said that there is an American psychology. Individual psychologists in America hold to the central core with greater or less deviation. In the land of the free, personal predilections count. The central core is, however, the thesis that mind is of use to the organism, or, in more general and modern terms, that it is with the adaptations of the organism to the exigencies of living that psychology is concerned. The proven value of psychology to national survival in the second World War is evidence as to how much American psychology involves use of the Darwinian principle.

NOTES

Antecedents and Beginnings

1. E. W. Scripture, *The New Psychology* (New York, Scribner, 1897).

2. On the nature of American psychology see E. G. Boring, *A History of Experimental Psychology* (2d ed. New York, Appleton-Century-Croft, 1950), pp. 505–583, 620–663, 693–734. To cite the 1950 edition of this book is an anachronism, for the present paper was written in 1946, and the revision of the book profited greatly by being able to draw upon the paper, whereas the paper had only the first edition of the book to which it could go. Hereinafter this book will be referred to as HEP. See also R. S. Woodworth, *Contemporary Schools of Psychology* (2d ed. New York, Ronald, 1948), especially pp. 11–36; G. Murphy, *Historical Introduction to Modern Psychology* (2d ed. New York, Harcourt, Brace, 1949), pp. 192–224, 234–283.

3. On the nature of German psychology see Boring, HEP, pp. 275–456; Murphy, *op. cit.*, pp. 79–102, 146–187; J. C. Flugel, *A Hundred Years of Psychology* (New York, Macmillan, 1933), pp. 144–214.

4. On British empiricism and associationism see Boring, HEP, *loc. cit.,* and pp. 168–202, 219–245.

5. On Fechner, *ibid.,* pp. 275–296.

6. On Helmholtz, *ibid.,* pp. 297–315.

7. On Wundt, *ibid.,* pp. 316–347.

8. On modern British psychology in general, see *ibid.,* pp. 459–502; also Murphy, *op. cit.,* pp. 99–126.

9. J. W. Fay, *American Psychology before William James* (New Brunswick, N. J., Rutgers University Press, 1939), complains that these early American psychologists are as important as the more recent ones and that their neglect is unjustified. They were not, however, functionally important, not if their importance is properly measured by their posthumous effects.

10. On James in 1867–90 see R. B. Perry, *The Thought and Character of William James* (Boston, Little, Brown, 1935), II, 3–50.

11. Henry James, *The Letters of William James* (Boston, Little, Brown, 1920), I, 118 f.; also Perry, *op. cit.*, II, 3.

12. On the controversy between James and Hall as to their professional priorities see Perry, *op. cit.*, pp. 6–10, 22 f. On James's early laboratory see R. S. Harper, "The Laboratory of William James," *Harvard Alumni Bull.*, 52 (1949), 169–173. Wundt also had a demonstrational laboratory at Leipzig as early as 1875; see Boring, HEP, pp. 323 f.

13. On the wave of laboratory founding in the United States see C. A. Ruckmick, "The History and Status of Psychology in the United States," *Amer. Jour. Psychol.*, 23 (1912), 517–531, especially p. 520.

14. On Wundt's American students see Boring, HEP, p. 347; Flugel, *op. cit.*, pp. 206–214.

15. On Cattell see Boring, HEP, pp. 532–540, 548 f.

16. On the effect of the free frontier on American character, see F. J. Turner, *The Frontier in American History* (New York, Holt, 1920), which reprints the famous original paper of 1893 (pp. 1–38) and other later essays on related topics. This general topic has now received discussion in Boring, HEP, pp. 8 f., 506–508.

17. On the American Creed and an analysis of it that differs from Turner's see G. Myrdal, *An American Dilemma* (New York, Harper, 1944), pp. 3–25.

18. On the way in which a democratic society favors a psychology of individual differences see J. Dewey, *Psychology and Philosophic Method* (Berkeley, University of California Press, 1899), 21 f.; cf. also his "The Need for Social Psychology," *Psychol. Rev.*, 24 (1917), 266–277, especially p. 273.

19. On the way in which the American character has led to psychologies of capacity, behavior, and physicalistic operations see G. W. Allport, "The Psychology of Participation," *Psychol. Rev.*, 53 (1945), 117–132, especially pp. 117–119; Boring, HEP, pp. 641–658.

20. It has been said that English science tends to be practical, like American, and that Newton and Maxwell (a Scot) were exceptions in their having theoretical breadth: J. D. Bernal, *The Social Function of Science* (New York, Macmillan, 1939), p. 197. That view makes Darwin appropriate to England, but implies that Darwin plus the practicality of a democracy are not alone a sufficient cause for the sudden growth of an applied psychology—for the reason that applied psychology thrived in America while it was starving in England. America had what England had not, a pioneer spirit and a readiness for shirt-sleeve science.

James

21. On James and Darwin and on James and Spencer see Perry, *op. cit.*, I, 468–470, 482; Harper, *loc. cit.*

22. On James's use of the word *function* see C. A. Ruckmick, "The Use of the Term Function in English Textbooks of Psychology," *Amer. Jour. Psychol.*, 24 (1913), 99–123, especially p. 111.

Functional Psychology

23. On Dewey and functional psychology see Boring, HEP, pp. 552–556, 578 f.; E. Heidbreder, *Seven Psychologies* (New York, Appleton-Century, 1933), pp. 201–233. On Dewey's philosophy and functional orientation see *The Philosophy of John Dewey* ed. by J. Ratner (New York, Holt, 1928); *Intelligence in the Modern World: John Dewey's Philosophy* (New York, Modern Library, 1939).

24. On Dewey and Darwinism see John Dewey, *The Influence of Darwin on Philosophy and Other Essays* (New York, Holt, 1910), especially pp. 1–10. The conception of special creation is essentially aristocratic because it gives divine rights to species; relative to it the theory of evolution is democratic, even though evolutionary change is slow and difficult.

25. The famous paper that started the ball rolling for the Chicago school is J. Dewey's "The Reflex Arc Concept in Psychology," *Psychol. Rev., 3* (1896), 357–370.

26. On Angell and functional psychology see Boring, HEP, pp. 556–558, 579; Heidbreder, *loc. cit.* The presidential address is J. R. Angell, "The Province of Functional Psychology," *Psychol. Rev., 14* (1907), 61–91. See also W. S. Hunter, "James Rowland Angell, 1869–1949," *Amer. Jour. Psychol., 62* (1949), 439–450. The standard textbook of functional psychology is Angell, *Psychology,* 1904 and later editions; see especially chap. iv on attention. For an analysis of functional systems of psychology in their accommodatory and teleological character see E. B. Titchener, *Systematic Psychology: Prolegomena* (New York, Macmillan, 1929), 158–193, especially pp. 177–193.

27. On the relation of functional psychology to phrenology see K. M. Dallenbach, "The History and Derivation of the Word 'Function' as a Systematic Term in Psychology," *Amer. Jour. Psychol., 26* (1915), 473–484. On the dependence of phrenology on the faculty psychology of the Scottish school see H. D. Spoerl, "Faculties vs. Traits: Gall's Solution," *Character and Pers., 4* (1936), 216–231.

Mental Evolution

28. On the effect of the theory of evolution on psychology in England see G. Murphy, *An Historical Introduction to Modern Psychology* (1929), pp. 111–126.

29. On Baldwin see Boring, HEP, pp. 528–532, 547 f. For negative criticisms of Baldwin's predilection for theorizing in the absence of facts see T. L. Bolton's review of the 1895 book, in *Amer. Jour. Psychol., 7* (1895), 142–145; M. F. Washburn, necrology of Baldwin, *ibid., 47* (1935), 168 f.

30. On Hall and his relation to the theory of evolution see G. S. Hall, *Life and Confessions of a Psychologist* (New York, Appleton, 1923), especially pp. 357–367, from which the quotations in the text are taken. See also S. C. Fisher, "The Psychological and Educational Work of Granvillé Stanley Hall," *Amer. Jour. Psychol., 36* (1925), 1–52, especially pp. 20–26; also Hall, "A Glance at the Phyletic Background of Genetic Psychology," *ibid., 19* (1908), 149–212. In general on Hall see Boring, HEP, pp. 517–524, and the commentaries and biographies cited on pp. 545 f.

31. On recapitulation see Fisher, *op. cit.,* pp. 22–24.

32. On the arboreal reverberations see J. O. Quantz, "Dendro-psychoses," *Amer. Jour. Psychol., 9* (1898), 449–506, especially pp. 450–467.

33. On the aquatic reverberations see F. E. Bolton, "Hydro-psychoses," *ibid., 10* (1899), 169–237, especially pp. 170–186.

Individual Differences

34. On phrenology, Scottish faculties, and functional psychology see Dallenbach and Spoerl, *locc. citt.,* n. 27 *supra;* M. Bentley, "The Psychological Antecedents of Phrenology," *Psychol. Monogr., 21,* No. 92 (1916), 102–115. On phrenology see Boring, HEP, pp. 50–60.

35. The popular appeal of phrenology has recently had its analogue in Sheldon's somatotypy, W. H. Sheldon et al., *The Varieties of Human Physique* (New York, Harper, 1940); *The Varieties of Temperament* (New York, Harper, 1942). Life becomes more interesting than usual if you can quickly assess the temperament of friends and strangers by estimating their constitutional types in respect of endomorphy, mesomorphy, and ectomorphy.

36. On Galton see Boring, HEP, pp. 476–488, 500 f., and references there cited.

37. On Cattell see Boring, HEP, pp. 532–540, 548 f., and references there cited. The articles mentioned in the text are: J. McK. Cattell, "Mental Tests and Measurements," *Mind, 15* (1890), 373–380; "Tests of the Senses and Faculties," *Educ. Rev., 5* (1893), 285–293; with L. Farrand, "Physical and Mental Measurements of the Students of Columbia University," *Psychol. Rev., 3* (1896), 618–648.

38. The important early paper in the French movement toward tests is A. Binet and

V. Henri, "La Psychologie individuelle," *L'année psychol.*, 2 (1896), 411–465. For their other papers see Peterson, *op. cit., infra.*

39. The early American reaction against Cattell is S. E. Sharp, "Individual Psychology: a Study in Psychology Method," *Amer. Jour. Psychol., 10* (1899), 329–391.

40. On the history of mental testing see J. Peterson, *Early Conceptions and Tests of Intelligence* (Yonkers, World Book, 1925), bibliography of 242 titles; Boring, HEP, pp. 570–578, 581–583.

Animal Psychology

41. On the development of animal psychology in general see Boring, HEP, pp. 472–476, 498, 622–631, 659 f.

42. On Romanes see Boring, HEP, pp. 473 f., 497, and references there cited.

43. Lloyd Morgan's reaction to Romanes is in C. Lloyd Morgan, *Animal Life and Intelligence* (London, Arnold, 1890–91); *Introduction to Comparative Psychology* (New York, Scribner, 1894) (the Canon of parsimony is in chap. iii); *Animal Behaviour* (London, Arnold, 1900). See also Boring, HEP, pp. 474 f., 497 f.

44. On tropism see J. Loeb, *Der Heliotropismus der Thiere und seine Ueberstimmung mit dem Heliotropismus der Pflanzen* (Würzburg, Hert, 1890); *Einleitung in die vergleichende Gehirnphysiologie und vergleichende Psychologie* (Leipzig, Barth, 1899, Eng. trans. 1900). See also Boring, HEP, pp. 475, 498.

45. On associative memory as evidence of the existence of consciousness see M. F. Washburn, *The Animal Mind* (New York, Macmillan, 1908 or any later ed.), chap. ii.

46. On protozoic consciousness see H. S. Jennings, *Contributions to the Study of the Behavior of the Lower Organisms* (New York, Columbia University Press, 1904), and the series of articles beginning in 1897. See Boring, HEP, pp. 622–626, 659.

47. For the early instance of protozoic learning see L. M. Day and M. Bentley, "A Note on Learning in Paramecium," *Jour. Animal Behav., 1* (1911), 67–73.

48. On R. M. Yerkes see Boring, HEP, pp. 628, 660.

Objective Psychology

49. For details of the history of objective psychology and of reflex action see F. Fearing, *Reflex Action* (Baltimore, Williams & Wilkins, 1930); Boring, HEP, pp. 631–641, 660 f.

50. On behaviorism see G. Murphy, *An Historical Introduction to Modern Psychology* (New York, Harcourt, Brace, 1929), pp. 251–268; Boring, HEP, pp. 641–653, 661–663.

51. On logical positivism and operationism in relation to psychology see S. S. Stevens, "Psychology and the Science of Science," *Psychol. Bull., 36* (1939), 221–263 and references there cited; Boring, *Sensation and Perception in the History of Experimental Psychology* (New York, Appleton-Century, 1942), pp. 13 f., 18 f., 33 f., 46 f.; HEP, pp. 653–659, 663; "Symposium on Operationism," by six authors, *Psychol. Rev., 52* (1945), 241–294. There is also a line of development from James and Dewey and C. S. Peirce through pragmatism to operationism, which has been held to be a form of pragmatism. See V. J. McGill, "Pragmatism," in D. D. Runes, *Dictionary of Philosophy* (Chicago, Alliance Book, 1942), pp. 245–247.

Nature Versus Nurture

52. On mental inheritance see Murphy, *op. cit.*, pp. 366–371.

53. On the supposed inheritance of feeble-mindedness see H. H. Goddard, *The Kallikak Family* (New York, Macmillan, 1912).

54. A representative book on eugenics is C. B. Davenport, *Heredity in Relation to Eugenics* (New York, Holt, 1911).

55. On the growth of intelligence testing see Murphy, *op. cit.*, pp. 351–372; J. Peterson, *Early Conceptions and Tests of Intelligence* (Yonkers, World Book, 1925), pp. 117–242.

56. On the relation of intelligence-test scores to social, economic, and cultural factors

see O. Klineberg, *Social Psychology* (New York, Holt, 1940), pp. 223–264, 282–316; *Race Differences* (New York, Harper, 1935), pp. 152–199.

57. On the startle reflex see C. Landis and W. A. Hunt, *The Startle Pattern* (New York, Farrar, 1939), especially pp. 20–51.

58. On nature, nurture, and twins see R. S. Woodworth, "Heredity and Environment: a Critical Survey of Recently Published Material on Twins and Foster Children," *Soc. Sci. Research Counc. Bull.,* No. 47 (1941).

59. On the inevitably concurrent contribution of heredity and environment to specific abilities see Woodworth, *loc. cit.;* L. Carmichael, "Heredity and Environment: Are They Antithetical?" *Jour. Abn. and Soc. Psychol.,* 20 (1925), 245–260.

60. On maturation of aptitudes see C. P. Stone, "Learning: the Factor of Maturation," in C. Murchison, *Handbook of General Experimental Psychology* (Worcester, Clark University Press, 1934), pp. 352–381. See also·L. Carmichael, "The Development of Behavior in Vertebrates Experimentally Removed from the Influence of External Stimulation," *Psychol. Rev.,* 33 (1926), 51–58; "A Further Experimental Study of the Development of Behavior, etc.," *ibid., 34* (1927), 34–47.

Case for Evolution

61. On Cattell's belief that Wundt's experimental psychology was the material on which to build mental tests see the references in n. 37 *supra.*

62. On the pioneer nature of American character see the references in nn. 16, 17 *supra.*

63. The synthesis in the Hegelian dialectic shows that consciousness in animals is relative to the point of view that you take up over against observable behavior. An analogous case appears in cosmology. Thesis: the Ptolemaic view—the sun goes around the earth. Antithesis: the Copernican view—the earth goes around the sun. Synthesis: Einstein's view—all motion is relative, and Ptolemy is right from one point of view and Copernicus from another.

64. On operationism as a form of pragmatism see n. 51 *supra.*

INTRODUCTION TO CHAPTER VIII

NATURALISM IN AMERICAN LITERATURE

THE early history of the naturalist movement in literature gives clear insight into a number of the social and intellectual tendencies of the late nineteenth century with which the evolutionary influence was associated. In rebelling against the genteel tradition the naturalists found in the theory of evolution useful symbolic devices for portraying the suffering, bewilderment, and despair, as well as the triumphs of the new industrial civilization. The use to which the theory was put varied with the respective purposes of each writer, the racism of London differing markedly from the social determinism of Dreiser. Mr. Cowley's appraisal of the evolutionary themes in naturalism, while acknowledging their immediate service in liberating the writing of fiction from stifling restraints, insists upon their ultimate barrenness of the insights essential to an enduring literature.

S. P.

VIII

NATURALISM IN AMERICAN LITERATURE

MALCOLM COWLEY

I

NATURALISM appeared thirty years later in American literature than it did in Europe and it was never quite the same movement. Like European naturalism it was inspired by Darwin's theory of evolution and kept repeating the doctrine that men, being part of the animal kingdom, were subject to natural laws. But theories and doctrines were not the heart of it. The American naturalists turned to Europe; they read—or read about—Darwin, they studied Spencer and borrowed methods from Zola because they were rebelling against an intolerable situation at home. What bound them together into a school or movement was this native rebellion and not the nature of the help that, like rebels in all ages, they summoned from abroad.

They began writing during the 1890's, when American literature was under the timid but tyrannical rule of what afterward came to be known as the genteel tradition. It was also called Puritanism by its enemies, but that was a mistake on the part of writers with only a stereotyped notion of American history. The original Puritans were not in the least genteel. They believed in the real existence of evil, which they denounced in terms that would have shocked William Dean Howells and the polite readers of the *Century Magazine*. The great New England writers, descendants of the Puritans, were moralists overburdened with scruples; but they were never mealymouthed in the fashion of their successors. Gentility—or "ideality" or "decency," to mention two favorite words of the genteel writers—was something that developed chiefly in New York and the Middle West and had its flowering after the Civil War.

Essentially it was an effort to abolish the various evils and vulgarities in American society by never speaking about them. It was a theory that divided the world into two parts, as Sunday was divided from the days of the week or the right side from the wrong side of the railroad tracks. On one side was religion; on the other, business. On one side was the divine in human beings; on the other, everything animal. On one side was art; on the other, life. On one side were women, clergymen, and university professors, all guardians of art and the ideal; on the other side were men in general, immersed in their practical affairs. On one side were the church and the school; on the other side were the saloon, the livery stable, and other low haunts where men gathered to talk politics, swap stories, and remember their wartime adventures with the yellow girls in New Orleans. In America during the late nineteenth century culture was set against daily living, theory against practice, highbrow against lowbrow; and the same division could be found even in the language itself—for one side spoke a sort of bloodless literary English, while the other had a speech that was not American but Amurrkn, ugly and businesslike, sometimes picturesque but not yet a literary idiom.

The whole territory of literature was thought to lie on the right side of the railroad tracks, in the chiefly feminine realm of beauty, art, religion, culture, and the ideal. Novels had to be written with pure heroines and happy endings in order to flatter the self-esteem of female readers. Magazines were edited so as not to disturb the minds of young girls or call forth protests from angry mothers. Frank Norris said of American magazines in 1895:

They are safe as a graveyard, decorous as a church, as devoid of immorality as an epitaph. . . . They adorn the center table. They do not "call a blush to the cheek of the young." They can be placed—oh, crowning virtue, oh, supreme encomium—they can be "safely" placed in the hands of any young girl the country over. . . . It is the "young girl" and the family center table that determine the standard of the American short story.

Meanwhile there were new men appearing year by year—Frank Norris was one of them—who would not write for the young girl or the center table and could not express themselves without breaking the rules of the genteel editors.

These new men, who would be the first American naturalists, were all in some way disadvantaged when judged by the social and literary standards then prevailing. They were not of the Atlantic seaboard, or not of the old stock, or not educated in the right schools, or not members of the Protestant churches, or not sufficiently respectable in their persons or in their family backgrounds. They were in rebellion against the genteel tradition because, like writers from the beginning of time, they had an urgent need for telling the truth about themselves, and because there was no existing medium in which they were privileged to tell it.

II

Instinctively the new writers began a search for older allies. There were a few of these to be found in America, but not enough of them to serve as the basis of a new literary movement. For most of their support the rebels had to look eastward across the Atlantic.

They were especially attracted by the English evolutionary scientists and pamphleteers. Most of the young writers read the works of this whole English group, beginning with Darwin, whose observations were too rigorously set forth to please their slipshod literary tastes. They could not find much to use in Darwin's books, except his picture of natural selection operating through the struggle for life; most of their Darwinism was acquired at second hand. Huxley they seem to have read with less veneration but more interest, chiefly because of his arguments against the Bible as revealed truth and because of his long war with the Protestant clergy. Young writers, feeling that the churches were part of a vast conspiracy to keep them silent, believed that Huxley was fighting their battle. It was Herbert Spencer, however, who deeply affected their thinking. Spencer's American popularity during the last half of the nineteenth century is something without parallel in the history of philosophic writing. From 1860 to 1903 his books had a sale of 368,755 copies in the authorized editions, not counting the many editions that appeared without his consent. In the memoirs of many famous Americans born in the 1860's and 1870's, one finds the reading of Spencer mentioned as an event that changed the course of their lives. Said John R. Commons, speaking of his father's cronies, "Every one of them in that eastern section of Indiana was a Republican living on the battle cries of the Civil War, and every one was a follower of Herbert Spencer. . . . I was brought up on Hoosierism, Republicanism, Presbyterianism and Spencerism."

What was a family inheritance for Commons was a personal

discovery for most of the young writers who belonged to the same generation. Hamlin Garland, when he was starving in Boston on three or four dollars a week, managed to borrow Spencer's books from the public library. After a five-cent breakfast of coffee and two doughnuts, he went "with eager haste," so he says, to Spencer's Synthetic Philosophy. Edgar Lee Masters read Spencer in Illinois, at the age of nineteen. Jack London read him in the little room in Oakland, Calif., where he was teaching himself to write. He says of his autobiographical hero, Martin Eden, that he opened Spencer's *First Principles* in bed, hoping that the book would put him to sleep after algebra and physics and an attempt at a sonnet. "Morning found him still reading. It was impossible for him to sleep. Nor did he write that day. He lay on the bed till his body grew tired, when he tried the hard floor, reading on his back, the book held in the air above him, or changing from side to side. He slept that night, and did his writing next morning, and then the book tempted him and he fell reading all afternoon, oblivious to everything." Theodore Dreiser read Huxley and Spencer in Pittsburgh, when he was working as a young reporter on the *Dispatch*. He tells us in *A Book about Myself* that the discovery of Spencer's *First Principles* "quite blew me, intellectually, to bits." And he goes on to say:

Hitherto, until I had read Huxley, I had some lingering filaments of Catholicism trailing about me, faith in the existence of Christ, the soundness of his moral and sociologic deductions, the brotherhood of man. But on reading *Science and Hebrew Tradition* and *Science and Christian Tradition,* and finding both the Old and New Testaments to be not compendiums of revealed truth but mere records of religious experiences, and very erroneous ones at that, and then taking up *First Principles* and discovering all I deemed substantial—man's place in nature, his importance in the universe, this too, too solid earth, man's very identity save as an infinitesimal speck of energy or a "suspended equation" drawn or blown here and there by larger forces in which he moved quite unconsciously as an atom—all questioned and dissolved into other and less understandable things, I was completely thrown down in my conceptions or non-conceptions of life.

Not many of Spencer's readers were left with this impression of being confused and "completely thrown down." There were many more who valued him because he fitted together the pieces of a universal scheme that had been shattered by their earlier loss of faith in Christian dogmas. Garland, for example, found that "the universe took on order and harmony" as he considered Spencer's theory of the evolution of music or painting or sculpture. "It was thrilling, it was joyful," he says, "to perceive that everything moved from the simple to the complex—how the bow-string became the harp and the egg the chicken." Spencer's chief value, for the generation of writers who studied him, was that he gave them another unified world picture to replace the Christian synthesis. In that early age of specialization, he was the only great lay scholar with the courage to expound a synthetic philosophy. Many young men worshiped him not merely as a teacher but as a religious prophet. "To give up Spencer," said Jack London's autobiographical hero, "would be equivalent to a navigator throwing the compass and chronometer overboard." Later, when he heard a California judge disparaging Spencer, the hero burst into a rage. "To hear that great and noble man's name upon your lips," he shouted, "is like finding a dewdrop in a cesspool." In his quieter way, Edwin Arlington Robinson was almost as loyal to the synthetic philosopher. He said in a letter written in 1898 to one of his Harvard friends:

Professor James's book is entertaining and full of good things; but his attitude toward Spencer makes me think of a dream my father once had. He dreamed he met a dog. The dog annoyed him, so he struck him with a stick. Then the dog doubled in size and my father struck him again with the same result. So the thing went on till the universe was pretty much all dog. When my father awoke, he was, or rather had been, halfway down the dog's throat.

But Spencer, enormous as he seemed, was no guide to young writers in the specific problems of their craft; nor was he a model to which they could point as justification for their dealing frankly with the world around them. In fiction and poetry they had to find other allies and, once again, most of them were transatlantic.

There were, for example, the English eighteenth-century classics, which could always be cited in arguments for honest realism. *Roxana, or the Fortunate Mistress* was one of Howells' favorites. "Did you ever read Defoe's 'Roxana'?" he said in a letter to his friend Samuel Clemens. "If not, then read it, not merely for some of the deepest insights into the lying, suffering, sinning, well-meaning human soul, but the best and most natural English that

a book was ever written in." Still, he was more than a little worried by the effect that novels like *Roxana* and even scenes from
Shakespeare might have on public morals. "I hope the time will
come," he said in an essay written not long after his letter to
Clemens, "when the beast-man will be so far submerged and
tamed in us that the memory of him in literature will be left to
perish; that what is lewd and ribald in the great poets shall be
kept out of such editions as are meant for public reading." But
this was only a pious wish, and perhaps not wholly sincere. General readers could still buy Defoe and Fielding and Smollett in
unexpurgated volumes printed in England.

They could also buy translations of living Continental writers,
sometimes in paper-bound reprints that sold for as little as ten
cents a copy. Turgeniev and Tolstoy both had a following among
literary people, and Tolstoy, because of his reputation for frankness, even had a popular sale. Ibsen was not often played, but he
was widely discussed. There was a complete translation of Balzac,
which stood on the shelves of the larger public libraries, and there
were many editions of his separate novels. Zola also had a large
public here and an extensive underground influence, in spite of the
fact that he was seldom mentioned in the critical journals without
being sweepingly condemned. "I read everything of Zola's that I
can lay hands on," Howells confessed in a letter to John Hay. "But
I have to hide the books from the children!" Theodore Dreiser
tells us in his memoirs that when he was working as a reporter
on the St. Louis *Republic,* in 1893, the city editor kept advising
him "to imitate Zola's vivid description of the drab and the gross
and the horrible, if I could—assuming that I had read him,"
Dreiser added, "which I had not, but I did not say so."

By that time, however, he had gained a fairly definite notion of
Zola's methods at second hand. Two of his colleagues on the St.
Louis *Globe-Democrat,* where he had worked the preceding year,
had written a novel in the Zola manner. It was about a young and
very beautiful actress named Theo, who was the mistress of a
French newspaper man. Though deeply in love with her, the hero
was unfaithful on at least one occasion; and this, Dreiser said
when he retold the story in his memoirs, "brought about a Zolaesque scene in which she spanked another actress with a hairbrush.
There was treacherous plotting on the part of somebody with regard to a local murder, which brought about the arrest and conviction of the newspaper man for something he knew nothing

about. This entailed a great struggle on the part of Theo to save him, which resulted in her failure and his death on the guillotine. A priest figured in it in some way, grim, jesuitical."

This novel, which never found a publisher, must have been one of the earliest attempts to write in the manner of the French naturalists. Dreiser read it in manuscript and was greatly impressed, though he also wondered why his friends found it necessary to deal with French, not American, life when they wished to write in terms of fact. He didn't read Zola till much later in his career, so he tells us; but he discovered Balzac in 1894, when he was a reporter in Pittsburgh. "It was for me," he says, "a literary revolution. Not only for the brilliant and incisive manner with which Balzac grasped life and invented themes whereby to present it, but for the fact that the types he handled with most enthusiasm and skill—the brooding, seeking, ambitious beginners in life's social, political, artistic and commercial affairs (Rastignac, Raphael, de Rubempré, Bianchon)—were, I thought, so much like myself." Doors had opened in his mind. "Coming out of the library this day," he says, "and day after day thereafter, the while I rendered as little reportorial service as was consistent with even a show of effort, I marveled at the physical similarity of the two cities"—Pittsburgh and Paris—"as I conceived it, at the chance for pictures here as well as there. American pictures here, as opposed to French pictures there."

This experience of Dreiser's brings to light a curious phenomenon connected with the whole stream of foreign influence. Not only did the rebels of Dreiser's generation learn technical methods from the European naturalists, and find examples of frankness that supported them in their struggle with the genteel tradition; they also were inspired by Europeans to write about American scenes. They had to read European books in order to discover their own natures, and travel in imagination through European cities before they gained courage to describe their own backgrounds. Hamlin Garland, who was the most dogmatically American of them all, and the most vehemently opposed to the imitation of foreign masters, was at the same time a disciple of Ibsen, Tolstoy, and the French Impressionist painters. "In my poor, blundering fashion," he said long afterward, "I was standing for all forms of art which expressed, more or less adequately, the America I knew. . . . Ibsen's method, alien as his material actually appeared, pointed the way to a new and more authentic

American drama. 'If we must imitate, let us imitate those who represent the truth and not those who uphold conventions,' was my argument."

III

Meanwhile there were a very few living American authors whose work seemed to represent the truth and could therefore serve as models to the new generation. There was Whitman, still living meanly in his little house in Camden and still saying over and over again that American books should deal with American life. There were the local-color novelists, scores of them, each studying the folkways of his native or deliberately chosen territory. Garland thought that they represented a national movement, but the truth was that they dealt with a very few sections of the country: chiefly New England, the Southern Highlands, Louisiana, or California.

There were, however, three local writers from the Middle West who described their respective backgrounds with less sentiment and decorum than those from other sections. Edward Eggleston, of southern Indiana, had published *The Hoosier Schoolmaster* in 1871, at a time when there were no American models for that sort of homely writing; his inspiration for the book, he said, was a translation of Taine's lectures on *Art in the Netherlands,* in which he first encountered the thesis that an artist should work courageously with the materials he finds in his own environment. Edgar Watson Howe, of Kansas, had failed to find a publisher for his *Story of a Country Town* and had printed it at his own expense in 1883. It was the first novel to suggest that there was narrowness, frustration, and sexual hypocrisy in Midwestern lives. Joseph Kirkland, of Illinois, had read *The Hoosier Schoolmaster* and had wondered whether a similar background couldn't be presented more honestly than in Eggleston's book; in 1885 he published *Zury, the Meanest Man in Spring County*. Later he said to Garland, who greatly admired his novel, "Why shouldn't our prairie country have its novelists as well as England or France or Norway? Our characters will not be peasants, but our fiction can be close to the soil." Kirkland recognized the imperfections of his pioneer work; "I began too late," he said.

All these early realists began too late in their lives, and with insufficient preparation. Eggleston, whose books were popular in Scandinavia, was the only one who became a professional man of letters, and that was only after he had abandoned fiction for lecturing on American history. Kirkland was a lawyer who wrote in his spare time. Ed Howe was a newspaper editor. "When I quit the newspaper," he wrote to Garland, "I will write my best book, but I am successful at newspaper work and afraid to give it up." He never quit the newspaper or wrote another book as good as *The Story of a Country Town*. Men like Howe had no assurance that they could earn a living merely by writing novels; no assurance that there was any large public for the sort of truth they had to tell. Their few honest books pointed toward a road that they were unable to follow. But meanwhile, as a model for young writers, there was also William Dean Howells, who, for all his timidity, was trying to present the American world that lay before his eyes. Howells was the real patron and precursor of naturalism in America.

Frank Norris, in one of his magazine pieces, "A Lost Story," described the old schoolmaster as he appeared to the literary rebels of 1898. "He was," Norris said, speaking of an imaginary character named Trevor, but undoubtedly thinking of Howells, "a short, rotund man, rubicund as to face, bourgeois as to clothes and surroundings, jovial in manner, indulging even in slang. One might easily set him down as a retired groceryman—wholesale, perhaps, but none the less a groceryman. Yet touch him upon the subject of his profession, and the *bonhomie* lapsed away from him at once." And Norris continued,

This elderly man of letters, who had seen the rise and fall of a dozen schools, was above the influence of fads, and he whose books were among the classics even before his death was infallible in his judgments of the work of the younger writers. All the stages of their evolution were known to him—all their mistakes, all their successes. He understood; and a story by one of them, a poem, a novel, that bore the stamp of his approval, was "sterling."

But the public, in 1898, had lost its taste for sterling. It had ceased to buy Howells' novels, let alone those of the young men he kept recommending in his many critical articles. Instead it was buying the romances of F. Hopkinson Smith and Kate Douglas Wiggin, brassy sentiment covered with a thin silver wash.

IV

Norris had dressed in tails to spend his first evening at the Howells'; he liked to be the dandy when he had money for good clothes. He was a big, engaging young man of twenty-eight with prematurely gray hair and a wide cupid's-bow mouth that curled into consciously boyish smiles. Unlike the other naturalists, he had been the rather spoiled child of a wealthy family; and he had formed a high opinion of himself that kept him from feeling professional jealousy and therefore permitted him to have a high opinion of others. Howells liked him so much at their first meeting that he consented to read the manuscript of the Zolaesque novel that his visitor had lately finished after working on it at intervals for four years. It was called *McTeague* and it was the story of an unlicensed San Francisco dentist who had murdered his miserly wife. A few evenings later Norris came back to hear the master's judgment. This time he was received by Howells in lounging slippers and they sat for a long time by the open fire talking about the novel. It wouldn't be popular, Howells said, but he gave it the stamp of his approval; it was sterling.

Most of the magazines were shocked by *McTeague* when it was published in February, 1899. The *Independent* called it a dangerous book that had "no moral, esthetical or artistic reason for being." The *Bookman* condemned it as "the unexpected revival of realism in its most unendurable form." Other critics were incensed by a page in *McTeague* that described a little boy wetting his pants; they said that Norris had mentioned the unmentionable. There was much in the book that worried Howells, too, but he reviewed it with something close to enthusiasm. It prompted him to raise a serious question in the weekly column he was writing for *Literature*. The question was "whether we shall abandon the old-fashioned American ideal"—to which Howells himself had always clung—"of a novel as something which may be read by all ages and sexes, for the European notion of it as something fit only for age and experience, and for men rather than women; whether we shall keep to the bonds of the provincial proprieties, or shall include within the imperial territory of our fiction the passions and motives of the savage world which underlies as well as environs civilization." Howells did not try to answer the question; but he did say with a sense of prophecy, "The time may come at last when we are to invade and control Europe in literature. I do not say that it has come, but if it has we may have to employ European means and methods."

McTeague was not the first novel in the manner of the French naturalists to be written in the United States, for there must have been others that remained in manuscript, like the wicked book by Dreiser's two St. Louis friends. It was not even the first naturalistic novel to be published here, for Stephen Crane's *Maggie, a Girl of the Streets* had been issued by D. Appleton & Company in 1896, after being privately printed in 1893. But *Maggie,* though it dealt with poverty and prostitution from a naturalistic point of view, was not so much American as metropolitan; it was an episode that might have taken place in any of the world's large cities. *McTeague* was localized; it was the first novel that applied Zola's massive technique, his objective approach and his taste for the grotesquely common to a setting that everyone recognized as American.

Today it has lost its power to shock, but it retains more vitality and clear-sightedness than any of Norris' later novels. The others, even *The Octopus,* are full of romantic situations in the taste of the time; we read them today as period pieces. And the author himself, when we follow his career in Franklin Walker's biography, arouses a good deal of affectionate amusement mingled with our respect for what he achieved. He was a giant who never grew up. He never got over his dependence on his strong-minded mother; every illness sent him scurrying home to her apron strings. Harry Thurston Peck, the editor of the *Bookman,* said of Norris in a letter, "The author of the terrible 'McTeague' is a pleasant, cultivated young gentleman, inclined to be obstreperous—and humorless—in arguments on realism, but in every other respect a very pleasant boy." He also thought that his face suggested "photographs of Hawthorne or of some classic actor." Another observer thought that he resembled "an old-time tragedian . . . Edwin Booth, perhaps." The truth was that Norris' writing was full of stage effects and that he never lost the actor's habit of looking at himself admiringly in the successive roles he played: the art student, the French dandy with sideburns and a cane, the fraternity brother, the breezy Westerner, the man about town, the Anglo-Saxon imperialist and explorer, the romantic lover, the struggling writer, the great novelist. Yes, even the last was a role; for his letters give the impression that Norris stood back and applauded himself as the author of books on big themes that he chose for their bigness, no matter how foreign they might be to his own experience.

About the time that *McTeague* appeared, he was getting launched on the biggest theme of all. "Tell Burgess I'm full of ginger and red pepper," he said in a letter, "and am getting ready to stand up on my hind legs and yell *big*." At the end of March, 1899, he wrote to Howells thanking him for his review of *McTeague*. "I have the idea of another novel or rather series of novels buzzing in my head these days," he added. "I think there is a chance for somebody to do some great work with the West and California as a background, and which will be at the same time thoroughly American. My idea is to write three novels around the one subject of *Wheat*. First, a story of California (the producer), second, a story of Chicago (the distributor), third, a story of Europe (the consumer) and in each keep to the idea of this huge Niagara of wheat rolling from West to East. I think a big epic trilogy *could* be made out of such a subject, that at the same time would be modern and distinctly American. The idea is so big that it frightens me at times but I have about made up my mind to have a try at it." He was in fact already working on his plans, and early in April he went to California in a search for characters, incidents, and local color.

The first volume of the trilogy was published just two years later, in April, 1901. *The Octopus* was on all counts his most ambitious novel, the most carefully composed, the broadest and most colorful in its background, the closest in its theme to great historical events. It was written after a period of sudden booms and depressions, when big business was swallowing little businesses and millions of individuals felt themselves the victims of impersonal corporations or uncontrollable forces. Norris gave expression to their sense of injustice and bewilderment; and he also introduced new technical methods, especially in his collective treatment of the California ranchers. His chapters on the barn dance and the rabbit hunt were almost the first portrayals in American fiction of a group that exulted and suffered as one man. *The Octopus,* in one of his favorite phrases, was a book "as big as all outdoors"; but its bigness was achieved at the expense of many strained effects and more concessions than he had made in *McTeague* to the bad taste of the day. At the end it declined into muzzy sentiments and fine writing. There is one long passage describing a dinner given by a railroad tycoon, with ortolan patties and Londonderry pheasants served at the exact moment when Mrs. Hooven, robbed of her home by the railroad, was dying of starvation in a vacant lot—one passage of twenty pages that belongs in an old-fashioned servant girls' weekly.

Howells admired *The Octopus* with reservations; after the comparatively unpretentious honesty of *McTeague,* he seems to have felt that it made too many compromises. But there were still more compromises in the second volume of the trilogy, *The Pit,* which appeared in January, 1903, after being serialized in the *Saturday Evening Post.* With its effort to romanticize the big gambler on the Chicago Board of Trade, and with its secondary plot about the wife who discovers that she really loves him after being tempted to run away with a freshwater esthete, who in turn is merely funny instead of being the sinister figure that Norris tried to present, it becomes a provincial melodrama rather than a second canto in the epic of the wheat. *The Pit* seems to indicate that the author had made his peace with genteel society. Perhaps the indication is false, for Norris was dissatisfied with this latest work. Perhaps the next book would have been better; but he died suddenly of peritonitis in the autumn of 1902, before *The Pit* was published and before he had even begun to collect material for the third volume of his trilogy.

It is easy now to see the faults of his work. He was a borrower of literary effects; he took those he needed wherever he found them, in Kipling, Stevenson, Tolstoy, Zola, or Maupassant. He depended on instinct rather than intelligence for his choice of borrowings, since he always thought viscerally, with his heart and bowels instead of his brain. In that respect he resembled the first Roosevelt; and Henry Adams' judgment on the President applies to the novelist equally: "We are timid and conventional, all of us, except T. R., and he has no mind." But T. R. was often timid and conventional in politics, for all his bluster, just as Norris was often conventional in writing his big dramatic scenes and timid in his moral judgments. One remembers how Presley, the poet in *The Octopus* who often speaks for the author, sets out to rescue the penniless Hooven family, finds that the daughter has become a prostitute and runs away from her in sick terror, feeling that with her first step into sin she has passed beyond all human help. Norris' moral rebellion, like T. R.'s political rebellion, stayed within the limits of what was then good form.

He had no feeling for any but the most obvious social values; I think it was Henry James who said that Norris' pictures of Chicago society would have been good satires if he had known they were satires. He was proud of not writing careful prose. He didn't live long enough to learn many subtleties of character or the use in portraying them of many shades between black and white. Yet it may be that his faults and failures helped to keep him close to a public that had missed the ironies in Henry B. Fuller's work and felt that Stephen Crane was cold, European and possibly corrupt. They were the faults of his time and they contributed, in their way, to his timely influence on American writing. His great virtues were also of a sort that the public could learn to respect: freshness, narrative vigor, a marvelous eye for the life around him and courage to portray it in its drama and violence, besides the ability to construct his novels like Zola's in massive blocks. During a literary career of only six years, he managed to impress his personality, some of his particular virtues, and many of his shortcomings on the whole naturalistic school that would follow him.

V

After half a century we can look back in an objective or naturalistic spirit at the work of the writers inspired by Dreiser and Norris. We can describe their principles, note how these were modified in practice and reach some sort of judgment on their achievements.

Naturalism in literature has been defined by Oscar Cargill as pessimistic determinism, and the definition is true so far as it goes. The naturalists were all determinists in that they believed in the omnipotence of natural forces. They were pessimists in that they believed in the absolute incapacity of men and women to shape their own destinies. They regarded the individual as merely "a pawn on a chessboard"; the phrase recurs time and again in their novels. They felt that he could not achieve happiness by any conscious decision and that he received no earthly or heavenly reward for acting morally; man was, in Dreiser's words, "the victim of forces over which he has no control."

In some of his moods, Frank Norris carried this magnification of forces and minification of persons to an even greater extreme. "Men were nothings, mere animalculae, mere ephemerides that fluttered and fell and were forgotten between dawn and dusk," he said in the next-to-last chapter of *The Octopus.* "Men were naught, life was naught; FORCE only existed—FORCE that brought men into the world, FORCE that made the wheat grow, FORCE that garnered it from the soil to give place to the succeeding crop." But Norris, like several other naturalists, was able to combine this romantic pessimism about individuals with romantic optimism about the future of mankind. "The individual suffers, but the race goes on," he said at the very end of the novel. "Annixter dies, but in a far distant corner of the world a thousand lives are saved. The larger view always and through all shams, all wickednesses, discovers the Truth that will, in the end, prevail, and all things, surely, inevitably, resistlessly work together for good." This was, in its magniloquent way, a form of the belief in universal progress announced by Herbert Spencer, but it was also mingled with native or Emersonian idealism, and it helped to make naturalism more palatable to Norris' first American readers.

Zola had also declared his belief in human perfectibility, in what he called "a constant march toward truth"; and it was from Zola rather than Spencer or any native sources that Norris had borrowed most of his literary doctrines. Zola described himself as "a positivist, an evolutionist, a materialist." In his working notes, which Norris of course had never seen, but which one might say that he divined from the published text of the novels, Zola had indicated some of his aims as a writer. He would march through the world observing human behavior as if he were observing the forms of animal life. "Study men as simple elements and note the reactions," he said. And again, "What matters most to me is to be purely naturalistic, purely physiological. Instead of having principles (royalism, Catholicism) I shall have laws (heredity, atavism)." And yet again, "Balzac says that he wishes to paint men, women and things. I count men and women as the same, while admitting their natural differences, and *subject men and women to things.*" In that last phrase, which Zola underlined, he expressed the central naturalistic doctrine: that men and women are part of nature and subject to the same indifferent laws.

The principal laws, for Zola, were those of heredity, which he assumed to be as universal and unchanging as the second law of thermodynamics. He fixed upon the hereditary weakness of the Rougon-Macquart family as a theme that would bind together his vast series of novels. Suicide, alcoholism, prostitution, and insanity were all to be explained as the result of the same hereditary taint. "Vice and virtue," he said, "are products like vitriol and sugar." Norris offered the same explanation for the brutality of McTeague. "Below the fine fabric of all that was good in him," Norris said, "ran the foul stream of hereditary evil, like a sewer. The vices and sins of his father and of his father's father, to the third and fourth and five hundredth generation, tainted him. The evil of an entire race flowed in his veins. Why should it be? He did not desire it.

Was he to blame?" Others of the naturalistic school, and Norris himself in his later novels, placed more emphasis on environmental forces. When Stephen Crane sent a copy of *Maggie* to the Reverend Thomas Dixon, he wrote on the flyleaf: "It is inevitable that this book will greatly shock you, but continue, pray, with great courage to the end, for it tries to show that environment is a tremendous thing and often shapes lives regardlessly. If I could prove that theory, I would make room in Heaven for all sorts of souls (notably an occasional street girl) who are not confidently expected to be there by many excellent people." Maggie, the victim of environment, was no more to blame for her transgressions than McTeague, the victim of hereditary evil. Nobody was to blame in this world where men and women are subject to the laws of things.

A favorite theme in naturalistic fiction is that of the beast within. As the result of some crisis—usually a fight, a shipwreck, or an expedition into the Arctic—the veneer of civilization drops or is stripped away and we are faced with "the primal instinct of the brute struggling for its life and for the life of its young." The phrase is Norris', but it might have been written by any of the early naturalists. When evolution is treated in their novels, it almost always takes the opposite form of devolution or degeneration. It is seldom that the hero evolves toward a superhuman nature, as in Nietzsche's dream; instead he sinks backward toward the beasts. Zola set the fashion in *L'Assommoir* and *La Bête humaine* and Norris followed him closely in the novel he wrote during his year at Harvard, *Vandover and the Brute*. Through yielding to his lower instincts, Vandover loses his humanity; he tears off his clothes, paddles up and down the room on his hands and feet and snarls like a dog.

A still earlier story, *Lauth,* was written at the University of California after Norris had listened to the lectures of Professor Joseph Le Conte, the famous evolutionist. The action takes place in medieval Paris, where Lauth, a student at the Sorbonne, is mortally wounded in a brawl. A doctor brings him back to life by pumping blood into his veins, but the soul had left the body and does not return. Without it, Lauth sinks back rapidly through the various stages of evolution: he is an ape, then a dog, then finally "a horrible shapeless mass lying upon the floor. It lived, but lived not as do the animals or the trees, but as the protozoa, the jellyfish, and those strange lowest forms of existence wherein the line between vegetable and animal cannot be drawn." That might have been taken as a logical limit to the process of devolution; but Jack London, who was two parts naturalist, if he was also one part socialist and three parts hack journalist, tried to carry the process even further, into the realm of inanimate nature. Here, for example, is the description of a fight in *Martin Eden:*

Then they fell upon each other, like young bulls, in all the glory of youth, with naked fists, with hatred, with desire to hurt, to maim, to destroy. All the painful, thousand years' gains of man in his upward climb through creation were lost. Only the electric light remained, a milestone on the path of the great human adventure. Martin and Cheese-Face were two savages, of the stone age, of the squatting place and the tree refuge. They sank lower and lower into the muddy abyss, back into the dregs of the raw beginnings of life, striving blindly and chemically, as atoms strive, as the star-dust of the heavens strives, colliding, recoiling and colliding again and eternally again.

It was more than a metaphor when London said that men were atoms and star dust; it was the central drift of his philosophy. Instead of moving from the simple to the complex, as Herbert Spencer tells us that everything does in this world, the naturalists kept moving from the complex to the simple, by a continual process of reduction. They spoke of the nation as "the tribe," and a moment later the tribe became a pack. Civilized man became a barbarian or a savage, the savage became a brute and the brute was reduced to its chemical elements. "Study men as simple elements," Zola had said; and many years later Dreiser followed his advice by presenting love as a form of electromagnetism and success in life as a question of chemical compounds; thus he said of his brother Paul that he was "one of those great Falstaffian souls who, for lack of a little iron or sodium or carbon dioxide in his chemical compost, was not able to bestride the world like a Colossus."

There was a tendency in almost all the naturalistic writers to identify social laws with biological or physical laws. For Jack London, the driving force behind human events was always biology—"I mean," says his autobiographical hero, Martin Eden, "the real interpretative biology, from the ground up, from the laboratory and the test tube and the vitalized inorganic right on up to the widest esthetic and social generalizations." London believed that such biological principles as natural selection and the survival of the fittest were also the laws of human society. Thomas Hardy often spoke as if men's destinies were shaped by the physical sciences. He liked to say that his characters were doomed by the stars in their courses; but actually they were doomed by human conflicts or by the still Puritan conventions of middle-class England. Norris fell into the same confusion between the physical and the social world when he pictured the wheat as "a huge Niagara . . . flowing from West to East." In his novels wheat was not a grain improved by men from various wild grasses and grown by men to meet human needs; it was an abstract and elemental force like gravity. "I corner the wheat!" says Jadwin, the hero of *The Pit*. "Great heavens, it is the wheat that has cornered me." Later, when he is ruined by the new grain that floods the market, Jadwin thinks to himself,

The Wheat had grown itself: demand and supply, these were the two great laws that the Wheat obeyed. Almost blasphemous in his effrontery, he had tampered with these laws, and roused a Titan. He had laid his puny human grasp upon Creation and the very earth herself, the great mother, feeling the touch of the cobweb that the human insect had spun, had stirred at last in her sleep and sent her omnipotence moving through the grooves of the world, to find and crush the disturber of her appointed courses.

Just as the wheat had grown itself, so, in the first volume of Norris' trilogy, the Pacific and Southwestern Railroad had built itself. This octopus that held a state in its tentacles was beyond human control. Even Shelgrim, the president of the railroad, was merely the agent of a superhuman force. At the end of the novel he gives a lecture to Presley which overwhelms the poet and leaves him feeling that it rang "with the clear reverberation of truth." "You are dealing with forces," Shelgrim says, "when you speak of Wheat and the Railroads, not with men. There is the Wheat, the supply. It must be carried to the People. There is the demand. The Wheat is one force, the Railroad, another, and there is the law that governs them—supply and demand. Men have little to do with the whole business." If the two forces came into conflict—if the employees of the railroad massacred the wheat ranchers and robbed them of their land—then Presley should "blame conditions, not men."

The effect of naturalism as a doctrine is to subtract from literature the whole notion of human responsibility. "Not men" is its constant echo. If naturalistic stories had tragic endings, these were not to be explained by human wills in conflict with each other or with fate; they were the blind result of conditions, forces, physical laws, or nature herself. "There was no malevolence in Nature," Presley reflects after meeting the railroad president. "Colossal indifference only, a vast trend toward appointed goals. Nature was, then, a gigantic engine, a vast, cyclopean power, huge, terrible, a leviathan with a heart of steel, knowing no compunction, no forgiveness, no tolerance; crushing out the human atom standing in its way, with nirvanic calm." Stephen Crane had already expressed the same attitude toward nature in a sharper image and in cleaner prose. When the four shipwrecked men in *The Open Boat* are drifting close to the beach but are unable to land because of the breakers, they stare at a windmill that is like "a giant standing with its back to the plight of the ants. It represented in a degree, to the correspondent, the serenity of nature amid the struggles of the individual—nature in the wind, and nature in the visions of men. She did not seem cruel to him, then, nor beneficent, nor treacherous, nor wise. But she was indifferent, flatly indifferent."

These ideas about nature, science, and destiny led to the recurrent use of words and phrases by which early naturalistic fiction can be identified. "The irony of fate" and "the pity of it" are two of the phrases; "pawns of circumstance" is another. The words that appear time and again are "primitive," "primordial" (often coupled with "slime"), "prehensile," "apelike," "wolflike," "brute" and "brutal," "savage," "driving," "conquering," "blood" (often as an adjective), "master" and "slave" (also as adjectives), "instinct" (which is usually "blind"), "ancestor," "huge," "cyclopean," "shapeless," "abyss," "biological," "chemic" and "chemism," "hypocrisy," "taboo," "unmoral." Time and again we read that "The race is to the swift and the battle to the strong." Time and again we are told about "the law of claw and fang," "the struggle for existence," "the blood of his Viking ancestors," and "the foul stream of hereditary evil." "The veneer of civilization" is always being "stripped away," or else it "drops away in an instant." The characters in early naturalistic novels "lose all resemblance to humanity," reverting to "the abysmal brute." But when they "clash together like naked savages," or even like atoms and star dust, it is always the hero who "proves himself the stronger"; and spurning his prostrate adversary he strides forward to seize "his mate, his female." "Was he to blame?" the author asks his readers; and always he answers, "Conditions, not men, were at fault."

VI

All these characteristics of the earlier American naturalists might have been deduced from their original faith in Darwinian evolution and in the need for applying biological and physical laws to human affairs. But they had other characteristics that were more closely connected with American life in their own day.

The last decade of the nineteenth century, when they started their literary careers, was an age of contrasts and sudden changes. In spite of financial panics, the country was growing richer, but not at a uniform rate for all sections: the South was hopelessly impoverished and rural New England was returning to wilderness. Cities were gaining in population, partly at the expense of the Eastern farms, industry was thriving at the expense of agriculture, and independent factories were being combined into or destroyed by the trusts. It was an age of high interest rates, high but uncertain profits, low wages and widespread unemployment. It was an age when labor unions were being broken, when immigrants were pouring through Ellis Island to people the new slums and when the new American baronage was building its magnificently ugly chateaux. "America," to quote again from Dreiser's memoirs, "was just entering upon the most lurid phase of that vast, splendid, most lawless and most savage period in which the great financiers were plotting and conniving at the enslavement of the people and belaboring each other." Meanwhile the ordinary citizen found it difficult to plan his future and even began to suspect that he was, in a favorite naturalistic phrase, "the plaything of forces beyond human control."

The American faith that was preached in the pulpits and daily reasserted on editorial pages had lost its connection with American life. It was not only an intolerable limitation on American writing, as all the rebel authors had learned; it also had to be disregarded by anyone who hoped to rise in the business world and by anyone who, having failed to rise, wanted to understand the reasons for his failure. In its simplest terms, the American faith was that things were getting better year by year, that the individual could solve his problems by moving, usually westward, and that virtue was rewarded with wealth, the greatest virtue with the greatest wealth. Those were the doctrines of the editorial page; but reporters who worked for the same newspaper looked around them and decided that wealth was more often the fruit of selfishness and fraud, whereas the admirable persons in their world—the kind, the philosophic, the honest, and the open-eyed—were usually failures by business standards. Most of the early naturalistic writers, including Stephen Crane, Harold Frederic, David Graham Phillips, and Dreiser, were professional newspaper men; while the others either worked for short periods as reporters or wrote series of newspaper articles. All were more or less affected by the moral atmosphere of the city room; and the fact is important, since the newspaper men of the 1890's and 1900's were a special class or type. "Never," says Dreiser, speaking of his colleagues on the Pittsburgh *Dispatch,* "had I encountered more intelligent or helpful or companionable albeit more cynical men than I met here"; and the observation leads to general remarks about the reporters he had known:

One can always talk to a newspaper man, I think, with the full confidence that one is talking to a man who is at least free of moralistic mush. Nearly everything in connection with those trashy romances of justice, truth, mercy, patriotism, public profession of all sorts, is already and forever gone if they have been in the business for any length of time. The religionist is seen by them for what he is: a swallower of romance or a masquerader looking to profit and preferment. Of the politician, they know or believe but one thing: that he is out for himself.

Essentially the attitude forced upon newspaper men as they interviewed politicians, evangelists, and convicted criminals was the same as the attitude they derived or might have derived from popular books on evolution. Reading and experience led to the same convictions: that Christianity was a sham, that all moral professions were false, that there was nothing real in the world but force and, for themselves, no respectable role to play except that of detached observers gathering the facts and printing as many of them as their publishers would permit. They drank, whored, talked shop, and dreamed about writing cynical books. "Most of these young men," Dreiser says, "looked upon life as a fierce, grim struggle in which no quarter was either given or taken, and in which all men laid traps, lied, squandered, erred through illusion: a conclusion with which I now most heartily agree." His novels one after another would be based on what he had learned in his newspaper days.

In writing their novels, most of the naturalists pictured themselves as expressing a judgment of life that was scientific, dispassionate, and, to borrow one of their phrases, completely unmoral; but a better word for their attitude would be "rebellious." Try as they would, they could not remain merely observers. They had to revolt against the moral standards of their time; and the revolt involved them more or less consciously in the effort to impose new standards that would be closer to what they regarded as natural laws. Their books are full of little essays or sermons addressed to the reader; in fact they suggest a naturalistic system of ethics complete with its vices and virtues. Among the vices those most often mentioned are hypocrisy, intolerance, conventionality, and unwillingness to acknowledge the truth. Among the virtues perhaps the first is strength, which is presented as both a physiological and a moral quality; it implies the courage to be strong in spite of social restraints. A second virtue is naturalness, that is, the quality of acting in accordance with one's nature and physical instincts. Dreiser's Jennie Gerhardt was among the first of the purely natural heroines in American literature, but she had many descendants. A third virtue is complete candor about the world and oneself; a fourth is pity for others; and a fifth is tolerance, especially of moral rebellion and economic failure. Most of the characters presented sympathetically in naturalistic novels are either the victors over moral codes which they defy (like Cowperwood in *The Financier* and Susan Lenox in the novel by David Graham Phillips about her fall and rise) or else victims of the economic struggle, paupers and drunkards with infinitely more wisdom than the respectable citizens who avoid them. A great deal of naturalistic writing, including the early poems of Edwin Arlington Robinson, is an eloquent hymn to loneliness and failure as the destiny, in America, of most superior men.

There are other qualities of American naturalism that are derived not so much from historical conditions as from the example of the two novelists whom the younger men regarded as leaders or precursors. Norris first and Dreiser after him fixed the patterns that the others would follow.

Both men were romantic by taste and temperament. Although Norris was a disciple of Zola's, his other favorite authors belonged in one way or another to the romantic school; they included Froissart, Scott, Dickens, Dumas, Hugo, Kipling, and Stevenson. Zola was no stranger in that company, Norris said; on one occasion he called him "the very head of the Romanticists."

Terrible things must happen [he wrote], to the characters of the naturalistic tale. They must be twisted from the ordinary, wrenched from the quiet, uneventful round of everyday life and flung into the throes of a vast and terrible drama that works itself out in unleashed passions, in blood and sudden death. . . . Everything is extraordinary, imaginative, grotesque even, with a vague note of terror quivering throughout like the vibration of an ominous and low-pitched diapason.

Norris himself wished to practice naturalism as a form of romance, instead of taking up what he described as "the harsh, loveless, colorless, blunt tool called Realism." Dreiser in his autobiographical writings often refers to his own romantic temper. "For all my modest repute as a realist," he says, "I seem, to my self-analyzing eyes, somewhat more of a romanticist." He speaks of himself in his youth as "a creature of slow and uncertain response to anything practical, having an eye to color, romance, beauty. I was but a half-baked poet, romancer, dreamer." The other American naturalists were also romancers and dreamers in their fashion, groping among facts for the extraordinary and even the grotesque. They believed that men were subject to natural forces, but they felt those forces were best displayed when they led to unlimited wealth, utter squalor, collective orgies, blood, and sudden death.

Among the romantic qualities they tried to achieve was "bigness" in its double reference to size and intensity. They wanted to display "big"—that is, intense—emotions against a physically large background. Bigness was the virtue that Norris most admired in Zola's novels. "The world of M. Zola," he said, "is a world of big things; the enormous, the formidable, the terrible, is what counts; no teacup tragedies here." In his own novels, Norris looked for big themes; after his trilogy on Wheat, he planned to write a still bigger trilogy on the three days' battle of Gettysburg, with one novel devoted to the events of each day. The whole notion of writing trilogies instead of separate novels came to be connected with the naturalistic movement, although it was also adopted by the historical romancers. Before Norris there had been only one planned trilogy in serious American fiction: *The Littlepage Manuscripts,* written by James Fenimore Cooper a few years before his death; it traces the story of a New York state landowning family through a hundred years and three generations. After Norris there were dozens of trilogies, with a few tetralogies and pentalogies: to mention some of the better known, there were Dreiser's trilogy on the career of a financier, T. S. Stribling's trilogy on the rise of a poor-white family, Dos Passos' trilogy on the United States from 1900 to 1930, James T. Farrell's trilogy on Studs Lonigan and Eugene O'Neill's trilogy of plays, *Mourning Becomes Electra.* Later O'Neill set to work on a trilogy of trilogies, on a theme that he planned to treat in nine full-length plays. Farrell wrote a tetralogy about the boyhood of Danny O'Neill and then attacked another theme that would require several volumes, the young manhood of Bernard Clare. Trilogies expanded into whole cycles of novels somehow related in theme. Thus, after the success of *The Jungle,* which had dealt with the meat-packing industry in Chicago, Upton Sinclair wrote novels on other cities (Denver, Boston) and other industries (oil, coal, whisky, automobiles); finally he settled on a character, Lanny Budd, whose adventures were as endless as those of Tarzan or Superman. Sinclair Lewis dealt one after another with various trades and professions: real estate, medicine, divinity, social service, hotel management, and the stage; there was no limit to the subjects he could treat, so long as his readers' patience was equal to his own.

With their eyes continually on vast projects, the American naturalists were careless about the details of their work and indifferent to the materials they were using; often their trilogies resembled great steel-structural buildings faced with cinder blocks and covered with cracked stucco ornaments. Sometimes the buildings remained unfinished. Norris set this pattern, too, when he died before he could start his third novel on the Wheat. Dreiser worked for years on *The Stoic,* which was to be the sequel to *The Financier* and *The Titan;* but he was never satisfied with the various endings he tried, and the book had to be completed by others after his death. O'Neill stopped work on his trilogy of trilogies. Lewis never wrote his novel on labor unions, although he spent months or years gathering material for it and spoke of it as his most ambitious work. In their effort to achieve bigness at any cost, the naturalists were likely to undertake projects that went beyond their physical or imaginative powers, or in which they discovered too late that they weren't interested.

Meanwhile they worked ahead in a delirium of production, like factories trying to set new records. To understand their achievements in speed and bulk one has to compare their output with that of an average novelist. There is of course no average novelist, but there are scores of men and women who earn their livings by writing novels, and many of them try to publish one book each year. If they spend four months planning and gathering material for the book, another four months writing the first draft (at the rate of about a thousand words a day), and the last four months in revision, they are at least not unusual. Very few of the naturalists would have been satisfied with that modest rate of production. Harold Frederic wrote as much as 4,000 words a day and often sent his manuscripts to the printer without corrections. At least he paused between novels to carry on his work as a foreign correspondent; but Jack London, who wrote only 1,000 words a day, tried to fulfill that quota six days a week and fifty-two weeks a year; he allowed himself no extra time for planning or revision. He wrote fifty books in seventeen years, and didn't pretend that all of them were his best writing. "I have no unfinished stories," he told an interviewer five years before his death. "Invariably I complete every one I start. If it's good, I sign it and send it out. If it isn't good, I sign it and send it out." David Graham Phillips finished his first novel in 1901 and published sixteen others before his death in 1911, in addition to the articles he wrote for muckraking magazines. He left behind him the manuscripts of six novels (including the two-volume *Susan Lenox*) that were published posthumously. Upton Sinclair set a record in the early days when he was writing half-dime novels for boys. He kept three secretaries busy; two of them would be transcribing their notes while the third was taking dictation. By this method he once wrote 18,000 words in a day. He gained a fluency that helped him later when he was writing serious books, but he also acquired a contempt for style that made them painful to read, except in their French translations. Almost all the naturalists read better in translation; that is one of the reasons for their international popularity as compared with the smaller audience that some of them found at home.

The naturalistic writers of all countries preferred an objective or scientific approach to their material As early as 1864 the brothers Goncourt had written in their journal, "The novel of today is made with documents narrated or selected from nature, just as history is based on written documents." A few years later Zola defined the novel as a scientific experiment; its purpose, he said in rather involved language, was to demonstrate the behavior of given characters in a given situation. Still later Norris advanced the doctrine "that no one could be a writer until he could regard life and people, and the world in general, from the objective point of view—until he could remain detached, outside, maintain the unswerving attitude of the observer." The naturalists as a group not only based their work on current scientific theories, but tried to copy scientific methods in planning their novels. They were writers who believed, or claimed to believe, that they could deliberately choose a subject for their work instead of being chosen by a subject; that they could go about collecting characters as a biologist collected specimens; and that their fictional account of such characters could be as accurate and true to the facts as the report of an experiment in the laboratory.

It was largely this faith in objectivity that led them to write about penniless people in the slums, whom they regarded as "outside" or alien subjects for observation. Some of them began with a feeling of contempt for the masses. Norris during his college years used to speak of "the canaille" and often wished for the day when all radicals could be "drowned on one raft." Later this pure contempt developed into a contemptuous interest, and he began to spend his afternoons on Polk Street, in San Francisco, observing with a detached eye the actions of what he now called "the people." The minds of the people, he thought, were simpler than those of persons in his own world; essentially these human beings were animals, "the creatures of habit, the playthings of forces," and therefore they were ideal subjects for a naturalistic novel. Some of the other naturalists revealed the same rather god-like attitude toward workingmen. Nevertheless they wrote about them, a bold step at a time when most novels dealt only with ladies, gentlemen, and faithful retainers; and often their contemptuous interest was gradually transformed into sympathy.

Their objective point of view toward their material was sometimes a pretense that deceived themselves before it deceived others. From the outside world they chose the subjects that mirrored their own conflicts and obsessions. Crane, we remember, said his purpose in writing *Maggie* was to show "that environment is a tremendous thing and often shapes lives regardlessly." Yet, on the subjective level, the novel also revealed an obsessive notion about the blamelessness of prostitutes that affected his career from beginning to end; it caused a series of scandals, involved him in a feud with the vice squad in Manhattan and finally led him to marry the madam of a bawdy house in Jacksonville. Norris's first novel, *Vandover and the Brute,* is an apparently objective study of degeneration, but it also mirrors the struggles of the author with his intensely Puritan conscience; Vandover is Norris himself. He had drifted into some mild dissipations and pictured them as leading to failure and insanity. Dreiser in *Sister Carrie,* was telling a story based on the adventures of one of his own sisters; that explains why Carrie Meeber in the novel is "Sister" Carrie, even though her relatives disappear after the first few pages. "My mind was a blank except for the name," Dreiser said when explaining how he came to write the novel. "I had no idea who or what she was to be. I have often thought that there was something mystic about it, as if I were being used, like a medium." In a sense he was being used by his memories, which had become subconscious. There was nothing mystic to Upton Sinclair about his fierce emotion in writing *The Jungle;* he knew from the beginning that he was telling his own story. "I wrote with tears and anguish," he says in his memoirs,

pouring into the pages all that pain which life had meant to me. Externally, the story had to do with a family of stockyards workers, but internally it was the story of my own family. Did I wish to know how the poor suffered in Chicago? I had only to recall the previous winter in a cabin, when we had only cotton blankets, and cowered shivering in our separate beds. . . . Our little boy was down with pneumonia that winter, and nearly died, and the grief of that went into the book.

Indeed, there is personal grief and fury and bewilderment in all the most impressive naturalistic novels. They are at their best, not when they are scientific or objective, in accordance with their own theories, but when they are least naturalistic, most personal and lyrical.

If we follow William James and divide writers into the two categories of the tough and the tender-minded, then most of the naturalists are tender-minded. The sense of moral fitness is strong in them; they believe in their hearts that nature *should* be kind, that virtue *should* be rewarded on earth, that men *should* control their own destinies. More than other writers, they are wounded by ugliness and injustice, but they will not close their eyes to either; indeed, they often give the impression of seeking out ugliness and injustice in order to be wounded again and again. They have hardly a trace of the cynicism that is often charged against them. It is the quietly realistic or classical writers who are likely to be cynics, in the sense of holding a low opinion of life and human beings; that low estimate is so deeply ingrained in them that they never bother to insist on it—for why should they try to make converts in such a hopeless world? The naturalists are always trying to convert others and themselves, and sometimes they build up new illusions simply to enjoy the pain of stripping them away. It is their feeling of fascinated revulsion toward their subject matter that makes some of the naturalists hard to read; they seem to be flogging themselves and their audience like a band of penitentes.

VII

So far I have been trying to present the positive characteristics of a movement in American letters, but naturalism can also be defined in terms of what it is not. Thus, to begin a list of negations, it is not journalism in the bad sense, merely sensational or entertaining or written merely to sell. It has to be honest by definition, and honesty in literature is a hard quality to achieve, one that requires more courage and concentration than journalists can profitably devote to writing a novel. Even when an author holds all the naturalistic doctrines, his books have to reach a certain level of observation and intensity before they deserve to be called naturalistic. Jack London held the doctrines and wrote fifty books, but only three or four of them reached the required level. David Graham Phillips reached it only once, in *Susan Lenox,* if he reached it then.

Literary naturalism is not the sort of doctrine that can be officially sponsored and taught in the public schools. It depends for too many of its effects on shocking the sensibilities of its readers and smashing their illusions. It always becomes a threat to the self-esteem of the propertied classes. *Babbitt,* for example, is naturalistic in its hostile treatment of American businessmen. When Sinclair Lewis defended Babbittry in a later novel, *The Prodigal Parents,* his work had ceased to be naturalistic.

For a third negative statement, naturalism is not what we have learned to call literature "in depth." It is concerned with human behavior and with explanations for that behavior in terms of heredity or environment. It presents the exterior world, often in striking visual images; but unlike the work of Henry James or Sherwood Anderson or William Faulkner—to mention only three writers in other traditions—it does not try to explore the world within. Faulkner's method is sometimes described as "subjective naturalism," but the phrase is self-contradictory, almost as if one spoke of "subjective biology" or "subjective physics."

Naturalism does not deal primarily with individuals in themselves, but rather with social groups or settings or movements, or with individuals like Babbitt and Studs Lonigan who are regarded as being typical of a group. The naturalistic writer tries not to identify himself with any of his characters, although he doesn't always succeed; in general his aim is to present them almost as if they were laboratory specimens. They are seldom depicted as being capable of moral decisions. This fact makes it easy to distinguish between the early naturalists and some of their contemporaries like Robert Herrick and Edith Wharton who also tried to write without optimistic illusions. Herrick and Wharton, however, dealt with individuals who possessed some degree of moral freedom; and often the plots of their novels hinge on a conscious decision by one of the characters. Hemingway, another author whose work is wrongly described as naturalistic, writes stories that reveal some moral quality, usually stoicism or the courage of a frightened man.

Many naturalistic works are valuable historical documents, but the authors in general have little sense of history. They present each situation as if it had no historical antecedents, and their characters might be men and women created yesterday morning, so few signs do they show of having roots in the past. "Science" for naturalistic writers usually means laboratory science, and not the study of human institutions or patterns of thought that persist through generations.

With a few exceptions they have no faith in reform, whether it be the reform of an individual by his own decision or the reform of society by reasoned courses of action. The changes they depict are the result of laws and forces and tendencies beyond human control. That is the great difference between the naturalists and the proletarian or Marxian novelists of the 1930's. The proletarian writers—who were seldom proletarians in private life—believed that men acting together could make a new world. But they borrowed the objective and exterior technique of the naturalists, which was unsuited to their essentially religious purpose. In the beginning of each book they portrayed a group of factory workers as the slaves of economic conditions, "the creatures of habit, the playthings of forces"; then later they portrayed the conversion of one or more workers to Marxism. But conversion is a psychological, not a biological, phenomenon, and it could not be explained purely in terms of conditions or forces. When the conversion took place, there was a shift from the outer to the inner world, and the novel broke in two.

It was not at all extraordinary for naturalism to change into religious Marxism in the middle of a novel, since it has always shown a tendency to dissolve into something else. On the record, literary naturalism does not seem to be a doctrine or attitude to which men are likely to cling through their whole lives. It is always being transformed into satire, symbolism, lyrical autobiography, utopian socialism, Communism, Catholicism, Buddhism, Freudian psychology, hack journalism or the mere assembling of facts. So far there is not in American literature a single instance in which a writer has remained a naturalist from beginning to end of a long career; even Dreiser before his death became a strange mixture of Communist and mystic. There are, however, a great many works that are predominantly naturalistic; and the time has come to list them in order to give the basis for my generalities.

I should say that those works, in fiction, were *Maggie* and *George's Mother* by Stephen Crane, with many of his short stories; *The Damnation of Theron Ware* by Harold Frederic; *Vandover, McTeague* and *The Octopus* (but not *The Pit*) by Frank Norris; *The Call of the Wild,* which is a sort of naturalistic Aesop's fable, besides *The Sea Wolf* and *Martin Eden* by Jack London; *The Jungle* by Upton Sinclair, as far as the page where Jurgis is converted to socialism; *Susan Lenox* by David Graham Phillips; all of Dreiser's novels except *The Bulwark* which has a religious ending written at the close of his life; all the serious novels of Sinclair Lewis between *Main Street* (1920) and *Dodsworth* (1929), but none he wrote afterward; Dos Passos' *Manhattan Transfer* and *U.S.A.*; James T. Farrell's work in general, but especially *Studs Lonigan;* Richard Wright's *Native Son;* and most of John Steinbeck's novels, including *In Dubious Battle* and all but the hortatory passages in *The Grapes of Wrath.* In poetry there is Robinson's early verse (*The Children of the Night*) and there is Edgar

Lee Masters' *Spoon River Anthology*. In the drama there are the early plays of Eugene O'Neill, from *Beyond the Horizon* to *Desire under the Elms*. Among essays there are H. L. Mencken's *Prejudices* and Joseph Wood Krutch's *The Modern Temper,* which is the most coherent statement of the naturalistic position. There are other naturalists in all fields, especially fiction, and other naturalistic books by several of the authors I have mentioned; but these are the works by which the school is likely to be remembered and judged.

And what shall we say in judgment?—since judge we must, after this long essay in definition. Is naturalism true or false in its premises and good or bad in its effect on American literature? Its results have been good, I think, in so far as it has forced its adherents to stand in opposition to American orthodoxy. Honest writing in this country, the only sort worth bothering about, has almost always been the work of an opposition, chiefly because the leveling and unifying elements in our culture have been so strong that a man who accepts orthodox judgments is in danger of losing his literary personality. Catullus and Villon might be able to write their poems here; with their irregular lives they wouldn't run the risk of being corrupted by the standards of right-thinking people. But Virgil, the friend of Augustus, the official writer who shaped the myth of the Roman state—Virgil would be a dubious figure as an American poet. He would be tempted to soften his values in order to become a prophet for the masses. The American myth of universal cheap luxuries, tiled bathrooms, and service with a smile would not provide him with the basis for an epic poem.

The naturalists, standing in opposition, have been writers of independent and strongly marked personalities. They have fought for the right to speak their minds and have won a measure of freedom for themselves and others. Yet it has to be charged against them that their opposition often takes the form of cheapening what they write about; of always looking for the lowdown or the payoff, that is, for the meanest explanation of everything they describe. There is a tendency in literary naturalism—as distinguished from philosophical naturalism, which is not my subject—always to explain the complex in terms of the simple: society in terms of self, man in terms of his animal inheritance, and the organic in terms of the inorganic. The result is that something is omitted at each stage in this process of reduction. To say that man is a beast of prey or a collection of chemical compounds omits most of man's special nature; it is a metaphor, not a scientific statement.

This scientific weakness of naturalism involves a still greater literary weakness, for it leads to a conception of man that makes it impossible for naturalistic authors to write in the tragic spirit. They can write about crimes, suicides, disasters, the terrifying, and the grotesque; but even the most powerful of their novels and plays are case histories rather than tragedies in the classical sense. Tragedy is an affirmation of man's importance; it is "the imitation of noble actions," in Aristotle's phrase; and the naturalists are unable to believe in human nobility. "We write no tragedies today," said Joseph Wood Krutch in his early book, *The Modern Temper,* which might better have been called "The Naturalistic Temper." "If the plays and novels of today deal with littler people and less mighty emotions it is not because we have become interested in commonplace souls and their unglamorous adventures but because we have come, willy-nilly, to see the soul of man as commonplace and its emotions as mean." But Krutch was speaking only for those who shared the naturalistic point of view. There are other doctrines held by modern writers that make it possible to endow their characters with human dignity. Tragic novels and plays have been written in these years by Christians, Communists, humanists, and even by existentialists, all of whom believe in different fashions and degrees that men can shape their own fates.

For the naturalists, however, men are "human insects" whose brief lives are completely determined by society or nature. The individual is crushed in a moment if he resists; and his struggle, instead of being tragic, is merely pitiful or ironic, as if we had seen a mountain stir itself to overwhelm a fly. Irony is a literary effect used time and again by all the naturalistic writers. For Stephen Crane it is the central effect on which almost all his plots depend: thus, in *The Red Badge of Courage* the boy makes himself a hero by running away. In *A Mystery of Heroism* a soldier risks his life to bring a bucket of water to his comrades, and the water is spilled. In *The Monster* a Negro stableman is so badly burned in rescuing a child that he becomes a faceless horror; and the child's father, a physician, loses his practice as a reward for sheltering the stableman. The irony in Dreiser's novels depends on the contrast between conventional morality and the situations he describes: Carrie Meeber loses her virtue and succeeds in her career; Jennie Gerhardt is a kept woman with higher principles than any respectable wife. In Sinclair Lewis the irony is reduced to an obsessive and irritating trick of style; if he wants to say that a speech was dull and stupid, he has to call it "the culminating glory of the dinner" and then, to make sure that we catch the point, explain that it was delivered by Mrs. Adelaide Tarr Gimmitch, "known throughout the country as 'the Unkies' Girl.' " The reader, seeing the name of Gimmitch, is supposed to smile a superior smile. There is something superior and ultimately tiresome in the attitude of many naturalists toward the events they describe. Irony —like pity, its companion—is a spectator's emotion, and it sets a space between ourselves and the characters in the novel. They suffer, but their cries reach us faintly, like those of dying strangers we cannot hope to save.

There is nothing in the fundamental principles of naturalism that requires a novel to be written in hasty or hackneyed prose. Flaubert, the most careful stylist of his age, was the predecessor and guide of the French naturalists. Among the naturalistic writers of all countries who wrote with a feeling for language were the brothers Goncourt, Ibsen, Hardy, and Stephen Crane. But it was Norris, not Crane, who set the standards for naturalistic fiction in the United States, and Norris had no respect for style. "What pleased me most in your review of 'McTeague,' " he said in a letter to Isaac Marcosson, "was 'disdaining all pretensions to style.' It is precisely what I try most to avoid. I detest 'fine writing,' 'rhetoric,' 'elegant English'—tommyrot. Who cares for fine style! Tell your yarn and let your style go to the devil. We don't want literature, we want life." Yet the truth was that Norris' novels were full of fine writing and lace-curtain English. "Untouched, unassailable, undefiled," he said of the wheat, "that mighty world force, that nourisher of nations, wrapped in Nirvanic calm, indifferent to the human swarm, gigantic, resistless, moved onward in its appointed grooves." He never learned to present his ideas in their own clothes or none at all; it was easier to dress them in borrowed plush; easier to make all his calms Nirvanic and all his grooves appointed.

Yet Norris wrote better prose than most of his successors among the American naturalists. With a few exceptions like Dos Passos and Steinbeck, they have all used language as a blunt instrument; they write as if they were swinging shillelaghs. O'Neill is a great dramatist, but he has never had an ear for the speech of living persons. Lewis used to have an ear, but now listens only to himself.

He keeps being arch and ironical about his characters until we want to snarl at him, "Quit patronizing those people! Maybe they'd have something to say if you'd only let them talk." Farrell writes well when he is excited or angry, but most of the time he makes his readers trudge through vacant lots in a South Chicago smog. Dreiser is the worst writer of all, but in some ways the least objectionable; there is something native to himself in his misuse of the language, so that we come to cherish it as a sign of authenticity, like the tool marks on Shaker furniture. Most of the others simply use the oldest and easiest phrase.

But although the naturalists as a group are men of defective hearing, they almost all have keen eyes for new material. Their interest in themes that others regarded as too unpleasant or ill-bred has immensely broadened the scope of American fiction. Moreover, they have had enough vitality and courage to be exhilarated by the American life of their own times. From the beginning they have exulted in the wealth and ugliness of American cities, the splendor of the mansions and the squalor of the tenements. They compared Pittsburgh to Paris and New York to imperial Rome. Frank Norris thought that his own San Francisco was the ideal city for storytellers; "Things happen in San Francisco," he said. Dreiser remarked of Chicago, "It is given to some cities, as to some lands, to suggest romance, and to me Chicago did that hourly. . . . Florence in its best days must have been something like this to young Florentines, or Venice to the young Venetians." The naturalists for all their faults were embarked on a bolder venture than those other writers whose imaginations can absorb nothing but legends already treated in other books, prepared and predigested food. They tried to seize the life around them, and at their best they transformed it into new archetypes of human experience. Just as Cooper had shaped the legend of the frontier and Mark Twain the legend of the Mississippi, so the naturalists have been shaping the harsher legends of an urban and industrial age.

INTRODUCTION TO CHAPTER IX

THE IDEA OF ORGANIC EXPRESSION
AND AMERICAN ARCHITECTURE

THE artistic principle of organic expression, while tracing its roots to sources which themselves nourished the evolutionary movement, was, like the naturalist current in literature, fully developed by men whose conscious use of insights derived from the post-Darwinian understanding of natural processes would hardly have been possible under other circumstances. The romantic current which appeared in other phases of evolutionary thought crops out again in the writings of Sullivan and Wright, as well as the typical confusion over individual and social values. Although Professor Egbert finds that the functionalism and environmentalism of the organicists sprang in part from the national character and from opposition to conscious artistic traditions, they were nevertheless strengthened and confirmed by the evolutionary influence.

S. P.

IX

THE IDEA OF ORGANIC EXPRESSION AND AMERICAN ARCHITECTURE

DONALD DREW EGBERT

I

ALTHOUGH there has been relatively little conscious connection between the arts of design and theories of evolution, indirectly such theories have had considerable influence on art. Furthermore, the history of art is an excellent medium for demonstrating the fact, not realized by many scientists, that scientific doctrines of evolution have been in large part an expression of tendencies long in the air and by no means solely scientific in either origin or spirit.

Of all the arts, architecture is the one which has most clearly reflected the general philosophic point of view which lies behind the chief theories of evolution, simply because it is the art most directly affected by changes in the physical or social environment. In this chapter, therefore, the subject matter will be limited to the art of architecture. And because the influence of evolutionary doctrine on architecture, as on the other arts, has generally been so indirect and imprecise, for greater clarity and precision we shall consider only a single important aspect of evolution, namely, the concept of organic expression. Moreover, for the sake of conciseness, the effects of this concept upon recent American architecture will be studied with special reference to only three great architects, all of them firm believers in the idea of organic expression. These three—Louis Sullivan, Frank Lloyd Wright, and Walter Gropius —have all exerted much influence not only because they have all designed important buildings, but also because each of them has been exceptionally effective in putting his own theories of architectural design into words. As a result, the idea of organic expression can be studied in the writings as well as in the architecture of these men, so that the theories of each of them can be checked against his practice.

In order to make clear the meaning of the term organic as used in this chapter, it will first be necessary to analyze briefly the numerous and somewhat confusing definitions to be found in any standard dictionary. For example, *Webster's New International Dictionary* (1932 ed.) gives the first, and oldest, meaning of the adjective as follows: "Serving as an organ, instrument or means; acting as an instrument of nature or art to a certain destined function or end; instrumental"—a meaning that goes back at least to the early sixteenth century.[1] Another chief meaning cited by Webster is, "Pertaining to, or inherent in, a certain organization; depending on the constitution or structure." In biology, says Webster, the word can be defined as, "Pertaining to or derived from living organisms. . . ." And an organism is defined as: "An individual constituted to carry on the activities of life by means of parts or organs more or less separate in function but mutually dependent; any living being. . . ." It was this meaning that Huxley had in mind when he said, "In speaking of the causes which lead to our present knowledge of organic nature, I have used it almost as an equivalent of the word 'living.' . . ."[2]

By philosophers "organic," used as either an adjective or a noun, is employed in ways which more or less combine the various meanings mentioned above. Thus the philosophical definition of the adjective is given by Webster as: "Possessed of a complex structure comparable to that of living beings; possessed of a structure, or forming a totality, in which the relation of the parts involves relations to the whole, which itself is free or comparatively free from external relationship. . . ."

At first glance all of this seems both hopelessly complex and hopelessly confused, and it must be admitted that the word organic is not only one which possesses multiple meanings, but one which has long been used with exceptional looseness. Nevertheless, on careful consideration not only can a few basic implications be distinguished, but a historical development in the use of the word can be traced, paralleling developments in science and philosophy including the philosophy of art.

Certainly throughout its history the words organic and organism have always connoted organization into a whole, which has a function or end. However, there has long existed a basic disagreement as to the exact nature of an organism. In one group have been those who insist that there is no essential difference between life and nonlife, and that therefore an organism is merely an assembly of parts to form a machine which is nothing but the sum of its parts, a machine determined by laws of physics and chemistry. In the opposing group have been those who insist that the controlling characteristic of an organism is a vital force above physics and chemistry, a life substance or principle independent of and in addition to the substances of inorganic nature. This opposition between the belief that the word organic connotes *mechanism,* and the belief that it connotes some form of *vitalism,* became especially pronounced in the eighteenth century and has not been completely resolved to this day. Moreover, while those who support mechanism have been united in opposing vitalism, they have disagreed among themselves as to whether purely mechanical laws, or other physical laws and chemical laws, control the organism and thus are fundamental to "life." Similarly, the concept of vitalism has been supported by at least two different groups for somewhat different reasons. On the one hand, it has been supported by those scientists who hold that life is fundamentally governed by something which transcends ordinary physical and chemical laws. But it has also been upheld by supporters of the romantic movement either because of their insistence on the uniqueness of the individual human organism and therefore of the individual's imagination, or because they believe that all of nature, including human beings, is pervaded by living spirit.

More recently the concepts of mechanism and vitalism, so long regarded as fundamentally opposed to one another, have for many now been replaced by a third concept, an *"organismic"* point of view in which mechanism and vitalism are, as it were, subsumed under a principle of organization and integration. Thus some biologists, some scientists in other fields, and some highly influential philosophers (including the late Alfred North Whitehead) have come to believe that the antithesis between mechanism and vitalism is essentially meaningless, because in their view neither sheer mechanism nor sheer vitalism alone can offer an adequate explanation of life as a whole and thus of organic evolution. To such scientists and philosophers the concept of organism means a living whole which, in possessing coordination or integration of functions, is fundamentally more than a mechanism and more, also, than a vague undefined vital force. In this view, then, the distinctive attributes of life are considered to be inherent in the total organism as an integrated and organized *whole*. But though these organicists agree that *organization* is a basic attribute of life, they in turn tend to differ among themselves as to whether the development of that organization is based solely on the substances of inorganic nature or involves a special vital principle.

Thus historically the word organic has implied three major related, but different, concepts, namely, mechanism, vitalism, and an organicism which is more than sheer mechanism or vitalism.[3] Each of these concepts has had profound implications for art as well as for philosophy and science. Each still has its highly influential supporters today (even though a very large number of scientists simply by-pass the problem on the grounds that the sciences can operate perfectly well without deciding it, and that therefore the whole question is unimportant or even meaningless).[4]

However, although fundamental differences continue to separate the supporters of mechanism, vitalism and organicism, it can at least be said that the members of all three groups have usually tended to agree upon one thing. For most, at least, of the philosophers or scientists who have subscribed to any one of these concepts have tended to agree that significance and truth reside primarily in nature, rather than either in man or in a God who is independent of nature and controls it for his own ends.

In this chapter all the different meanings of "organic" will have to be dealt with, and as the chapter develops will be defined in more detail, particularly with reference to their bearing on architecture. But before considering them any further, it must be emphasized and re-emphasized that to this day the concept of "life," which the word organic implies, has never been defined to the complete satisfaction of scientists and philosophers. Indeed, the word has even become increasingly difficult to define since each quality that biologists usually stress as characteristic of living organisms (such as capacity for reproduction, movement, irritability, and perhaps even self-repair of injuries) has also been found in some form of inorganic matter. Primarily for this reason the biological concept of the living organism suggested by the word "organic" has often been applied also to aspects of the inorganic world. This has been especially true since 1828 when Wöhler produced synthetically the first "organic compound" by transforming ammonium cyanate into urea, and thereby helped to blur the earlier belief in a fundamental distinction between the products of living organisms and the nonliving world.

Largely as a result of the ambiguities introduced by discoveries of this sort, it became easier to regard the whole universe as a single organism. It became easy, also, for Auguste Comte, and for Herbert Spencer and his followers, the Social Darwinists, to consider society as a kind of living organism, because the total concept of an organism involves the concept of the interaction of organisms. Similarly, Hegel could regard the state, and Karl Marx the social class, as a kind of organism; while Spengler and others were enabled to look upon a single civilization, a single culture, in this way. And because works of art and art styles can be considered as the expressions of a given society, civilization, or class, organicists could look upon them as if they too were natural organisms, each endowed with a significant life of its own, a life which should be fully expressed. Consequently Frank Lloyd Wright could state in his Princeton lectures on *Modern Architecture,* published in 1931, "The word [organic] applies to 'living' structure—a structure or concept wherein features or parts are so organized in form and substance as to be, applied to purpose, *integral*. Everything that 'lives' is therefore organic." Thus to Wright a building that is "integral" (by which he means a building whose every part is a direct result of the process of construction for use) is a "living" organism.

In so far as Wright holds that the best architectural form is the one which has the best organization for survival so that it will "live" while poorer forms "die," he clearly agrees with the Darwinian doctrine of the survival of the fittest. But it must not be forgotten that there is a fundamental difference between the views of Wright as an artist, and Darwin as a scientist. For the Darwinian scientist believes that the characteristics which enable an organism to survive are selected by *nature* itself through nature's laws, whereas to Wright it is the *artist* who is the selector on the basis of what he considers to be natural. Consequently, one artist can regard as "living" and "vital" various art forms that are very different from those chosen by another. And this, of course, means that in fundamental respects architecture, like any other art, is necessarily different from science in general and Darwinian science in particular.

Obviously, what anyone in any field considers to have "life," whether actual or metaphorical, he will tend to believe is particularly real and significant. Since whatever he believes to be real and significant will determine what he considers to give meaning and order to the world, it will necessarily determine the character of his general philosophy and thus of his philosophy of art. In other words, the beliefs and assumptions of any individual—beliefs in part peculiarly his own but in part produced by the age and by the environment—will in the end decide what he considers to be worthy of expression in architecture or any other art.

Because works of architecture thus necessarily reflect the philosophy of life held by their designer, and also customarily reflect the points of view prevailing at the time and place of their creation, the various aspects of the doctrine of organic expression, so increasingly important since the eighteenth century, have been increasingly reflected in the architecture of the period. And because the concept of organic expression usually implies that the ultimate reality lies within nature itself as a single great organism, rather than either in man or in a God who created and transcends nature, it has usually connoted some form of philosophical naturalism in architecture as in other aspects of life. As a result of this belief in nature as fundamental, those who insist upon the necessity for organic expression in art have often been much interested in natural science. They have therefore often sought to take over the findings of the natural sciences, particularly those of paleontology, botany, and zoology, which, during the last two centuries, have given a new emphasis to the fact that the natural world is characterized by change, growth, and development—in short, by evolution. For this reason, those who have come to hold the doctrine of organic expression have customarily believed in that of evolution as well, so that the two have jointly affected architectural design. Moreover, the naturalistic point of view which so often lies behind organic expression (and which will shortly be defined in more detail) has tended to encourage a very different kind of philosophy of architecture from those produced, say, under the humanism of the Renaissance, or under the theocentric point of view dominant during the Middle Ages. It is a philosophy of architecture based not on principles of design considered forever valid and universal, like those of the Renaissance, and not on that subordination of man to God implicit in the religious architecture of the Middle Ages. It is based on a belief that buildings should be in harmony with the phenomena of the natural world and nature's laws; and since the forms of architecture are held to be so largely determined by natural environmental conditions, buildings—like man or even God—have been thought of as part of nature itself.

However, buildings have been thus conceived from two major and very different points of view, one of which can be loosely termed "romantic," the other "functionalistic." Because these two terms as applied to architecture are so fundamental to this chapter, it will be necessary to define them, as used herein, at some length and to clarify them by contrasting them with other historically distinctive points of view toward architecture. And since both the romantic and functionalistic aspects of the organic concept of architecture will be discussed primarily as aspects of naturalism, our use of the word naturalism will also have to be defined as the chapter develops. Once these terms have been clarified, the remainder of the chapter—less abstract and consequently more readable—can be devoted to the history and meaning of the idea of organic expression with reference to American architecture.

Turning first to the romantic aspect of organic expression, it is of course true that the word "romanticism," like "naturalism," is one of multiple meanings, and one which has stirred up an enormous amount of controversy. It is also true that not all kinds of romanticism are naturalistic. Yet even though there are thus many different varieties of romanticism, it can perhaps be said with some truth that practically all of them have sought to achieve for the individual a more vital existence, and this primarily by means of his imagination and feelings. And certainly one type of romanticism, at least, has naturalistic connotations because it has maintained that a more vital existence for the individual can best be achieved by a return to an informal, more-or-less "primitive" kind of nature to which, in effect, God as well as man and all his works are subordinated as part of nature itself. According to this kind of romanticism, the phenomenal world of nature is to be regarded as most real and most significant because in it God and man come together. Those who subscribe to this type of romanticism are thus customarily pantheists in so far as they believe that man is natural and significant only when he is *in* nature, even though they interpret the life of the universe through the soul of man rather than through nature itself. Just as such romanticists consider either the

"noble savage" or pastoral man to be the most natural and significant of mankind because he is in harmony with nature, so also
they believe that only those buildings which similarly harmonize
with the surrounding natural environment are natural and worth
while.

Typical of this romantic point of view toward architecture is
Horace Walpole's celebrated Gothic Revival villa, Strawberry Hill
(Fig. 1) at Twickenham, England, begun about 1750. It is romantic not only because of the conscious harmony between the picturesque forms of the architecture and the picturesque nature
around it, a harmony contrived by artificially altering the natural
site if necessary, but also because of its intentional appeal to
the emotions of the individual. Walpole deliberately revived the
Gothic style here as a style which, by its inherently picturesque
and often informal character, could have a more direct appeal to
his feelings than could the formal and rationally conceived Pal-
ladian architecture then predominant in Georgian England under
the influence of the Italian Renaissance. While the plans of Pal-
ladian buildings (Fig. 12) consist of simple geometric forms
arrived at primarily by means of abstractly rational principles of
design considered good for all time and thus independent of evolution, the plan of Strawberry Hill (Fig. 2) was determined very
largely by the individualistic whims of Horace Walpole himself.
As the word "whim" suggests, Walpole designed Strawberry Hill
by relying on his own emotions and intuition rather than on any
kind of abstract logic. For the romantic holds that truth lies in
intuitively emotional—rather than rational—expression, insisting
that the characteristic quality of the mind evinces itself in feeling
and especially in the feeling of individuality.

However, the romantic emphasis on individuality often gives
rise to the belief that all individuals are equally important, and so
to an equalitarianism and humanitarianism in which the relation
of man to his social environment becomes paramount. In other
words, because other men also partake of nature, the romantic
may hold that truth and goodness reside in a harmony between
man and his social, as well as natural, environment, so that romantic architecture—like the romantic philosophy of a Rousseau—can
display considerable variation as to what constitutes "natural" expression. Sometimes, as at Strawberry Hill, essentially individualistic values are stressed, but at other times cooperative, equali-

tarian, and humanitarian social values are emphasized, as for example in a typical English garden city of the twentieth century (Fig. 4).

To a very considerable degree the individualistic approach to romantic harmony between architecture and its picturesque natural environment which is so characteristic of Strawberry Hill, is also exemplified by the house known as Falling Water, on Bear Run, Penn. (Figs. 5 and 6), a house designed by Frank Lloyd Wright in 1936 nearly two hundred years after Walpole began Strawberry Hill. Because the philosophies of architecture reflected in Falling Water on the one hand, and in the romantic Gothic of Strawberry Hill on the other, are in this respect so similar, it is not surprising to find that Frank Lloyd Wright admires the Gothic architecture of the Middle Ages. But he admires it primarily because he feels that the spirit behind Gothic architecture is fundamentally identical with his own organic point of view: in 1910 he wrote, "I have called this feeling for the organic character of form and treatment the Gothic spirit, for it was more completely realized in the forms of that architecture, perhaps, than any other." [5] Yet in praising the true Gothic of the Middle Ages for its organic qualities, Wright implies criticism of romantic Neo-Gothic buildings like Strawberry Hill which, even though possessing some characteristics in common with Wright's architecture, in most respects are hardly "organic." For example, at Strawberry Hill Walpole often did not hesitate to imitate stone forms in plaster (Fig. 3) if necessary for most easily producing the emotional effect best suited to his feelings of the moment. Whereas at Falling Water, Wright has characteristically made a conscious effort to express the character natural to each specific material— notably the character natural to reinforced concrete and glass and to local stone. To a far greater degree than Walpole, Wright has also given direct and natural expression to the specific use of the edifice: whether one admires Falling Water or not, it cannot be denied that the building does express what it is, a country house primarily for summer and week-end use.

Thus, together with certain romantic characteristics, Wright has consciously and directly suggested both the "natural" function of the materials and methods of construction, and the "natural" function and use of the building itself, insisting that both of these must be expressed if a truly organic form is to be achieved. In his own words, "Form is organic only when it is natural to materials and natural to function." [6] It can therefore be said with truth that Falling Water reflects a functionalistic as well as a romantic point of view, and so combines *both* of the two chief points of view which so often come together in a naturalistic philosophy of architecture. For it reflects a philosophy which, in both its romantic and functionalistic aspects, encourages man to be "natural" by living in accord with what he judges the phenomenal world of nature to be.

Such is the meaning of the term naturalism as used in this chapter, a meaning somewhat wider than that found elsewhere in this book. It is—to repeat—a meaning which includes aspects of the romantic approach to architecture (according to which the architectural form is to be organized in harmony with environmental nature for emotional purposes), and includes also the functionalistic approach (according to which the form should harmonize with the natural qualities of the building materials and with the nature of the use to which the building is put). Now this second, or functionalistic, aspect of naturalism can be discussed in more detail.

As the functionalist tends to believe that nature, man, and God (if any) are all one, he necessarily tends to have a monistic philosophy of life, which, however, differs from the monistic pantheism of most romanticists. For the functionalist holds that man, as the most highly developed of all natural organisms, can investigate the phenomena of nature and arrive at nature's laws by means of his reason, so that intuition, glorified by the romantic, is thrown aside. Moreover, he is likely to look upon the universe as a mechanism operating according to natural laws, and to regard the laws of nature as basically the laws of physics and chemistry. Because the functionalist thus tends to hold that reality lies in the phenomena of nature, and specifically in the laws which he believes give order to matter, he frequently subscribes to a materialistic philosophy; and in architecture he correspondingly tends to give direct expression to the natural qualities of materials as ends in themselves. However, in the last analysis, the functionalist is usually forced to adopt an organismic (and hence fundamentally biological rather than mechanistic) point of view. For monism and sheer mechanism are contradictory: the idea of nature as a simple machine is fatal to monism because a machine implies something outside of itself to design and construct it. [7] Consequently, in order to maintain his monistic position, in order to continue to identify nature, man, and God, the functionalist looks upon nature as a great organism with a life of its own, an organism developing according to its own laws. In this way he often adopts a fundamentally biological point of view, which—particularly since Darwin—has lent itself to the concept of evolution.

In believing that an ultimate order and truth reside in the laws, mechanistic or biological, through which nature operates, the functionalist necessarily considers scientific knowledge to be especially important. He not only maintains that the laws of nature discovered through science must be made use of (so that technology and immediately "practical" values are highly esteemed), but he insists that they must be directly expressed in art. As a result, the scientifically direct expression of function and structure is for him of first importance.

In so far as architecture is an art, however, it necessarily requires more than the narrowly literal expression of purpose. Obviously enough, an edifice whose design has been completely and literally determined by bald function would not be architecture as art, but only construction, since it would lack the intent of the artist to "say something" by means of the medium of his art. In other words, because such a building would be the sheerly impersonal result of brute natural fact, natural fact unshaped by the highly individual imagination of a great artist, it must necessarily lack the significant uniqueness which is one characteristic of works of art. For this reason, when in this chapter a great architect like Frank Lloyd Wright or Walter Gropius is called a functionalist, we obviously mean, not that he is a literal functionalist who restricts himself solely to engineering or sheer building, but merely that he is an artist who places a *relatively* high importance on function and its direct expression.

Like Wright himself, his master, Louis Sullivan, also emphasized the necessity for expressing "organically" the nature and function of the specific building materials and the nature of the function and use of the given building. It is worthy of note that Sullivan was the first to employ—in 1896—the phrase which is still the slogan of the functionalists, "Form follows function." Six years before, in the Wainwright Building at St. Louis (Fig. 7), Sullivan had designed the first skyscraper in which really direct architectural expression was given both to a modern, tall office building, and also to a fireproofed steel-frame construction (even though the expression of the steel frame here is not so completely literal as it looks, because only every other one of the vertical members actually contains a structural column). A few years later (1899) Sullivan built the Schlesinger and Mayer store in Chicago, today Carson Pirie Scott & Co. (Fig. 8), in which, while expressing a fireproofed steel frame even more directly than in the Wainwright Building, he also gave conscious visual expression to the specific functions of a department store. Furthermore, in theory at least, Sullivan customarily insisted that the natural environment of a given edifice—the site, climate, etc.—must also be functionally expressed in the very forms of the architecture itself. And as will be seen later, the importance which he thus gave to environmental conditions as determining structure and design resulted in part from the direct influence of theories of evolution on his philosophy of architecture.

Sullivan's pupil, Wright, was to go still further than his master in expressing environmental conditions in his architecture. For example, his so-called "prairie-style" houses, such as his Robie House (Fig. 9), built at Chicago in 1909, were consciously given a particular kind of horizontal composition admirably suited to harmonize with and express the flatness of the Middle Western site whenever an adequate lot was available. When faced with very different climatic and site conditions, however—as in the case of the winter studio residence, Taliesin West (Fig. 10), which Wright has been building for himself and his pupils in Arizona ever since 1938—he has changed the architectural treatment to fit the location. At Taliesin West he has used a more jagged silhouette and brilliant color harmonizing with its desert setting, so that the architecture might seem to grow organically out of its own particular environment.

Clearly, then, the buildings of Louis Sullivan, and, even more, those of Frank Lloyd Wright, reflect an organismic kind of architectural philosophy which, in both its romantic and functionalistic aspects, tends toward naturalism. As already noted, a naturalistic philosophy is likely to imply an interest in the processes of development or change in nature for their own sake, an interest also in the effects of environmental conditions on structure and form, and so lends itself to belief in doctrines of evolution. It is primarily for this reason that both Wright and Sullivan have shown a considerable degree of direct and indirect sympathy with Darwinian and Spencerian thought. While it is true that, from the organismic point of view now accepted by many biologists, Darwin and Spencer were not yet complete organicists in so far as they both believed that a biological organism is no more than a mechanistic aggregate of its cells; in this they were simply accepting the prevailing view of their day. In physiology, for example, the concept that the human organism is a system of organized functions and thus more than a mere assemblage of parts like a machine did not become widely accepted until about 1865. For only then—six years after Darwin first published the *Origin of Species*—had this concept at last been clearly stated in the *Introduction à la médicine expérimentale* of Claude Bernard, whose naturalistic belief in the adaptation of means to ends in animals and plants, could, however, still give strong support to the Darwinian principle of natural selection. Yet although Darwin and Spencer were restricted to a mechanistic view of organism, they nevertheless greatly aided in spreading the idea of organic expression by stressing the importance of nature's processes and the influence of the natural environment on change and development. And in so doing they helped to pave the way for the architectural philosophies of Louis Sullivan and Frank Lloyd Wright.

II

Before going further the evolutionary and naturalistic point of view reflected in the architecture of Sullivan and Wright should perhaps be more adequately defined by contrasting it in more detail with basically different philosophies of architecture and of life. Specifically, it will be contrasted now with (1) the humanistic point of view so characteristic of the Renaissance version of the classic tradition, and (2) the theocentric point of view so typical of the Middle Ages and so clearly reflected in medieval religious architecture.

To the humanist—as the word itself suggests—man, rather than nature or God, is most significant, because man is the focus and mediator between nature and God. Yet Renaissance humanism never quite decided whether God and nature, Creator and created, are separate and distinct, or whether nature, man, and God are all part of a single great hierarchy of Being. In other words, the Renaissance never quite made up its mind whether to accept a Christian dualism, or the pantheism characteristic of the Neoplatonic philosophy which had then been revived as part of the rebirth of classicism. But in making man the focus, humanism clearly differs from romanticism. It differs in the fact that the humanist emphasizes the universal qualities of the individual rather than his uniqueness, and seeks not to live in nature but to transcend and control nature by imposing an ideally rational pattern upon it. For the humanist relies primarily on the logical powers of the human reason, and not on romantic intuition and feeling.

It is true that the functionalist also relies on reason, applying it to the task of determining the specific laws of nature, laws which are to be expressed differently in each specific work of architecture because each building is considered an answer to a different set of conditions, including environmental conditions. However, while the functionalist thus applies his reason to the expression of highly specific characteristics in what he considers to be a scientific and practical way, the humanist, on the contrary, emphasizes a more abstract kind of reasoning, avoiding any conception of art that can be designated as either personal or local. For this reason the architect who holds to the humanistic tradition is likely to maintain that, by means of the rational faculty common to all men, mankind has arrived at principles of design which are superior to time and place, and therefore eternally and universally valid for all architecture. This point of view—sharply opposed in Darwin's statement that "the idea of what is beautiful is not innate or unalterable" [8]—is reflected with especial clarity in the architecture of Renaissance Italy. Not only did the Renaissance (and the seventeenth century as well) usually subscribe to the Aristotelian view that whatever is universal is necessarily superior to the specific facts of nature on which, according to Aristotle, the universal is based; but often the Renaissance also adopted the Neoplatonic belief in an ideal beauty which is independent of, as well as superior to, the particulars of the world of the senses, and which is therefore universally valid for all time.

Certainly the very form of characteristic buildings of the Italian high Renaissance, such as Palladio's celebrated Villa Capra (1552–) near Vicenza (Figs. 11 and 12), could not be regarded as "organic" by Wright or Sullivan because it was not primarily determined by the specific nature of the materials or of the site, or even by the particular functions of the building itself. It was determined instead mainly by what were considered to be universal and abstractly rational principles of design, principles more or less implicit in the general classic tradition to which the Renaissance subscribed. Because of this fact it is difficult to make out at a glance what the specific materials of the Villa Capra are—whether its walls are of stone, or of brick and stucco as is actually the case. Nor is the specific function of the building immediately clear: in plan, rooms of quite different function have been given exactly the same shape in order to permit that high degree of symmetry and axiality which so well expresses the abstractly logical spirit of the Renaissance. Palladio would no doubt have followed much the same general principles in designing a house for a different location in a very different climate—many years later, indeed, Thomas Jefferson could submit an almost literal copy of the Villa Capra as his design for the White House in Washington without violating in any fundamental way the principles of the Renaissance tradition. But because the composition of Renaissance buildings does not grow primarily out of natural and environmental conditions, it is obvious that the Renaissance philosophy of architecture must necessarily be anathema to an organicist. This fact explains Frank Lloyd Wright's fervent cry, "Instinctively, I think, I hated the empty pretentious shapes of the Renaissance," because, like all cultural organicists (including, one might add, such diverse figures as John Dewey, James Harvey Robinson, Charles Beard, Mr. Justice Holmes, and Thorstein Veblen), Wright is bitterly opposed to formalism, abstractionism, and traditional method.[9]

Turning now to the theocentric point of view under which the great cathedrals of the Middle Ages were built, it too is widely different in its ends (though not so much so in means) from that of the organicist, and different also from that of the humanist of the Renaissance tradition. For from this medieval point of view, neither man nor nature is most real, but God; therefore it is the *super*natural, the *super*human, and the *super*rational which are considered most real and significant, and are held to impose order on both nature and man. It is true that man and nature are also considered real, but primarily because they have been created by God. A sharp distinction is made between Creator and created, and, in contrast to the Renaissance, God and not man is the focus. Consequently, while a great medieval church, such as Chartres Cathedral (Fig. 13), does stir the emotions by means of an extraordinarily functional structure rationally conceived, the chief end in view is not emotion for the sake of emotion, as it so often is for the romanticist. Nor is its chief aim the organic expression of structure and use, even though relative functionalists such as Wright (who was much influenced by the great French Gothic Revivalist and proto-functionalist, Viollet-le-Duc), have tended to glorify the functionalism of the Gothic as an end in itself. Nor, indeed, is it the primary purpose of a medieval cathedral to express abstractly rational principles of formal design, as was the tendency in Renaissance buildings, even though the form of the Gothic cathedral, too, was partly determined by mathematics. Instead, the chief end of the cathedral is a spiritual one, because the purpose of its architecture is to lead the human spirit from this world to God, with the connection between the individual worshiper and Deity made through the elaborate hierarchy and ritual of the Roman Catholic church as expressed in the complex but rationally ordered forms of the building itself.

This, then, is the theme on which the rest of this chapter will be based, namely, that the idea of organic expression usually reflects, not a theocentric or humanistic philosophy, but a naturalistic one which, while always existing to some degree, has been especially dominant since the eighteenth century. For the eighteenth century gave rise almost simultaneously to the romantic return to a more or less primitive nature and to that functionalistic glorification of science and technology known as the industrial revolution. And both of these, in different ways, have tended to exalt the phenomenal world of nature or its laws more than ever before. It was as part of the overwhelming development of these largely naturalistic tendencies in which the powers of nature and of the physical and social environment are so heavily emphasized, that theories of evolution first became of prime importance, well before the time of Darwin, Spencer, or even of Lamarck.

With this general theme in mind, the implications for architecture of the idea of organic expression, as one important aspect of romantic and functionalistic naturalism in art, can now be more thoroughly analyzed. In the pages that follow, these implications—already broadly indicated with reference to individual buildings designed by Louis Sullivan and Frank Lloyd Wright—will be still more specifically illustrated by quotations from the respective writings of these two men.

III

As organicists, both Sullivan and Wright constantly reiterate the general naturalistic and evolutionary thesis that great architecture must evolve organically out of the specific architectural problem to be solved, a thesis which clearly suggests the necessity for direct and "natural" expression, and particularly for direct expression of function. Says Wright, "A sense of the organic in nature is indispensable to an architect, and the knowledge of the relation of form to function is at the root of his practice." [10] Earlier, in 1901, Sullivan had written: "All life is organic. It manifests itself through organs, through structures, through functions." [11] Out of this general doctrine of organic expression, thus stated by Sullivan and Wright, there come certain major beliefs and implications for architecture, nearly all of which are also directly reflected in the theories of these great American architects, and which have profoundly affected modern architecture in the United States.

In the first place, there is the belief that the process of creation should be natural in being intuitive, and not—as the Renaissance humanist would ordinarily have it—in being based on abstractly rational principles which can be codified and learned from books. Moreover, dislike of such codification can, in a negative way, help to encourage belief in change and evolution. All this is illustrated by such statements of Sullivan as: "To create is an absolutely natural process";[12] and again, ". . . we in our art are to follow Nature's processes, Nature's rhythms, because those processes, those rhythms, are vital, organic, coherent, logical above all book logic. . . ." [13] And he also said, "In Darwin he [Sullivan] found much food. The Theory of Evolution seemed stupendous." [14] Taken together, all these statements suggest not only a belief in evolution, but a kind of evolution with vitalistic overtones not found in Darwin's own thought.

Sullivan also reflects a further belief of the organicist, namely, that great architecture must necessarily evolve out of, and express, the specific conditions from which it arises, a point of view in entire harmony with the importance given to the environment in Darwinian doctrine. For the organicist maintains that environmental conditions—physical, social, etc.—should determine the design of architecture. In the words of Sullivan, the architect "must cause a building to grow naturally, logically, and practically out of its conditions";[15] while Wright has said, "An organic form grows its structure out of conditions as a plant grows out of soil . . . both unfold similarly from within."[16] In this concept of growth as an unfolding from within, there is again a suggestion of vitalism that is further borne out by Wright's statement, "An inner-life principle is a gift to every seed. An inner-life principle is also necessary for every idea of a good building."[17] And when this is combined with Wright's insistence that "form changes with changing conditions,"[18] a vitalistic kind of evolutionism is again clearly implied.

If a work of art, like an organism, "grows its structure out of conditions," both the work as a whole and its individual parts will naturally tend to express their own particular functions. Here the organic concept as held by Sullivan and Wright becomes related to pragmatism and instrumentalism, for a "good" building is one which is suited to its functions; which is, in short, a practical working instrument. And in so far as the specific needs to be answered by any given building almost inevitably differ from those to be answered by any other, a work of architecture becomes considered a unique event, the uniqueness of which should be expressed. It is for this reason that the organicist holds that great architecture must, by its very form, express not only the function of the specific materials in construction but also the specific purpose and function of the whole building and of each of its parts. Or, as Wright has phrased it in the statement already quoted, "Form is organic only when it is natural to materials and natural to function."[19] Yet to anyone who upholds the humanism of the Renaissance such a statement is fallacious; consequently Geoffrey Scott, in his famous defense of Renaissance architecture entitled *The Architecture of Humanism* (1914), has referred to the doctrine of the direct expression of structure as "the Mechanical Fallacy."[20]

This belief of the organicist that form must follow function raises, in turn, a further implication inherent in the idea of organic expression, namely, that architecture must be *truthful* in expressing quite literally its structure and purpose; indeed, the organicist often implies that lack of such factual expression is even a moral failing. While Geoffrey Scott holds that this point of view represents a confusion of esthetic and moral values which is part of what he calls "the Ethical Fallacy," Frank Lloyd Wright on the contrary maintains firmly that "All forms stands prophetic, beautiful, and forever insofar as they were in themselves truth embodied. They become ugly and useless only when forced to seem and be what they are not and cannot be." [21]

Out of such truthfulness will arise the natural simplicity which, to the organicist, is absolutely necessary for good architecture. This is not easily accomplished: as Wright himself states, "Nothing is more difficult to achieve than the integral simplicity of organic nature. . . ." [22] Yet he maintains again and again that only this "organic simplicity . . . [gives rise to] significant character in the harmonious order we call nature." [23] Similar praise of simplicity as organic and natural was expressed by Louis Sullivan when he said, "I have shown to you the difference between things inorganic, miscellaneous, complicated, and things organic, simple, complex; and again I have taken you to Nature for inspiring proofs." [24]

Since the organic approach to architecture involves the expression of all factors contributing to the specific character of a building, one factor which the organicist believes should be expressed is the specific personality of the architect himself. For the concept of organism is implicit in the idea of the artist as a unique creative personality.[25] Here the doctrine of organic expression tends to fuse with the romantic doctrine of original genius and its belief that individuality is particularly significant and must be expressed in art. For example, Wright constantly reiterates, "Individuality is sacred";[26] while Sullivan has said, "And why is he [the architect] a genius? Because he is a child of Nature, single and simple as the weed in the field." [27] To Sullivan, furthermore, "The 'style is the man.' . . . Where there is no man, there can be no style, no matter how 'classic' or historic is the imitation." [28] The romantic regard for individual genius is thus usually accompanied by opposition to all traditional architectural forms, and especially to those of classic and Renaissance architecture in which individual self-expression is largely subordinated to traditional and universal principles of design. On this count also Wright despises the Renaissance, insisting that "This soulless thing, the Renaissance . . . has betrayed the artist. . . . Let us have done with it forever." [29]

In opposing or disregarding tradition the organicist tends to glorify the present, as can be seen in Wright's words, "I stand before you preaching *organic* architecture; declaring organic architecture to be the modern ideal . . . , holding no traditions essential to the great TRADITION." [30] Such glorification of modernity tends to carry with it the glorification of technology and of industry simply because they are highly characteristic features of modern life, particularly modern American life; so that organicists today generally hold that the machine must be made use of and expressed in contemporary American architecture. As early as 1901 Wright remarked (in sharp contrast to Gothic Revivalists such as Ruskin and William Morris, who usually had opposed industrialization by favoring a return to handicraft): "The machine does not write the doom of Liberty, but is waiting at man's hand as a peerless tool, for him to use to put foundations beneath a genuine democracy." [31]

Notice, however, that in stressing the machine as tool, Wright implicitly attacks those who would subordinate human personality to the machine, and who in this way would deny that dignity and worth of the individual which is part of American democracy. For to Wright, and to Sullivan also, democracy is a characteristic condition of the American environment and of American individualism which must also be expressed in architecture. According to Wright, "Our ideal is democracy; the highest possible expression of the individual, as a unit not inconsistent with a harmonious whole," [32] and it is significant that the lectures which he delivered in London in 1939 were published under the title, *An Organic Architecture: The Architecture of Democracy*. Similarly, Wright's master, Sullivan, wrote, "Arrange your architecture for Democracy," [33] because ". . . a certain function, democracy, is seeking a certain form of expression, democratic architecture. . . ." [34]

Such statements as these last clearly imply a belief in a *national* architecture. Sullivan was, as he says, under the influence of Taine's doctrine that "the art of a people is a reflex or direct expression of the life of that people," [35] and himself called for "an art of and for democracy, an art of and for the American people of your own time." [36] Moreover, both Sullivan and Wright have believed that one particular region of the United States is more truly American, and hence more truly democratic, than any other: like so many other organicists, Sullivan and Wright have upheld regionalism in art, and for them the most truly American region is the Middle West, especially Chicago. Says Wright, "America begins *West* of Buffalo," [37] because to him "Chicago is the national capital of the essentially American spirit." [38] And Sullivan—to whom New York, with its susceptibility to foreign influences, was "the plague-spot of American architecture" [39]—was delighted with Chicago of which he had said at very first sight, "This is the place for me!" [40]

Actually, American democracy was so all important to Sullivan that he wished to set out consciously to train democratic architects; indeed, his desire for a truly democratic architecture was one major reason why he hated the whole classic tradition which he felt was fundamentally aristocratic. In Sullivan's day most of the leading American architects were greatly influenced by that French academic version of classic architecture which was taught at the École des Beaux-Arts in Paris, and which had originated with the foundation of the Académie d'Architecture in the seventeenth century during the highly aristocratic age of Louis XIV. Therefore, to Sullivan (who was a rebel against his own training at the École) most contemporary American architecture was "in the main . . . viciously undemocratic. From which it must further follow," he said, "that the great bulk of contemporary American architects, as their characters are reflected in the buildings made by them—are not good citizens; and still further must it follow in reverse from this, that the first duty of our architectural educators must be to make of our pupils good citizens; and that this can never be accomplished so long as they continue to cram their confiding pupils full of trashy notions concerning 'the classic,' and utterly ignore their own land and people." [41]

In this single statement, Sullivan has managed to make a characteristic attack on the classic tradition, while insisting that the period and the national character must both be expressed in art. At the same time, he has included other concepts related to the idea of organic expression, among them the ethical concept that because the character of an architect is reflected in the character of his architecture, only good men can build good architecture. One of the chief protagonists of this point of view—which to a classicist is only another aspect of what Geoffrey Scott calls "the Ethical Fallacy"—was John Ruskin, so it is worth noting that Ruskin was a favorite author of the young Frank Lloyd Wright.

Sullivan further resembled Ruskin—and also Taine—in holding that architecture necessarily reflects the specific character of the society under which it is produced. In calling for an architecture specifically of our "own time and people," he indicated his belief that American architecture, to be organic and functional, must be an expression of contemporary American society. "Architecture is not merely an art," he said, ". . . it is a social manifestation. . . . By this light, the study of architecture becomes naturally and logically a branch of social science." [42] Wright has similarly implied that architecture must express its particular society, for he has said that "we cannot have an organic architecture unless we achieve an organic society!" [43]

The importance placed by Sullivan on expressing our "own time" in architecture not only reflects his Hegelian belief that a given period is an organic whole, but it also reflects his insistence that art must evolve with the passage of time, a thesis likewise implicit in Wright's statement that "form changes with changing conditions." [44] Both of these men, therefore, have maintained that no architectural forms can be forever valid, and in this respect, also, they have necessarily opposed the Renaissance version of the classic tradition. Moreover, they insist that tradition must never be allowed to dominate the naturally evolving genius of the architect. As Sullivan said, "no architectural dictum, or tradition, or superstition, or habit should stand in the [architect's] way"; [45] while according to Wright, "Human traditions like styles are garments to be put on or taken off." [46]

Such a point of view inevitably lends itself to a belief in change or development, and consequently in evolution. However, during the nineteenth and twentieth centuries there have existed side by side (in addition to the theory of purely chance variation) at least three important and widely different concepts as to the general manner in which change, development, and evolution take place. All three of them have greatly affected the philosophy of art, and at least two are represented in the writings of Louis Sullivan and Wright.

The first of the three concepts—and the one most influential in the United States where it has been re-enforced by the American doctrine of manifest destiny—is the idea of continuous progress. It is this concept of progress which seems to be implicit in Sullivan's remark that "the past is dead, and has been buried by a past that is dead. . . ." [47] It is implicit also in numerous statements by Wright, such as, "The average of human intelligence rises steadily . . ."; or such as, "Life has gone by succession into following forms. Creation never imitates, creation assimilates. . . ." [48] Or again, "The law of organic change is the only thing that mankind can know as beneficial or as actual; we can only know that all things are in process of flowing into some continuous state of becoming," [49] a statement almost Bergsonian in spirit. Because quotations such as these suggest belief not only in a process of continuous change but also in progressive development, they reflect the optimism usually characteristic of organicists and evolutionists alike. For in modern times—at least until recently—there have been comparatively few pessimists who, like Henry Adams, have applied the idea of continuous change, not to the progress of civilization but to its decline, maintaining that civilization, far from forging ahead, is actually running down.[50]

Within the idea of progress several different emphases are possible, each with very different effects for architecture and art. If the emphasis is placed on the *most recent* development as being the most important—an emphasis encouraged by the Darwinian and Spencerian doctrine of the "survival of the fittest"—that glorification of modernity already noted as characteristic of both Sullivan and Wright will result. But if the chief emphasis is placed instead on the *beginning* of the development, either for its own sake or for understanding the present, a special interest in such things as the history of origins, of archaeology, philology, or primitive man will arise. Such primitivism is likely to be especially glorified in art because it is also supported by the romantic belief that primitive man is the most "natural" man whose arts and crafts therefore most directly express universal fundamentals of art.

There is, however, a third possibility, but one that is sharply opposed by Wright and Sullivan. This consists in placing the emphasis, not on the end or on the beginning of the development, but upon any or several of the *intermediate* phases at the whim of the individual, a point of view which inevitably produces the eclecticism that has been so strong in the art and architecture of the nineteenth and twentieth centuries.

In addition to the idea of continuous progress, Sullivan and Wright have also subscribed to a cyclical theory of the development both of artistic style and of the work of art. Various versions of the cyclical theory of development have, of course, been held by philosophers and historians of ancient Greece and Rome such as Plato and Polybius, by Renaissance historians such as Machiavelli and Campanella, and by Vico, Hegel, Nietzsche, Spengler, and Toynbee, among others, in more recent times. According to one type of cyclical theory—a type that ordinarily prevailed in classical antiquity—it is primarily the geometric *form* of the cycle which gives order and therefore significance to history. According to another and later type, the important thing is not so much the form of the cycle as the fact that it is believed to be *mechanically* described, whether by a rotating wheel, a swinging pendulum, a moving spiral, or some other mechanical means; so that those who hold this theory are customarily mechanists. However, still another kind of cyclical theory, and the one emphasized by Sullivan and Wright, is based upon a concept of historical and artistic development like the life cycle of a biological organism, a cycle which consequently involves a period of growth, followed by one of maturity and then of decay. Those who apply this organismic kind of cyclical theory to fields outside of biology itself usually imply—as do Sullivan and Wright—some kind of *vital* force which produces the cycle and gives it significance.

This concept, applied outside of biology, has had to vie with several other ideas of development. Not only has it had to compete with the belief in straight-line progress in this world but it has had to meet the attacks of those who uphold the Christian concept of progress, under God's grace, to another and better world. In recent years, it has also encountered the criticism of the pragmatists who regard as significant not cycles but particular events, their duration and their context. Consequently, pragmatists consider a cyclical curve to be only one of a large number of possible relations between specific events, and one, indeed, that is not truly cyclical because it probably would never be repeated in exactly the same form.

In so far as architectural organicists like Sullivan and Wright regard each work of architecture as a unique event resulting from a set of specific conditions which can hardly recur in exactly the same form, their point of view is closely related to pragmatism, particularly as, like the pragmatists, they too stress functional usefulness as a major criterion. However, in subscribing to a biological concept of cyclical development as well as to the idea of progress, Sullivan and Wright differ from the pragmatists.

Perhaps the sharpest attack on the transfer of a biological cycle of growth, maturity, and decay to art is made by those who subscribe to the humanistic tradition stemming from the Renaissance. For while humanist critics usually accept the classical view that historical development is cyclical, they—like Plato and Aristotle—seek to transcend history by regarding as fundamental, not history, not cycles, not change and progress, and not events as such, but Platonic and Aristotelian norms which are considered to be universal and fixed and so good for all time. As a consequence, most humanist critics, like Geoffrey Scott, insist that the application of the life cycle to nonliving things, including works of art and artistic styles, constitutes a "biological fallacy." Yet Louis Sullivan clearly subscribed to this very "fallacy" when he said: "a great work of art must first of all be an organism, that is, possessed of a life of its own; an individual life that functions in all its parts. . . ." [51] And in direct relation to architecture Sullivan has written of "the two fundamental rhythms of Nature, the rhythm of growth . . . , *the rhythm of life;* and the rhythm of decadence . . . , *the rhythm of death.*" [52]

Though Sullivan and Wright have thus subscribed both to a belief in progress and to a biological-cyclical concept of development, neither of them has subscribed to the third great theory of development, the dialectical theory of Hegel and Marx which itself is in part a kind of variation on the cyclical theme, yet also involves the idea of progress. According to the dialectical concept, progress takes place only through a constant struggle in which any one tendency, called a thesis, inevitably produces a countertendency or antithesis. Out of the struggle between the two there finally comes a synthesis, after which the whole process begins again, and eventually higher levels of attainment are reached. Thus cyclical repetition is combined with the idea of progress to produce a spiral or zigzag development, and one that is full of life as well as of violent movement because the element of struggle implies an underlying vitalism.

While this Hegelian and Marxist theory has not directly influenced Sullivan and Wright, some forms of Marxism (as will be indicated later in this chapter) have at times exerted direct or indirect influence on that other modern architectural movement known as the International Style, particularly through a common interest in the social problem of housing the proletarian masses. For this reason it may be mentioned here that Marxists have long accepted with approval, if with reservations, the Darwinian theory of biological evolution. To them the Darwinian belief in a struggle for survival resulting in the survival of the fittest is simply a bourgeois version of the Marxist doctrine of class conflict, even though Darwin conceived of the struggle as never ending, while Marx held that it would cease with the triumph of the proletariat. Said Marx, "Darwin's book is very important and serves me as a basis in natural science for the class struggle in history"; and his friend, Friedrich Engels, remarked that the fundamental proposition of Marxism, as expressed in the *Communist Manifesto,* "is destined to do for history what Darwin's theory had done for biology." [53] Engels also stated: "Just as Darwin discovered the law of the evolution of organic nature, so Marx discovered the evolutionary law of human history: . . . that . . . the production of the material necessaries of life and the corresponding stage of the economic evolution of a people or a period provides a foundation upon which the national institutions, legal systems, *art* [my italics], and even the religious ideas of the people in question have been built and upon which, therefore, their explanation must be based." [54]

Such, then, are some of the major implications for architecture of the idea of organic expression. All of them are linked to theories of evolution, and nearly all (aside from the Marxian ones) are reflected in the architectural theories of Louis Sullivan and Frank Lloyd Wright. With these implications in mind, the history of the doctrine of organic expression can now profitably be traced as part of a general naturalistic point of view which includes both romantic and functionalistic beliefs that evolving nature constitutes reality and truth.

IV

In discussing the history of the doctrine of organicism in relation to architecture, we shall start from the theories of Wright and Sullivan indicated above, and in a summary way endeavor to trace them back to their chief scientific-technological and romantic sources. Very often the connection with those sources will be found to be vague, tenuous, and unconscious, because, as already suggested, many of the beliefs of Sullivan and Wright have long been in the air and have been quite widely accepted for at least two centuries.

Nevertheless, some of their beliefs have grown directly from specific theories of evolution, including those of Darwin and Spencer. We have already pointed out that Sullivan himself said in his book, *The Autobiography of an Idea,* "In Darwin he [Sullivan] found much food. The Theory of Evolution seemed stupendous." [55] And in the same volume Sullivan not only likewise acknowledged the influence of Spencer, but also mentioned having read the works of other evolutionists, notably Huxley and Tyndall.[56] It is, of course, not at all surprising that Sullivan was interested in Darwinism for the doctrines of Darwin re-enforced his own belief that changes in environmental conditions must be expressed in architecture: Darwin had said in the *Origin of Species,* "Changed conditions of life are of the highest importance in causing variability. . . ." In this respect the theories of Darwin resemble those of his great predecessor, Jean Baptiste Lamarck, who had written in 1801, ". . . it is not the form either of the body or of its parts which has given rise to habits and to the mode of life of animals, but, on the contrary, it is the habits, the mode of life, and all the other influential circumstances which have with time produced the form of the bodies and organs of animals. With new forms new faculties have been acquired, and gradually Nature has reached the state in which we actually see it." [57] Here clearly is the implication that in living beings the form follows the function.

Transferring this general thesis to architecture, not only could Sullivan and other architects insist (quite like Lamarck and the Neo-Lamarckians, who were not, however, mentioned by Sullivan) that function is a key to change, but they could in a sense apply the Darwinian doctrine of natural selection to architectural forms and styles, although only by making the architect the selector rather than nature itself. Furthermore, natural selection could support Sullivan's belief that architectural styles of the past, especially those of the classic past, are outmoded, and being outmoded, are unfitted to survive, with the implication that the latest architectural forms to develop are the only ones really fit to survive. As the Darwinian and Spencerian doctrines of the "survival of the fittest" thus contained—despite Darwin's attempts to be objective —an implicit belief in progress, and hence an implicit optimism, they served to strengthen the optimism inherent in the doctrine of organic expression and characteristic of the theories of Sullivan and Wright.

Because this optimism is much stronger in the writings of Herbert Spencer than in those of Darwin, Spencer could exert a particularly strong influence over Sullivan who wrote: "Spencer's definition implying a progression from an unorganized simple through stages of growth and differentiation to a highly organized complex, seemed to fit his [Sullivan's] own case." [58] Here Sullivan is referring to Spencer's idea of progress from the homogeneous to the heterogeneous, a theory which possesses highly optimistic overtones because Spencer not only stressed change as the most characteristic feature of living matter but he was also thoroughly convinced that such change is for the better. Unlike the more objective Darwin, Spencer specifically maintained that evil results from the nonadaptation of the organism to the conditions of the environment, just as, for Sullivan and Wright, bad architecture results when a building is not well adapted to the specific environment. Spencer also maintained that, in art, adaptation to environment produced a vital economy which, as a result of the law of least effort, gives a distinctive direction to the sense of beauty; and this vital economy is really the "integral simplicity of organic nature"[59] glorified by Wright and by Sullivan.

Furthermore, it was Spencer who, in his *Principles of Sociology,* especially developed the concept that society is itself an organism, a concept which was specifically taken over by Louis Sullivan, and which seems to be implicit in Wright's statement, already quoted, that ". . . we cannot have an organic architecture unless we have an organic society." This Spencerian belief in the social organism—unlike the somewhat similar belief of Marx—did not result in a denial of individuality, because Herbert Spencer always maintained that individuals participate *voluntarily* in social action, so that he was able to insist upon the extreme importance of individuality in an un-Darwinian way. Consequently, Spencer's doctrines appealed with particular force not only to supporters of laissez faire capitalism in general but also to upholders of that romantic individualism which, in its specifically American democratic form, is so clearly reflected in the theories and personalities of Sullivan and Wright. Because in this respect the doctrines of Spencer could be greatly re-enforced by the vogue for the Nietzschean superman and the Carlylean hero, it is worth noting that one of Sullivan's favorite books was Nietzsche's *Thus Spake Zarathustra,* and that he also greatly admired Carlyle, who was likewise one of the favorite authors of the young Frank Lloyd Wright.

It is well known that Spencer's writings clearly reflect a tendency to romanticize science and technology, much as Sullivan and other architectural functionalists were later to do. For example, Spencer—who had been trained as an engineer—wrote, "The highest Art of every kind is based on Science."[60] Somewhat similarly Louis Sullivan remarked in his *Autobiography of an Idea,* "That which at once impressed Louis as new to him and vital was what was known as 'The Scientific Method.'"[61] Like Spencer, Sullivan, too, glorified the role of technology in making practical use of this scientific method, with the result that he "found himself drifting towards the engineering point of view, or state of mind . . . ," [62] and "the chief engineers became his heroes. . . ." [63] Thus Sullivan—more than his younger friend Wright—subscribed to a mechanistic point of view, even though he did so in a romantic mood of hero worship.

In view of this tendency to romanticize scientific method and technology, it is a significant that, although Sullivan's architectural theories can in part be traced directly back to scientific theories of evolution as indicated above, these scientific sources of his thought cannot be completely separated from doctrines originating in that many-sided movement known as romanticism. Not only was the idea of organic expression itself in major part an outgrowth of romantic philosophies, but various aspects of romanticism helped to pave the way for, and even to produce, the theories of evolution which directly or indirectly influenced Sullivan. For romanticism not only aided in paving the way for Darwinism, but, as will be indicated later, it directly gave rise to vitalistic theories of evolution.

It was these romantic tendencies, also, which have helped to make both Sullivan and his pupil, Wright, particularly sympathetic to the writings of Walt Whitman and of Emerson and his circle. Emerson, in turn, was sympathetic to the theories of Coleridge and of the German romantics, as F. O. Matthiessen, has so clearly shown in his book, *American Renaissance* (1941).

Without doubt their common belief in the idea of organic expression made Sullivan and Wright especially partial to the ideas of Whitman. In his *Autobiography* Wright cited Whitman as one of his favorite authors,[64] and wrote, "Dear old Walt, we need you more than ever. . . ." [65] Nor is it surprising that when Louis Sullivan died a well-thumbed copy of Whitman's *Leaves of Grass* was found among his effects. For Sullivan had implied in the *Autobiography of an Idea* that Whitman had given him the most compelling suggestion toward his idea, described by Sullivan, in pantheistic fashion, as an "idea of power" in which "the powers of nature and the powers of man coalesce." [66] Moreover, Sullivan had again and again made use of the words "democratic vistas," the title of the well-known essay by Whitman.

Because Wright and Sullivan so directly admired Whitman, it is noteworthy that Whitman, too, was an organicist: he even said that he thought of his book of poems, *Leaves of Grass,* as an organism. Like Sullivan and Wright he glorified nature, natural fact, science, and democracy. "I shall endeavor to copy nature," [67] he wrote; and again, "the true use of the imaginative faculty of modern times is to give ultimate vivification to facts, to science, and to common lives, endowing them with glows and glories and final illustriousness which belong to every real thing, and to real things only." [68] Furthermore, Whitman's organic and functional approach to life and art is clearly reflected in his words, "that which distorts honest shapes . . . is a nuisance and revolt. . . . [Only] those ornaments can be allowed that . . . flow out of the nature of the work and come irrepressibly from it. . . ." [69] Whitman himself evidently realized that this point of view was related to the concept of evolution because he stated that first-class literature and its poems inevitably "grow out of circumstances, and are evolutionary." [70] Like Wright and Sullivan, also, Whitman considered the organic expression of the period and place to be highly important, for he believed in "a subjective and contemporary point of view appropriate to us alone, and to our new genius and environments, [and] different from anything hitherto. . . ." [71] He likewise maintained that American democracy was a particularly important factor of his own day and environment, and therefore necessarily to be expressed in his art: "I know very well," said he, "that my 'Leaves' could not possibly have emerged . . . from any other era than the latter half of the Nineteenth Century, nor any other land than democratic America. . . ." [72]

Whitman addressed Emerson (1803–82) as "Master," and Emerson was one of the few to praise Whitman's *Leaves of Grass* when the volume was first published. As might be expected, Emerson and the members of his immediate circle were also firm believers in the idea of organic expression. Said Emerson, "We feel, in seeing a noble building . . . , that it is spiritually organic; that is, had a necessity, in Nature, for being"; [73] and he spoke sharply against the tendency "to detach the beautiful from the useful." [74] In the *American Scholar* he characteristically attacked the use of traditional styles in architecture as follows: "And why need we copy the Doric or Gothic model? Beauty, convenience, grandeur of thought, and quaint expression are as near to us as to any, and if the American artist will study with hope and love the precise thing to be done by him, considering the climate, the soil, the length of the day, the wants of the people, the habit and form of the government, he will create a house in which all there will find themselves fitted. . . ." [75]

As is well known, Thoreau (1817–62), whom Frank Lloyd Wright has called one of his favorite authors, read Emerson's essay, *Nature,* during his senior year at Harvard and built his life upon it, so that he, too, believed in organic expression. In *Walden* he wrote: "What of architectural beauty I now see, I know has gradually grown from within outward, out of the necessities and character of the indweller. . . ." [76] This very sentence was quoted on the title page of a special number of the *Architectural Forum* devoted to Wright's works in January, 1938, a number dedicated by Wright to Louis Sullivan and to Sullivan's one-time partner, Dankmar Adler.

Of all of Emerson's friends, however, it was Horatio Greenough (1805–52)—the American sculptor from whom Emerson drew many of his ideas on art—who most clearly expressed the idea of organic expression and the related idea of functionalism in art and architecture. Greenough spoke of "the subordination of the parts to the whole, of the whole to the function." [77] In a letter to Emerson he said, "Here is my theory of structure: A scientific arrangement of spaces and forms to functions and to site; an emphasis of features proportioned to their *gradated* importance in function; color and ornament to be decided and arranged and varied by strictly organic laws. . . ." [78] However, it was in his essay, *American Architecture,* that Greenough best expressed his theories of organic functionalism. "Instead of forcing the functions of every sort of building into one general form, adopting an outward shape for the sake of the eye or of association, without reference to the inner distribution," he said, "let us begin from the heart as a nucleus, and work outward." [79] "When I define Beauty as the promise of Function; Action as the presence of Function; Character as the record of Function; I arbitrarily divide that which is essentially one." [80] That Greenough was in some respects an evolutionist is clearly indicated by his statement: "The law of adaptation is the fundamental law of nature in all structure. So unflinchingly does she modify type in accord with a new position, . . . so entirely does she limit the modifications to the demands of necessity. . . ." [81]

Because of the importance which Greenough thus placed on adaptation to environmental circumstances, he—like Sullivan, Wright, and other organicists—insisted that the art and architecture of the United States must express a characteristically American spirit and American democracy. It is true that he admired the art of the Greeks, and even said, "In the Greek alone, beauty," [82] but he admired Greek art primarily because he considered the Greeks to be free men living, like Americans, under republican forms of government. For this reason Greenough's celebrated statue of George Washington (Fig. 14), originally intended to stand under the dome of the Capitol of the United States, represents Washington in classic garb, nude to the waist like some Plutarchean hero-leader of an ancient Greek republic. However, although Greenough thus imitated the Greeks to achieve a republican expression, he also had said that "the American builder, by a truly philosophic investigation of ancient art, will learn of the Greeks to be American." [83] It was in this spirit that he used a purely American subject in the sculptured group which he executed to flank the steps on the east façade of the Capitol, for this group, called "The Rescue" (Fig. 15), represents (albeit not too successfully) an American frontiersman defending his family against an Indian.

As already noted, the ideas of Greenough and the other members of Emerson's group on the subject of organic expression were in part derived from, or influenced by, those of Coleridge and of the German romantics. The doctrine is clearly reflected in Coleridge's lectures on Shakespeare, for example, in which Coleridge pointed out the—to him—fundamental mistake of "confounding mechanical regularity with organic form. The form is mechanic," he said, "when on any given material we impress a pre-determined form, not necessarily arising out of the properties of the material. . . . The organic form . . . is innate; it shapes, as it develops, itself from within, and the fulness of its development is one and the same with the perfection of its outward form. . . . Nature, the prime general artist, inexhaustible in diverse powers, is equally inexhaustible in forms. . . ." [84]

It might parenthetically be mentioned here that the organismic and functionalistic point of view to which Coleridge subscribed was carried still further by later English romantics, especially by William Morris, who, like Frank Lloyd Wright later, exalted Gothic architecture because he felt that it was organic. "We should take Gothic architecture by the hand," Morris said, "and know it for what it was and what it is: a magnificent manifestation of organic order. Proceeding on such a tradition, one avows a prin-

ciple of structure that evolves its forms in the spirit of strict truthfulness, following the conditions of use, material, and construction." [85]

As will shortly be indicated in more detail, Morris' ideas were
highly influential in Germany as well as in England, no doubt
largely because they stemmed in part from German thought. For
Morris, like Coleridge and many other English romantics, like
Emerson and his circle, or like Sullivan and Wright, was by temperament sympathetic to many of the ideas of the German romantic philosophers. Coleridge himself had frequently cited German
philosophers such as Kant, Schelling, Fichte, Herder, and the
Schlegels, among others. It must be admitted, however, that
the doctrine of organicism had become so widespread in the intellectual climate of the time that it is difficult to tell to what degree
Morris, Coleridge, or for that matter, Emerson and his group,
borrowed from the Germans, and to what degree they each
formed their ideas independently. Nevertheless, without question
the doctrine of organic expression was developed in large part
under German romanticism; Coleridge and Emerson were to some
degree influenced by German romantic thought; and partly from
Emerson, by way of Thoreau and Whitman, the doctrine was to
reach Sullivan and Wright.

Yet both Sullivan and Wright had more immediate connections
with German romantic philosophy. Sullivan specifically mentioned
"the Germans," along with Darwin, Spencer, Huxley, and Tyndall, as having greatly influenced him. [86] As a young man he first
came into contact with German philosophy through his friend
John Edelmann, a fellow draftsman in the office of William
LeBaron Jenney at Chicago. Not only, said Sullivan, did Edelmann
know "the highest transcendentalisms of German metaphysics,"
but it was from Edelmann, also, that Sullivan derived his "theory
of *suppressed functions*," [87] the theory on which he based his doctrine that form follows function. Like Sullivan, Frank Lloyd
Wright, too, has acknowledged the direct influence of various German philosophers in whose writings the doctrine of organic expression is expressed, and has cited, among others, Goethe, Herder, and Nietzsche.

Obviously, then, the organic point of view toward architecture
is not only in large part a product of romantic thought in general,
but of German romantic philosophy in particular. As Walzel, the
leading historian of German literary romanticism, has said: "The

organic conception of nature and art is the key to romantic philosophy," [88] and he might have added that it is a conception to be found in the works of all the chief German romantic philosophers.

It is clearly reflected, for example, in the ideas of August Wilhelm von Schlegel (1767–1845), who stated, in his lectures on Shakespeare delivered in Vienna during 1808, "Organic form . . . is an inherent quality; it proceeds from within. . . ." [89] Schlegel's brother, Friedrich von Schlegel, was one of the first to express the doctrine that one of the environmental conditions to be given organic expression in art is the spirit of the nation, when he said, "Springing from what is near and peculiar to us, the character of the art will infallibly be local and national," [90] Friedrich von Schlegel, also, was the first to apply the word romantic to what he considered to be more truly *modern* (and therefore nonclassical) art,[91] so that Schlegel's romanticism is different from that of earlier romantics in looking forward rather than back, and in this resembles the romanticism of Sullivan and Wright. For Schlegel developed a new kind of romantic philosophy which held that art should achieve vitality, not by returning to a simpler, more primitive state of nature, but by seeking a constant enlargement of its boundaries and an endless progression toward an unattainably remote ideal. Thus, unlike earlier romantics, he came to admire Gothic architecture, not for its supposed naturalness or wild primitiveness, but because to him it conveyed a spirit of infinity, of boundless Christian aspiration which he considered to be truly modern.[92]

Friedrich von Schlegel was especially inspired by the "Philosophy of Nature" of Schelling (1775–1854). In opposition to the natural scientists who attempted to explain nature as a pure mechanism, Schelling had made *life* the central conception of his philosophy. For this reason he considered nature from the point of view of the organism, and held that the connection between nature's various forces is understandable if the ultimate end of nature is the production of organic life. Schelling is said, also, to have been the first to conceive of nature and humanity as a single mighty, unified organism.[93] This concept, developed further by his disciple Oken, was destined to exert tremendous influence in encouraging and diffusing the doctrine of organic evolution. For Schelling and Oken maintained that the classes and species of organic life are arranged in a connected and ordered system in which each species is the preliminary stage for that which the next accomplishes. And Oken eventually began to regard the ascending of such classes and species as an actual process in time, as actual evolution.

In 1807 Schelling, to whom the universe, as the total manifestation of the Absolute, was not only the most perfect organism but the most perfect work of art, wrote as follows concerning the relation between the plastic arts and nature: ". . . that which gives beauty to the whole [work] . . . is . . . the aspect and expression of the in-dwelling spirit of nature."[94] And also: "[The essence in art] might indeed be injured by form which was forced upon it, but never by that which flows from itself. . . ."[95] Furthermore Schelling, like other organicists, emphasized the necessity of giving organic expression to the period: "To different ages," he said, "is accorded different inspiration. . . . An Art, indeed, which should be in all respects the same as that of former centuries, will never recur, for nature never repeats herself."[96]

Another important source for the doctrine of organic expression in art was the philosophy of Herder, one of the German philosophers and writers occasionally quoted by Frank Lloyd Wright. Herder had said, "All that we call matter is . . . more or less imbued with life"; and "every art . . . has had its period of growth, bloom and decline."[97] Believing that history, like everything else, unfolds according to the laws of the growth of living things, he was chiefly responsible for spreading the concept of history as the unbroken progress of natural development, a concept which led him to become particularly interested in the origins of that development. In thus relating the concept of evolution in nature to that of development in human history, Herder merely helped to further a tendency which was rapidly increasing during the second half of the eighteenth century. For at that time the hypothesis of evolution in nature was being "greatly strengthened, if not actually suggested, by the study of human history, where the forms of political and social organization can be seen to have undergone an evolution of the same kind."[98] This kind of history —which made the idea of progress, change, and development the fundamental category of historical thought—grew up in the Renaissance and post-Renaissance along with the idea of progress. It appears in a fully developed form by the middle of the eighteenth century in such writings as Turgot's *Discours sur l'histoire universelle* (1750), and Voltaire's *Le Siècle de Louis XIV* (1751).

Fostered by the *Encyclopédie* (1751–65), it soon became a commonplace.[99]

In addition to the concept of history as development, Herder emphasized the influence of climate in molding men, and on the basis of this idea it later became easy for architects to give a new emphasis to climate as molding the dwellings of mankind. Furthermore Herder stressed the concept that the peculiar character of a people proceeds from its natural endowments, arguing—even earlier than Friedrich von Schlegel—that the natural state is that of a people with a national character (though Herder, unlike Schlegel, still reflected the cosmopolitanism of the Enlightenment in believing that national characteristics were dying out). From this it was easy to pass to the Hegelian concept of the state as an organism and also to the concept that the national character must be expressed in art.

Herder's contemporary, Goethe, was likewise a chief contributor to the organic conception of nature and art. In *Die Natur* he set forth the concrete idea of a living unity of nature, which, however, he approached primarily from the point of view of natural history (and not just from the aesthetic point of view usual among the early romantics). For Goethe was, among other things, a distinguished scientist, who, in proving erroneous a supposed physical distinction of man from the higher animals—the lack of an intermaxillary bone—was a precursor of Darwin. Yet although Goethe became a scientist, and although he eventually sought to bring romanticism and classicism into a kind of synthesis, it is worth recalling that originally he was in many respects a romantic. In view of Goethe's connection with the early history of organicism it is significant that his name was included by Frank Lloyd Wright in a list of Wright's favorite authors,[100] and significant also that Emerson, in speaking of the leaders of the intellectual revival in New England in which he himself was prominent, said, "Goethe was the cow from whom their milk was drawn." [101] For Goethe had clearly shown himself to be a believer in organic expression by such statements as, "A universal knowledge of organic nature is necessary in order to understand and develop the artist through the labyrinth of his structure." [102]

Another major contributor to the idea of organic expression was Immanuel Kant, whose ideas not only influenced all the German philosophers mentioned above but were also a chief source for the transcendentalism of Emerson and his followers. Like Goethe, Kant was, of course, more than a romantic, although he admired Rousseau so much that he was accustomed to wear Rousseau's picture in a locket. Like Goethe, too, Kant was also a scientist; he has often been called—with considerable exaggeration—one of the originators of the nebular hypothesis, a theory which implies not fixed creation but a gradual evolution of the planets. Yet although Kant did subscribe to the idea of planetary evolution, he also believed that this mechanistic evolutionary explanation, which was sufficient for the solar system, was inadequate when applied to the blade of grass or the caterpillar, so that to him the living organism seemed a kind of vitalistic miracle in the world of mechanics. Nevertheless, Kant was greatly impressed by the relatively recent developments in science made by Galileo and Newton among others, developments which have contributed so much to the belief, fundamental to modern science, that all of nature is a single ordered and organic system.

Kant himself believed that nature can be looked upon as purposive, as adapted to ends. Since, in his view, the beautiful is characterized by an "undesigned fitness" or appropriateness to its end, he maintained that art should be "natural." "Beautiful Art," he said, "is an art insofar as it seems like nature." [103] He spoke of "the Principle of the formal Purposiveness of nature . . . ," [104] and of "the objective purposiveness of nature," [105] statements in which not only the concept of organism is implicit, but also the notion of continuous ascent which Kant saw in conscious artistic development.[106] However, it should be noted that Kant carefully distinguished between *fine art* (which he said is beautiful, works directly upon the feeling as does a purposeless product of nature, and consequently must "be able to be regarded as nature") and *technical art* (which, because it produces objects designed to satisfy definite interests, is more narrowly utilitarian). Here Kant differs sharply both from the functionalist, who makes no distinction between fine art, craft art, and industrial design, and from those romantics who glorify utilitarian folk crafts as part of their love for the primitive in art.

Although in this respect Kant's point of view was neither romantic nor functionalistic, nevertheless because his philosophy summed up so many aspects of the thought of his time, it necessarily included many ideas which were scientific or romantic in spirit and which contributed to the doctrine of organic expression.

For in the thought of Kant, as in that of Goethe, the scientific rationalism of the day—combining, as it were, the rationalism of Descartes with the scientific spirit of a Newton or a Leibnitz—was fused with the new romantic philosophy which had developed in eighteenth-century England largely out of the philosophies of Locke and of Shaftesbury. And herein lie the chief sources of the concept of organic expression.

To be more specific, even at the risk of great oversimplification: the basing of philosophy upon the presupposition of organism can be traced to Leibnitz (1646–1716). For Leibnitz considered the universe to be made up of atomlike substances which he called "monads" but which differ from atoms in the fact that each is held to possess distinct individuality based on a psychic life of its own. Thus not only the concept of organism is implicit in the monad but that of vitalism as well. Since the monads of Leibnitz are said to be the source of the concept of organism it is worth noting that Leibnitz has also been credited with being the first to suggest, at least by implication, a general law of organic evolution.[107] Moreover, it was Leibnitz' Neoplatonic belief in continuity within the whole scale of living beings which suggested to Herder that human society might be better understood by analogy with an organism.[108]

The doctrine that beauty is associated with fitness and utility, and consequently with function—a doctrine which forms part of the idea of organic expression and which has been strongly emphasized by Sullivan and Wright—arose partly out of the concept of the well-functioning organism and partly out of the mechanistic concept of the well-functioning machine. It could be especially fostered by the empiricism deriving from Locke which stressed the practical utility of everyday experience. This in turn was fostered by the mechanistic philosophy of those followers of Descartes and Newton who—combing Descartes' belief that animals, though not men, are machines with the Newtonian doctrine that the physical universe operates according to laws of mechanics—went further and insisted that men and men's works, including works of art, must also be well-working machines. This eventually became the view of the later "Moderns" in the famous struggle between the Ancients and Moderns, and increasingly pervaded the whole philosophy of the Enlightenment in its reaction against the abstract traditional formulas of Renaissance and post-Renaissance classicism. The new functionalistic spirit which resulted from all this can be illustrated (to cite just one example) by the writings of the eighteenth-century English critic, Archibald Alison, who approvingly, if somewhat inaccurately, quoted the painter Hogarth as saying, "A ship which is well built and which promises to sail well is called by sailers a beauty." And Alison himself added, "In every other profession in like manner, all Machines or Instruments are called beautiful by the Artists, which are well adapted to the end of their Arts." [109]

As is well known, the empiricism of Locke, with its basis in the experience of the individual, also helped to produce a relativism and a final reliance upon individual sentiment which were among the chief characteristics of the romantic movement, and which also fostered a related, and democratic, belief in the worth of the individual human organism. But perhaps the ultimate source of both romanticism and the idea of organic expression was the Neoplatonism which underlay the philosophy not only of Leibnitz but also of the English philosopher, Lord Shaftesbury (d. 1713), who contributed the theory of inner form to German romanticism and thus to Coleridge, Emerson, Sullivan, and Wright. Once the German romantics had fallen under the influence of Leibnitz and Shaftesbury, whose Neoplatonism was derived at second hand from that of Renaissance Italy, it was easy for some of the leading romantics to turn directly to the writings of Plotinus (d. 269 A.D.), originator of the Neoplatonic version of Plato's philosophy. So important was Neoplatonism for the philosophy of romanticism that one leading authority has gone so far as to say, "If we are to speak of a 'key' to early Romanticism, it is to be found in one of the thinkers of antiquity, Plotinus. For this Neoplatonic philosopher not only inspired the entire system of [the early German Romantic] Novalis, . . . and many of the ideas of Schelling; . . . [but] through Novalis and Schelling he exercised an influence . . . upon both the Schlegels." [110]

It can certainly be said with truth that the concept of the organic unity of nature, a concept fundamental both to romantic and mechanistic theories of evolution and also to the related idea of organic expression, grew in large part from Neoplatonism. The Neoplatonists had ever held that reality lies in a system of Platonic "Ideas" organized in accordance with principles of continuity and of hierarchical classification developed by Plato's greatest pupil, Aristotle; and had come to maintain that this system forms a great continuous "chain of being" which links together nature, man, and God, so that nature is spiritualized and man himself partakes of nature.

In the eighteenth century the doctrine of the chain of being—the history of which has been so well traced by Arthur O. Lovejoy[111]—had become part and parcel of everyday thought, largely because it had also been insisted upon by two of the most influential thinkers of the later seventeenth century, Locke and Leibnitz. It is particularly well illustrated in the well-known lines of Alexander Pope:

> Vast chain of being; which from God began,
> Natures aethereal, human, angel, man,
> Beast, bird, fish, insect, what no eye can see,
> No glass can reach; from Infinite to thee,
> From thee to nothing. . . .

In the eighteenth century, also, this Neoplatonic belief in a continuous natural system at last developed into a major source of doctrines of evolution and organic expression for natural scientists and romantics alike. It is true that some foreshadowings of such doctrines are to be found in ancient Greek thought, which usually tended to regard nature itself as a great organism characterized by life and permeated by mind. Indeed, this concept had dominated the first Greek school of philosophy, the Ionian school of Miletus, in the sixth century B.C. The leading philosophers of this school even followed a kind of evolutionary scheme; while a foreshadowing of the principle of the "survival of the fittest" was shortly to be found in the philosophies of Empedocles and Epicurus. However, it was especially in the works of Aristotle that intimations of the concepts of evolution and organism occurred, because not only was he the chief progenitor of the great chain of being but he also, like so many earlier Greek philosophers (including his master Plato, in the *Timaeus*), conceived of nature as a being in itself alive. Nevertheless Aristotle's concept of organism differed from that of modern organicists in that he regarded the motion of the great organism which is nature as an effect of the divine reason; also, Aristotle conceived of an "organic whole" as a whole which logically *preceded* its parts. And, most important, although the Aristotelian philosophy—including the scholastic philosophy of the Middle Ages—was fundamentally organismic, Aristotle and his followers always regarded the chain of being as basically a *static* scheme of things. For to Aristotle evolution was a *mental* concept involving logical order and continuity in thought but not an actual sequence of events in time.

Only in the eighteenth century did the chain of being at last tend to become temporalized, a development which constituted one of the chief contributions of eighteenth-century thought,[112] and which, of course, was to be carried much further in the nineteenth century by romantic philosophers such as Schelling and Oken, as well as by scientists such as Darwin. The ultimate source of this development was doubtless the Hebrew-Christian belief in a progress toward another and better world. When, following the scientific developments of the seventeenth century, the Christian belief in divine Providence was weakened by a growing emphasis on the invariability of the laws of nature, the idea of progress was increasingly shifted to *this* world. And whereas formerly the chain of being had been looked upon as a completed system in which change or novelty was hardly possible (a point of view which had encouraged the academic kind of neoclassicism in architecture), now for the first time it came to be conceived by some as the program through which nature is ever operating and changing, a never ending program evolving gradually in cosmic history. Hence Kant could say, "Creation is never completed. It is forever busy achieving new ascents of nature, bringing into existence new things and new worlds." [113] It was with the increasing acceptance of this point of view during the third quarter of the eighteenth century, that theories which may in a broad sense be called evolutionistic had first really tended to multiply. And almost simultaneously, the related concepts of organism and of organic expression had begun to assume major importance.[114]

Such, in brief, is the history of the idea of organic expression. Now that it has been summarily traced back from Wright and Sullivan through Emerson and his circle to its chief sources, its later influence in Germany since the early nineteenth century must be briefly indicated. For in the second and third decades of the twentieth century a new influx of the doctrine of organicism was to come to the United States from Germany, and was destined to affect American architecture profoundly.

V

Ever since the time of Kant, of Herder, Goethe, Schelling, and the Schlegels, the concept of organic expression has continued to dominate much German thought. It can be seen, for example, in the statement of Schopenhauer (1788–1860)—one of the German philosophers to whose works Louis Sullivan had been introduced by his friend Edelmann[115]—that "the beauty . . . of a building lies in the obvious adaptation of every part . . . directly to the stability of the whole, to which the position, dimensions, and form of every part must have so necessary a relation that, . . . if any one part were taken away, the whole would fall to pieces." [116]

It is noteworthy that Schopenhauer, who was an older contemporary of Spencer and Darwin, was not only a believer in the idea of organic expression but an important figure in the history of evolutionary theory. For Schopenhauer has even been called the first great protagonist of a general vitalistic evolutionism, based on his doctrine of a timeless will working in time and in the form of a blind purposiveness which gives rise to the organs and potencies in new species.[117] Actually, however, Schopenhauer's vitalism (the direct or indirect influence of which was to be felt by many well-known figures including Nietzsche, Bernard Shaw, and Bergson, as well as Louis Sullivan) had long been foreshadowed in the writings of such well-known philosophers as Leibnitz and Shaftesbury, as well as of German romantics such as Schelling, Friedrich von Schlegel, and especially Herder. It was Herder who had conceived of the whole basis of the universe as "force" (*Kraft*), something not unlike "energy" in modern scientific terminology.[118] And Herder's "force"—like all such vitalistic concepts, including Sullivan's "idea of power"—arose out of the Neoplatonic pantheism and panpsychism which were the basis of the romantic belief that all nature is pervaded by a vital spirit.

One important respect in which Schopenhauer went beyond Herder and other German romantics was in his concept of the artist as an intuitive mystic seer, a view later echoed by Sullivan.[118a] This, also, Schopenhauer developed out of Neoplatonism. For where Plato had frowned upon art as dealing with mere particulars rather than with the general and the "ideal," as being a mere copy of appearance and therefore lacking in reality and truth, Plotinus, on the contrary, had indicated that an artist may through his insight pass beyond the physical world of appearances to reveal the highest reality, the Platonic "Ideas" themselves. However, where Plotinus based the insight of the artist upon intellect, Schopenhauer in romantic fashion based it upon intuition. And since Schopenhauer, unlike most romantics, pessimistically regarded the everyday world as evil, his philosophy, even more than that of Plotinus, encouraged the artist to disregard the forms of nature in favor of nonnaturalistic symbols arrived at by sheer intuition. Eventually, therefore, Schopenhauer's philosophy helped to encourage the antinaturalistic artistic movements known as symbolism in literature, and cubism in painting and sculpture.[118b]

But although Schopenhauer is a key figure in the history of vitalism, we must recall that scientists regard as the father of modern vitalism not Schopenhauer or some earlier romantic but a scientist, the German physiologist G. E. Stahl (d. 1734).[119] Stahl held that the living body is governed not by ordinary physical and chemical laws but by a vital principle he called the "sensitive soul." In this he was reacting sharply against the mechanistic aspects of the Cartesian philosophy so influential in his own day; for by the eighteenth century followers of Descartes had come to believe that men as well as animals are machines. In calling his vital principle the "sensitive soul" Stahl was probably influenced not only by Neoplatonic pantheistic vitalism but also by the Christian insistence on the worth of the individual soul in the sight of God.

Obviously, vitalistic evolutionism—whether stemming from the vitalism of Schopenhauer and the romantics or from the scientific vitalism of Stahl—is sharply opposed to the mechanistic kind of evolution. And this, in turn, although it derives ultimately from the mechanistic aspects of Descartes' philosophy, stems more immediately, of course, from that alliance between mechanism and evolution which was completed in the middle of the nineteenth century, and was so greatly fostered not only by Spencer's mechanistic theory of the universe but by Darwin's quasi-mechanistic biology. For while it is true that Darwin did not establish any direct connection between the laws of mechanics and organic evolution, nevertheless many of his followers have implied that nature, with its "laws" of the survival of the fittest, has brought about the formation and development of species by a kind of mechanical process like that believed to be operating in the inorganic world and in the universe. This mechanistic kind of biological evolutionism was to reach its peak with the German Darwinian, Haeckel (1834–1919), who firmly asserted the essential unity of organic and inorganic nature and so stood for an uncompromising monism.

Thus in Germany and and elsewhere the extreme mechanistic evolutionism represented by Haeckel was eventually to be found

side by side with the vitalistic evolutionism supported not only by
followers of Schopenhauer and the romantics but by a scientific
tradition descended from Stahl. The conflict between these points
of view still goes on even though, as mentioned early in this
chapter, some biologists and other scientists, as well as some influential philosophers, have in recent years insisted that the antithesis
between vitalism and mechanism is meaningless, maintaining
that the fundamental fact is the organism as an organized whole,
which is more than mechanism or vitalism but in a sense can include them both. Somewhat similarly, the architectural philosophies of Sullivan, and especially of Wright, include both mechanism and vitalism because both concepts have come to be regarded
as subsumed within a more fundamental concept, that of organic
expression. And this organismic point of view is equally characteristic of the architectural philosophy of Walter Gropius and many
other German-born architects today.

Because the dual romantic and scientific origins of the doctrine
of organic expression have had such direct parallels in German
philosophy and science ever since the eighteenth century, it is not
surprising that both the romantic and functionalistic aspects of
the doctrine can be traced also in the writings and buildings of
some of the most influential German architects of the period down
to and including those of Gropius himself. For example, doubtless under the influence of both romantic and scientific thought,
the greatest German architect of the early nineteenth century,
Karl Friedrich Schinkel (1781–1841), expressed his belief in organic expression, and therefore in the direct expression of specific
function. Said Schinkel, in words remarkably similar to those of
Sullivan and Wright, "Architecture is the setting forth of Nature
in its constructive activity." [120] "Emphasize construction; use materials frankly; no useless parts; all clear and natural." [121] Also,
"All great ages have left a record of themselves in their style of
building. Why should we not try to find a style for ourselves?" [122]
Because Schinkel, like all organicists, stressed contemporaneity
in this way, he considered it important to make use of the new inventions made possible by advances in technology and science.
Furthermore, he sought to give direct expression to various new
architectural problems: he was much interested, for example, in
the new forms of the factory architecture of Manchester which he
saw on a trip to England in 1826. And during the following year
he made a design for a department store (Fig. 16) in which—

largely by means of huge windows and a relatively small amount of wall—he achieved a surprisingly advanced expression for what was then a very new architectural problem.

The point of view of Schinkel was carried on in Germany into the second half of the nineteenth century, particularly by the architect Gottfried Semper (1803–79), who was a friend of Schinkel. In his books *Wissenschaft, Industrie und Kunst* (1851) and *Der Stil in den technischen und tektonischen Künsten* (1860–63), Semper conceived art to be a special process of development, of becoming in time, and thus of evolution. For this reason he dealt especially with the principles of style in their adaptation to new inventions. He investigated structure from a genetic point of view, and explained it as derived from the specific nature of the material, from the nature of the tools and methods of construction, and also from the nature of the use to which the structure is to be put.[123] In developing this genetic, empirical, and comparative method, he originated an objective science of art destined to have a wide influence, even though it tended to reduce art to a resultant of purely mechanical and social forces.[124]

Semper's aesthetic materialism and empirical method were immediately adopted by several eminent philosophers of art, chiefly on the Continent; and soon many architects in Germany, Austria, and Holland also fell under the influence of his ideas. Even earlier, Semper had been sympathetically received in England by a group who had already been working along similar lines. For after the Revolution of 1848, Semper—a political liberal—had gone to London as a refugee, and there had been called upon to arrange parts of the great Exhibition at the Crystal Palace in 1851.

Eventually, therefore, Semper's influence on the Continent could easily be re-enforced by similar influences from England, and particularly by that of William Morris. As already mentioned, Morris once said in words very like those of Semper, "one avows a principle of structure that evolves its forms in the spirit of strict truthfulness following the conditions of use, material and construction." Such aesthetic materialism as this was in harmony not only with the materialism of Semper but with the rising materialism of Karl Marx. As a result, Morris himself eventually became a Marxist, at least in name. And when his concepts of society and art were carried to Germany they fitted in both with the liberalism which had become widespread with the Revolution of 1848, and with the socialism which also had accompanied that revolution but had become particularly widespread after the founding of the Social Democratic Workingmen's party in 1869. For Morris' attempt to revive the guild system of the Middle Ages was an effort to improve not only the arts and handicrafts but the social condition of the individual workingmen as well. Consequently it could appeal not only to many artists and craftsmen but to humanitarian liberals, and also—in so far as the guild system involved collective action—to many socialists as well. It might be noted here, however, that Morris was by no means the first in modern times to glorify the medieval guilds; the tendency originated in the early days of the romantic movement, and is to be seen in Germany itself at a relatively early date: Herder, for example, in praising Gothic architecture, insisted that it was a product of the towns and of their craft guilds.[125]

Many of the ideas of both Morris and Semper were to a considerable degree reflected in the Deutsche Werkbund, founded in 1907, "to ennoble industrial labor through the cooperation of art, industry, and handicraft—by means of education, propaganda and united action on relevant questions," [126] and also to form a "rallying point for all those who are able and willing to work for quality." [127] While the emphasis here on handicraft particularly suggests the influence of Morris,[128] the importance given to modern industry and its possibilities for expression in art is more in the tradition of Schinkel and Semper. And it is significant that quality, the central idea of the Werkbund, was defined as meaning "not only excellent solid work and the use of blameless, genuine materials, but also the attainment of an *organic whole* [my italics] rendered significantly real (*sachlich*), noble, and artistic by such means." [129]

One of the youngest of the Werkbund leaders was Walter Gropius (1883–   ), who is proud of the fact that he belongs "to a Prussian family of architects in which the tradition of Schinkel . . . was part of our heritage." [130] Moreover, Gropius received an important part of his architectural training in the office of Peter Behrens, who, in turn, had been greatly influenced, directly or indirectly, by Semper's pupil, Otto Wagner. In 1919 Gropius was made head of the Bauhaus at Weimar, which under his leadership moved to Dessau in 1925 and became a great and influential school of handicraft, industrial design, art, and architecture. The first proclamation issued by the Weimar Bauhaus under Gropius' direction contains the words, "Let us create a new *guild of crafts-*

men, without the class distinctions which raise an arrogant barrier between craftsman and artist." [131] The Morris-like emphasis on the "guild of craftsmen," and also the humanitarian and equalitarian emphasis on doing away with class distinctions are to be noted, for Gropius, though a liberal and not a Marxist, nonetheless considers himself a follower of Morris in his views on art.[132]

In *The Theory and Organization of the Bauhaus* (1923), Gropius directly set forth his belief in the idea of organic expression. "We want," he said, "to create a clear organic architecture whose inner logic will be radiant and naked, unencumbered by lying façades and trickeries, . . . an architecture whose function is clearly recognizable in the relation of its forms." [133] In the same document he spoke of "universal unity," and of "this dawning recognition of the essential oneness of all things . . . ," [134] thereby displaying the monism characteristic of one who is, relatively speaking, a functionalist. His statement that "the Bauhaus believes the machine to be our modern medium of design and seeks to come to terms with it," is not only very much in the tradition of Schinkel and Semper, but reflects that emphasis on contemporaneity which is so typical of functionalism.[135] Yet the vitalism which also underlies his philosophy of architectural evolution is reflected in his remark that at the Bauhaus, "We did not base our teaching on any preconceived ideas of form, but sought the vital spark behind life's ever-changing forms." [136]

In many respects, therefore, Gropius' point of view toward architecture is similar to that of Frank Lloyd Wright. Indeed, one of his most important works executed before the first World War —the administration building and model factory (Fig. 17) which, in collaboration with Adolf Meyer, he designed for the Werkbund Exposition at Cologne in 1914—apparently showed the direct influence of Wright. For here the roof was treated as a projecting slab in the manner so characteristic of many of Wright's works (e.g., Fig. 18) and, in more rudimentary form, characteristic also of some of Sullivan's buildings, notably the Wainwright Building at St. Louis (Fig. 7).

In 1910, four years before Gropius had designed the building for the Werkbund Exposition at Cologne, the first great publication ever made of Wright's architecture had been brought out in Germany, long before Wright was very widely known in his own country. Wright himself believes that it was Kuno Francke, professor of the history of German culture at Harvard, who first spread his fame to Germany. According to Wright, Francke visited his Oak Park, Ill., workshop about 1908 or 1909, and became so enthusiastic about Wright's work that he said, "I see that you are doing organically what my people are feeling for only superficially. They would reward you. It will be long before your own people will be ready for what you are trying to give them." [137] In other words, Francke saw clearly how Wright's architecture would appeal to the Germans because Wright had carried organic expression in architecture even further than they themselves had.

Nevertheless, there are highly significant differences between the German tradition of organic expression as reflected in the buildings and theories of Gropius, and the Emersonian tradition of organic expression continued by Sullivan and Wright. In the first place, Gropius—like many other Continental architects—was much more directly and consciously affected by that movement which in painting and sculpture is known as cubism, a movement which originated on the Continent and is usually said to have been "invented" in France about 1907 by the painters Picasso and Braque.

While it is true that Wright's architecture sometimes has shapes that appear to be cubistic, these shapes are simply an expression of the naturally rectangular shapes of most building materials. Whereas European cubism, in theory at least, employs geometric shapes as abstract symbols in an effort to get away from the natural forms of the everyday world.[138]

The variety of European cubism which particularly influenced Gropius is known as Neoplasticism, and this became especially popular at the Bauhaus in 1922 when the Dutch Neoplasticist painter, Van Doesburg, visited Weimar where the Bauhaus was then located.[139] It was in the same year that Gropius, in collaboration with Adolf Meyer again, submitted a design in the competition for the Chicago Tribune Tower (Fig. 19) which seems to reflect the influence of Neoplasticism. Indeed, this design was in part so abstractly cubistic, as well as so nonhistorical in style, that it had no appeal to the prevailing American eclecticism of the time, based as the latter was on historical precedent; and Gropius did not win a prize or even one of the numerous honorable mentions in the competition.

Because of the influence of Neoplasticism on Gropius, it is worth noting here that the whole cubist movement in art has been, in part at least, a continuation of that kind of romanticism which has sought to return to the primitive. For primitivism—like cubism—usually carried with it the suggestion of a program of simplification, of reform by elimination.[140] And the cubists, largely inspired by Cézanne's statement, ". . . treat nature by the cylinder, the sphere and the cone . . . ," have sought to achieve a higher reality by means of geometric abstractions in which the literal details of the everyday world are largely eliminated. Moreover, the close historical connection of European cubism with symbolism in literature, and their common derivation from Baudelaire and certain phases of French literary romanticism, are well known.[141] We have already seen that the theory behind both cubism and symbolism stems in large part from Schopenhauer's romantic conception of the artist as one who, through his intuition, attains a reality which transcends the world of appearances.

Thus the architectural philosophy of Gropius, like that of Frank Lloyd Wright, combines, as it were, aspects of functionalism with aspects of romanticism in direct relation to the concept of organic expression, while differing sharply from that of Wright in regard to cubism. There are, moreover, several other important differences between the philosophies of the two men which should be pointed out here. One of them is that Wright, like his master Sullivan, has ever insisted upon expressing the specific region in his buildings, whereas Gropius' design for the Tribune Tower is a characteristic example of what became known as the International Style in showing relatively little attempt to express a specifically national or a regionalistic character. It is true that Gropius, like several other leaders of the "modern" movement in architecture, dislikes being considered a proponent of the International Style; for he maintains that the International Style is neither international nor a style. He insists that he had no intention of founding a "style," but has sought merely to return to the fundamentals of architecture which had been so long neglected for eclectic imitations of past styles. Nevertheless, many of the particular fundamentals which he and like-minded modern architects stress are based primarily upon the direct expression of the materials and techniques of the Machine Age, and upon the abstract forms derived from cubism. As these materials and techniques are much the same in any industrialized country, and as cubistic shapes easily can be similar in widely separated regions, the resulting architectural forms transcend national boundaries. It is therefore not surprising that the name, International Style, has been generally accepted in spite of the protests of founders of the movement, or even that the same international spirit is in other respects sometimes reflected in their writings, as for example in Gropius' own statement that "what we preached in practice [at the Bauhaus] was the common citizenship of all forms of creative work. . . ." [142]

The tendency of the architects of the International Style to glorify the machine in an effort to achieve a completely twentieth-century character in architecture can clearly be seen in the machine-like quality of Gropius' design for the Tribune Tower, which, in addition to cubism, shows a mechanistically literal expression of a fireproofed steel frame. This machine-like quality also appears clearly in the building (Fig. 20) which Gropius designed during the middle 1920's for the Bauhaus itself. As in so many other examples of the International Style, particularly in its earlier phases, there is a tendency to glorify the machine as an end in itself, even though many of the leading architects of the International Style in theory often deny this fact. Thus Gropius constantly attacks "the much too materialistic attitude of our times," and has insisted that, "no one who has explored the sources of the movement I have called the New Architecture [i.e., the International Style] can possibly subscribe to the claim that it is based on an anti-traditional obsession for mechanistic technique *qua* mechanistic technique, which blandly seeks to destroy all deeper national loyalties and is doomed to lead to the deification of pure materialism." [143] Yet no less a critic than Frank Lloyd Wright has subscribed vigorously to this very claim in saying, "The 'international style' [is] a style that could never be democratic because it is *the use of man by the machine.*" [144] While Wright, too, seeks to express the machine in modern architecture, he insists that he expresses it only as a tool controlled by the creative imagination of the artist.

Another and perhaps more significant difference between the point of view of Gropius and the Bauhaus and that of Sullivan and Wright, lies in the fact that many members of the Bauhaus group have tended to place much emphasis on humanitarian, social, and collective values, on the welfare of man in the mass and on the use of the power of the state to aid that welfare. Interestingly enough, Gropius attacks the academic point of view because of its "preoccupation with the idea of individual genius," [145] whereas Wright, like Sullivan, has attacked it primarily because it pays insufficient attention to individualist values. Significantly, although Gropius himself can be justly described as a liberal, several of his colleagues at the Bauhaus had socialist leanings, while his immediate successor as director, Hannes Meyer, was a thorough-going Marxian communist. The importance which the Bauhaus tended to give to a collective spirit and to collective action in art is reflected in Gropius' statement, ". . . a resolute band of fellow workers can rear a higher embodiment of creative unity than the individual artist," [146] a point of view contrasting sharply with that of Wright who has said again and again, "Individuality is sacred." [147] For while it is true that Wright's master, Louis Sullivan, spoke of architecture as a branch of social science, and true also that even Wright himself read with approval the writings of Kropotkin[148] who stressed mutual aid as a factor in evolution, nevertheless both Sullivan and Wright, like Herbert Spencer, have held that the participation of the individual in the social organism is entirely voluntary, and therefore on a fundamentally individualistic basis.

Because of the special emphasis which Gropius has given to the humanitarian and social aspects of the art of architecture, it is not surprising that he has long been particularly interested in the problem of housing the masses. In 1928 he left the Bauhaus after a dispute with a faction under the leadership of Hannes Meyer who upheld a more completely mechanistic theory of art. Gropius then returned to private practice in Berlin, where, as he said, he "could devote more of my time to the sociological and structural aspects of housing." [149] In the following year he built in the Berlin suburb of Siemensstadt a housing group for workers (Fig. 21) which, with similar German designs, was to exert great influence on housing elsewhere. At Siemensstadt, Gropius and other architects erected a series of row houses having nearly identical apartments for economy, and all the rows identically oriented to the sun with mechanical precision (Fig. 22). It was this type of continental row house that was to be the model for much of the urban housing built in the United States under the New Deal.

To Frank Lloyd Wright such housing completely denies the personality of the individuals who live in it, and he has even referred to housing of this sort as "the slums of tomorrow." [150] His own more individualistic point of view is reflected in his model for an ideal community which he calls "Broadacre City" (Fig. 24). In "Broadacre City," which to Wright represents "Organic Capitalism," [151] each individual family would have its own house and at least an acre of ground; and because each house would be suited to the needs of the particular family, it would necessarily be quite different in plan, composition, and orientation from neighboring houses. To Wright only in this way can the truly American democratic spirit be given adequate architectural expression, although such housing is, of course, more expensive than the row-housing of Gropius.

During the middle 1920's the influence of Gropius and the other leading continental architects of the International Style began to spread in the United States. In 1933 the Bauhaus was closed by the Nazis to whom its international spirit was "degenerate" or "bolshevistic";[152] and, like so many other German architects, Gropius soon left Germany. After three years in England he came to the United States in 1937 as senior professor in the department of architecture at Harvard, of which he was made chairman the following year. By his teaching as well as by his practice he still exerts great influence on architectural design in the United States, where he continues to build in an only slightly modified version of his earlier International Style work. His own house (Fig. 23) at Lincoln, Mass., for example, reflects much the same architectural principles as his design for the Bauhaus itself, even though constructed mostly of wood as a regionalistic concession to a local material. Yet even here the local material is not treated as horizontal clapboarding in the manner traditionally characteristic of the region, for on the exterior the finish boards are set vertically and with no overlapping.

Today, then, the idea of organic expression as seen in modern architecture in the United States particularly reflects two important but different currents of thought which nevertheless have in common an organismic and—in major respects—essentially naturalistic philosophy of architecture. One of them, derived in part from German romanticism, stems from Emerson and his circle, and has been greatly strengthened by Darwinian evolutionary doctrine, especially by the individualistic variety promulgated by Herbert Spencer and his followers. The second main current of organic expression, also springing largely from German romanticism as well as from scientific concepts, has entered the United States with the spread of the International Style since the first World War, especially under the influence of European émigré architects, including Walter Gropius.

Thus today the Emersonian version of organic expression—a version reflecting the individualistic spirit which is one aspect of the American democratic tradition and which is so well expressed in Sullivan's phrase, "Democracy is primarily of the individual" [153]—is encountering a somewhat more collectivistic version stemming chiefly from Germany. This, in turn, has a strong appeal to the equalitarianism which likewise has always been characteristic of American democracy. In other words, the problem of the relation of the individual to society as a whole, of democratic individualism to democratic equalitarianism, a problem always inherent in American democracy but peculiarly intense today, is reflected with especial clarity in those many examples of contemporary American architecture which have been designed under the influence of the idea of organic expression, and therefore of related theories of evolution.

No doubt this concept of organic expression, now so powerful in many fields of American thought, has of late been fostered by the works of Frank Lloyd Wright and Walter Gropius. Conversely, its wide acceptance—fostered also by the wide acceptance of the related philosophies of John Dewey[154] and of Alfred North Whitehead, among others[155]—has undoubtedly helped to popularize the ideas and buildings of Wright and Gropius among Americans. Certainly in recent years Wright's work, like that of Gropius, has achieved wide recognition, whereas it was Louis Sullivan's personal tragedy that, during middle and later life, his ideas and architecture were temporarily rejected by the American public. And they were rejected primarily because at that time the influence of the French academic point of view—the direct heir of Renaissance classicism, and as such fundamentally opposed to organic expression—was temporarily dominant in American architecture.

But although the history of the idea of organic expression as a philosophical and scientific doctrine has significant implications for the history of American architecture as well as of American life in general, the fact that aesthetic values are never identical with philosophical, historical, social, or scientific values must now finally be emphasized. For even though a work of art is a historical and philosophical document determined in large part by the philosophy of the artist and by his historical and social background, in the end it must be judged on its unique value as a work of art, and not as a mere document in the history of ideas. In other words, the tendency today—a tendency resulting from the primacy of the concept of evolution—to regard all ideas and institutions as social products, as springing from the necessity of effecting some kind of adaptation between human nature and its environment,[156] must not be allowed to obscure the significance of art as art.

This does not mean, however, that the philosophical concept of organic expression and its history possess no significance for art. Surely, history and philosophy, properly understood, can cast light on the intent, conscious or unconscious, of an artist, and also on the different ways in which his works have been regarded at different times. For this reason, knowledge of the history of so influential a concept as that of organic expression, by adding greater understanding to feeling, can help enrich the total experience which a beholder receives from a work of art created under the influence of that concept. And in a sense it is a concept highly relevant to all art, for any significant work of art is an expression of a very exceptional organism, the artist who created it.

Thus in some respects, from artistic points of view as well as from the point of view of the history of ideas, the idea of organic expression has profound meaning for architecture as art. And this despite the fact that it is primarily a biological concept, naturalistic in tendency, whose complete validity for art has justly been questioned, especially by those critics whose philosophy of art has either a humanistic or a supernaturalistic basis.

NOTES

1. The *New English Dictionary,* which gives this as the first meaning of the word organic, states that this usage is rare, but cites examples of it ranging from the early sixteenth century through the nineteenth century. The earliest examples given by the *New English Dictionary* for the other meanings cited in this paragraph range from the early eighteenth to the middle of the nineteenth century.

2. "On Our Knowledge of the Causes of the Phenomena of Organic Nature" [Six Lectures to Working Men—1863], *Darwiniana, Essays by Thomas H. Huxley* (London, Macmillan, 1893), p. 306.

3. See Sir William Dampier, *A History of Science* (New York, Macmillan, 1939, also other editions), index, under mechanism, vitalism, and organicism; and especially George Gaylord Simpson, *The Meaning of Evolution* (New Haven, Yale, 1949), pp. 125–129. Also consult Ernst Cassirer, *The Problem of Knowledge* (New Haven, Yale, 1950), chap. xi (pp. 188–216), "Vitalism."

4. The logical positivists, who first became influential in the late 1920's, are among those who insist that the whole question of "vitalism or mechanism" is really meaningless because it is not a simple question of fact with a solution which can satisfy all men. Instead, they hold that the real question is simply this: "In which style—mechanistic or vitalistic or both—can the picture of the world best be painted?" They regard the contemporary organismic point of view as a return to the anthropomorphic and Aristotelian

philosophy of the Middle Ages, and hence outmoded. See Philipp Frank, *Modern Science and Its Philosophy* (Cambridge, Mass., Harvard, 1949), especially pp. 59–60 and 195.

5. Quoted in *Frank Lloyd Wright on Architecture,* ed. by Frederick Gutheim (New York, Duell, Sloan & Pearce, 1941), p. 66, from *Ausgefürte Bauten und Entwürfe* (Berlin, 1910).

6. Frank Lloyd Wright, *Modern Architecture* (Princeton, Princeton University Press, 1931), front end paper.

7. See R. G. Collingwood, *The Idea of Nature* (Oxford, Clarendon, 1945), pp. 99–100.

8. Charles Darwin, *The Origin of Species* (New York, Modern Library, n.d.), p. 147.

9. For Wright's statement see his *Modern Architecture,* p. 47. The "cultural organicism" of Dewey, Beard, Holmes, Veblen, and others is discussed in Morton G. White, *Social Thought in America; the Revolt against Formalism* (New York, Viking, 1949), chap. i.

10. Quoted by Walter Curt Behrendt, *Modern Building* (New York, Harcourt, Brace, 1937), p. 127.

11. Quoted by Hugh Morrison, *Louis Sullivan* (New York, Museum of Modern Art and W. W. Norton, 1935), p. 247, from *Kindergarten Chats,* originally published in *Interstate Architect and Builder* (1901–2).

12. Louis Sullivan, *Kindergarten Chats* (Scarab Fraternity Press, 1934), p. 114.

13. *Ibid.,* p. 158.

14. Louis Sullivan, *The Autobiography of an Idea* (New York, Norton [1934]), pp. 254–255.

15. Sullivan, *Kindergarten Chats,* p. 114.

16. Wright, *Modern Architecture,* front end paper.

17. *Loc. cit.*

18. *Ibid.,* front flyleaf.

19. *Ibid.,* front end paper; see also n. 6 herein.

20. It is true, however, that Geoffrey Scott's own variety of humanism differs from that of the Renaissance in being largely based on the modern—and subjective—theory of *Einfühlung,* or empathy. The first appearance of the verb *einfühlen* occurred in the writings of the German romantic, Herder, in 1774: see Emory Neff, *The Poetry of History* (New York, Columbia, 1947), pp. 23 and 225.

21. Wright, *Modern Architecture,* front flyleaf.

22. Gutheim, *op. cit.,* p. 158, quoting from Wright, "Why I Love Wisconsin," *Wisconsin Magazine* (1932).

23. Frank Lloyd Wright, *An Autobiography* (London, etc., Longmans, Green, 1932), p. 136.

24. Sullivan, *Kindergarten Chats,* p. 184.

25. As Stephen C. Pepper points out in his analysis of organicism in *World Hypotheses* (Berkeley and Los Angeles, University of California, 1942), p. 314.

26. Wright, *Modern Architecture,* back end paper.

27. Sullivan, *Kindergarten Chats,* p. 198.

28. *Ibid.,* p. 243.

29. Gutheim, *op. cit.,* p. 95, quoting Wright, "Chicago Culture" (1918).

30. Wright, *An Organic Architecture: The Architecture of Democracy* (London, Lund, Humphries, 1939), p. 4.

31. Wright, *Modern Architecture,* p. 23.

32. Gutheim, *op. cit.,* p. 23, quoting Wright, "The Art and Craft of the Machine" (1901).

33. Sullivan, *Kindergarten Chats,* p. 83.

34. *Ibid.,* p. 127.

35. Sullivan, *The Autobiography of an Idea,* p. 233.

36. Sullivan, *Kindergarten Chats,* p. 20.

37. Wright, *An Organic Architecture*, p. 26.
38. Gutheim, *op. cit.*, p. 85, quoting Wright, "Chicago Culture."
39. Sullivan, *Kindergarten Chats*, p. 91.
40. Sullivan, *The Autobiography of an Idea*, p. 197.
41. Sullivan, *Kindergarten Chats*, p. 169.
42. Morrison, *op. cit.*, p. 257, quoting Sullivan, "The Young Man in Architecture" (1900).
43. Wright, *An Organic Architecture*, p. 6.
44. Wright, *Modern Architecture*, front flyleaf.
45. Sullivan, *The Autobiography of an Idea*, p. 257.
46. Wright, *Modern Architecture*, front end paper.
47. Sullivan, *Kindergarten Chats*, p. 174.
48. Gutheim, *op. cit.*, p. 36, quoting Wright, "In the Cause of Architecture" (1908); and Wright, *Modern Architecture*, front flyleaf.
49. Quoted by Gutheim, *op. cit.*, p. 257.
50. Henry Adams, *The Degradation of the Democratic Dogma* (New York, Macmillan, 1919). Adams arrived at his conclusions on the basis of Lord Kelvin's principle of the dissipation of energy.
51. Sullivan, *Kindergarten Chats*, p. 223.
52. *Ibid.*, p. 162.
53. For Marx's statement see his letter to Lassalle in *Marx-Engels Selected Correspondence* (New York, International Publishers, 1934), p. 125; for that of Engels see *Communist Manifesto* (Rand School ed., 1919), Preface, p. vii.
54. Quoted by M. Beer, *Life and Teaching of Karl Marx* (Boston, Small, Maynard, 1925), p. 63.
55. Sullivan, *The Autobiography of an Idea*, pp. 254–255; see also n. 14 herein.
56. *Ibid.*, p. 249.
57. For the quotation from Darwin see Charles Darwin, *The Origin of Species*, p. 37. The quotation from Lamarck—called to my attention by Mr. R. W. Steblay—is from Lamarck's *Système des animaux sans vertèbres* (1801), quoted in Alpheus S. Packard, *Lamarck* (New York, Longmans, 1901), p. 247.
58. Sullivan, *The Autobiography of an Idea*, p. 255.
59. Gutheim, *op. cit.*, p. 58.
60. Herbert Spencer, *Essays on Education* (London, etc., Everyman's Library, 1911, etc.), p. 32.
61. Sullivan, *The Autobiography of an Idea*, p. 250.
62. *Ibid.*, p. 246.
63. *Ibid.*, p. 247.
64. Frank Lloyd Wright, *An Autobiography* (New York, Duell, Sloan & Pearce, revised and enlarged ed. 1943), p. 561.
65. Wright, *op. cit.*, p. 415.
66. Sullivan, *The Autobiography of an Idea*, pp. 248–249.
67. Quoted by F. O. Matthiessen, *American Renaissance* (New York, etc., Oxford, 1941), p. 598.
68. "A Backward Glance o'er Travel'd Roads," *Leaves of Grass by Walt Whitman*, ed. by E. Holloway (Garden City and New York, Doubleday, Page, 1925), p. 525.
69. Preface to 1855 edition, *ibid.*, pp. 500–501.
70. "A Backward Glance," *ibid.*, p. 525.
71. *Ibid.*, p. 527.
72. *Ibid.*, p. 526.
73. Quoted by Matthiessen, *op. cit.*, p. 135.
74. *Ibid.*, p. 133.
75. Ralph Waldo Emerson, "Self-Reliance," in Essays: First Series, *The Complete Essays and Other Writings* (New York, Modern Library, 1940), pp. 165–166.

76. Henry David Thoreau, *Walden and Other Writings* (New York, Modern Library, 1940), p. 42.

77. Quoted by Matthiessen, *op. cit.*, pp. 151–152.

78. Quoted in Emerson, "English Traits," *The Complete Essays*, p. 525.

79. Greenough, "American Architecture," in Henry T. Tuckerman, *A Memorial of Horatio Greenough* (New York, Putnam, 1853), p. 125.

80. Greenough, "Relative and Independent Beauty," in *ibid.*, p. 132.

81. Greenough, "American Architecture," in *ibid.*, pp. 122–123.

82. Quoted by Matthiessen, *op. cit.*, p. 148.

83. Greenough, "American Architecture," in Tuckerman, *op. cit.*, p. 129.

84. Samuel Taylor Coleridge, *Lectures on Shakespeare, Etc.* (London and New York, Everyman's Library, 1907, etc.), pp. 46–47.

85. Quoted by Behrendt, *op. cit.*, p. 61. Viollet-le-Duc, the French Gothic Revivalist and proto-functionalist so highly regarded by Frank Lloyd Wright, had a similar definition of truthfulness in architecture, also based on an admiration for the Gothic: see E. E. Viollet-le-Duc, *Discourses on Architecture*, trans. by Henry van Brunt (Boston, Osgood, 1875), p. 474.

86. Sullivan, *The Autobiography of an Idea*, p. 249.

87. *Ibid.*, pp. 206–207. Frank Lloyd Wright has said that Sullivan "venerated none except Adler [his partner], Herbert Spencer, Richard Wagner, Walt Whitman, John Edelman, and himself"; see Wright, *Genius and the Mobocracy* (New York, Duell, Sloan & Pearce, 1949), p. 54.

88. Oskar Walzel, *German Romanticism*, trans. by A. E. Lussky (New York, etc., Putnam, 1932), p. 20.

89. Quoted by Walzel, *op. cit.*, p. 283.

90. "Description of Paintings in Paris and the Netherlands in the Years 1802–1804," Letter IV, in *The Aesthetic and Miscellaneous Works of Frederick von Schlegel*, trans. by E. J. Millington (London, Bohn, 1849), p. 116.

91. See Arthur O. Lovejoy, "The Meaning of 'Romantic' in Early German Romanticism," *Essays in the History of Ideas* (Baltimore, Johns Hopkins, 1948), pp. 183–206.

92. Lovejoy, "Schiller and the Genesis of German Romanticism," in *ibid.*, p. 216; also his essay "On the Discrimination of Romanticisms," especially pp. 242–249.

93. See Walzel, *op. cit.*, p. 19, who says that Schelling arrived at this concept largely as a result of the influence of Herder. The concept of the universe as an organic whole in which everything implies and is implied by everything else is to be found also in Hegel.

94. F. W. J. von Schelling. *The Philosophy of Art, An Oration on the Relations between the Plastic Arts and Nature*, trans. by A. Jackson (London, John Chapman, 1845), p. 10.

95. *Ibid.*, p. 11.

96. *Ibid.*, pp. 32–33.

97. The two quotations from Herder are taken from Neff, *op. cit.*, pp. 66 and 22, who cites Herder's *God: Some Conversations*, trans. by Frederick Burckhardt (New York, Veritas Press, 1940), p. 172; and Herder's *Still Another Philosophy of History for the Culture of Humanity* (1774).

98. Collingwood, *The Idea of Nature*, p. 134.

99. *Ibid.*, p. 10; and J. B. Bury, *The Idea of Progress* (New York, Macmillan, 1932), chap. vii.

100. Wright, *An Autobiography* (1943 ed.), p. 561, also p. 56.

101. Quoted by Vernon L. Parrington, *Main Currents in American Thought* (New York, Harcourt, Brace, n.d.), II, 389.

102. Quoted by Behrendt, *op. cit.*, p. 127, from one of Goethe's Essays on Art.

103. *Kant's Critique of Judgement*, trans. by J. H. Bernard (London, Macmillan, 1914), p. 187, heading of Section 45 in Part I, Division I.

104. *Ibid.*, p. 20, heading of Section 5 in Introduction.

105. *Ibid.*, p. 259, Section 61 in Part II, Division I.

106. See Walzel, *op. cit.*, p. 37.

107. For Leibnitz's presupposition of organism see A. N. Whitehead, *Science and the Modern World* (New York, Macmillan, 1939), p. 223, who cites Bertrand Russell, *The Philosophy of Leibniz*. Whitehead himself states (p. 224), that Leibnitz' system presupposed an aggregate of independent entities. Leibnitz once said that his concept of the monad was based on the discoveries of Malpighi, Swammerdam, and Leeuwenhoek, discoveries made possible by the development of the microscope: see Cassirer, *The Problem of Knowledge*, p. 152. Lovejoy, "Monboddo and Rousseau," *Essays in the History of Ideas*, p. 61, points out that a general law of organic evolution had been early implied by Leibnitz, and then by Maupertuis, Diderot, Robinet, and Monboddo: see also Lovejoy's articles, "Some Eighteenth-Century Evolutionists," *Popular Science Monthly*, LXV (1904), 238–251, 323–340, and "The Argument for Organic Evolution before *The Origin of Species*," *ibid.*, LXXV (1909), 499–514, 537–549. G. G. Simpson, *op. cit.* (see n. 3), pp. 265–266, cites among the early evolutionists Hooke, Ray, De Maillet, Maupertuis, Buffon, and Erasmus Darwin; and states that all of them "openly considered evolution as a possibility, and most of them proclaimed it as a reality."

108. See Neff, *op. cit.*, p. 38.

109. Archibald Alison, "Of the Relative Beauty of Forms," in *Essays on the Nature and Principles of Taste* (1790), p. 301. The quotation from Hogarth was taken by Alison from William Hogarth, *The Analysis of Beauty* (1753). The nearly contemporary proto-functionalism of the French "Moderns," which, with that of Locke, probably influenced Hogarth as well as Alison, can best be seen in the *Nouveau traité de toute architecture* (Paris, 1706) of Chanoine L. G. de Cordemoy, who in turn apparently inspired such theorists on architecture as Abbé Laugier and Carlo Lodoli. Laugier's influential *Essai sur l'architecture* was first published in Paris in 1753, and in London in 1755.

110. Quoted from P. Rieff in *Euphorion* (1912), pp. 591 ff., by Arthur O. Lovejoy, *The Great Chain of Being* (Cambridge, Mass., Harvard, 1936), p. 298.

111. Lovejoy, *The Great Chain of Being*.

112. *Ibid.*, p. 244.

113. Quoted from *Allgemeine Naturgeschichte* (4th ed. 1755), p. 84, in Lovejoy, *op. cit.*, p. 268.

114. Lovejoy, *op. cit.*, p. 268, states that evolutionary theories began to multiply in the third quarter of the eighteenth century. D'Arcy Thompson, *On Growth and Form* (New York, Macmillan, new ed. 1942), p. 1020, note, mentions that the words "organism" and "organization" had come into use among biologists and zoologists in the early eighteenth century, citing Charles Robin, "Recherches sur l'origine et le sens des termes organisme et organization," *Journal de l'anatomie* (1880), pp. 1–55. See also n. 1 herein.

115. Sullivan, *The Autobiography of an Idea*, p. 209.

116. Schopenhauer, *The World as Will and Idea*, Section 43, trans. by DeWitt H. Parker, *Schopenhauer Selections* (New York, etc., Scribner, 1928), p. 140.

117. See Arthur O. Lovejoy, "Schopenhauer as an Evolutionist," *Monist*, XXI (1911), 195–222. Lovejoy points out that Schopenhauer's pessimism is dropped by those who continue his vitalism, because most believers in evolution believe in progress and hence are optimists.

118. See Neff, *op. cit.*, p. 65; also Robert T. Clark, Jr., "Herder's Conception of 'Kraft,'" *Publications of the Modern Language Association of America*, LVII, No. 3 (Sept., 1942), 737–752, especially p. 750.

118a. Sullivan, *The Autobiography of an Idea*, pp. 269–270.

118b. For the influence of Schopenhauer's philosophy upon the origins of literary symbolism and cubism, see the excellent account in Frances B. Blanshard, *Retreat from Likeness in the Theory of Painting* (New York, Columbia, 1949), pp. 54 ff. Unlike Schopenhauer, however, much cubist theory emphasized intellect as well as intuition.

119. Dampier, *A History of Science* (1938 ed.), p. 202.

120. Alfred Freiherrn von Wolzogen, *Aus Schinkel's Nachlass* (Berlin, R. Decker, 1863), III, 365.

121. Quoted by Behrendt, *op. cit.*, p. 40.

122. *Ibid.*, p. 39, quoting Schinkel's diary.

123. Gottfried Semper, *Der Stil in den technischen und tektonischen Künsten* (Munich, Bruckmann, 1878), I, 7.

124. Earl of Listowel, *A Critical History of Modern Aesthetics* (London, Allen & Unwin, 1933), p. 209.

125. See Neff, *op. cit.*, p. 77. This concept of Gothic architecture appears also in Viollet-le-Duc's insistence that the Gothic was produced by laymen.

126. Quoted by Behrendt, *op. cit.*, p. 101.

127. See N. Pevsner, *Pioneers of the Modern Movement from William Morris to Walter Gropius* (London, Faber & Faber, 1936), p. 39.

128. For the influence of William Morris on German architecture and especially on the Werkbund see particularly N. Pevsner, *op. cit.*, pp. 38 ff. In spite of his emphasis on handicraft, however, Morris did not always oppose the industrial revolution: for instance, he praised the new iron steamships as the cathedrals of the Industrial Age. Like Morris, Viollet-le-Duc also stressed the importance of handicraft as the basis of art: see his *Discourses, op. cit.*, p. 339.

129. *Ibid.*, p. 39.

130. Walter Gropius, *The New Architecture and the Bauhaus*, trans. by P. M. Shand and J. Hudnut (New York, Museum of Modern Art; and London, Faber & Faber, n.d.), pp. 79–80.

131. Quoted in *Bauhaus, 1919–1928*, ed. by H. Bayer, W. Gropius, I. Gropius (New York, Museum of Modern Art, 1938), p. 18.

132. N. Pevsner, *op. cit.*, p. 42, and p. 216, n. 91, cites Gropius, *Idee und Aufbau des Staatlichen Bauhauses Weimar* (Munich, 1925), p. 2, as showing that Gropius regards himself "as a follower of Ruskin and Morris, of Van de Velde and the Werkbund." Van de Velde, who was partly responsible for spreading the ideas of Morris to the Continent, said that his own theory of architecture was influenced chiefly by the theories of Morris, Viollet-le-Duc, and Semper: see Behrendt, *op. cit.*, p. 86.

133. Quoted in *Bauhaus, 1919–1928*, p. 29.

134. Quoted in *ibid.*, p. 22.

135. For Gropius' statement see *ibid.*, p. 27. In 1948, however, Gropius said, "The word 'functionalism' has been taken too materially. This is evident from my own writings, from writings by Le Corbusier and others of the period. . . . Looking back I think we dealt not too *much* with the machine but too *little*. We are still enslaved by the machine and its possibilities for business instead of making it our obedient slave for the good life." See the *Museum of Modern Art Bulletin*, XV, No. 3 (New York, Spring, 1948), 11.

136. Gropius, *The New Architecture and the Bauhaus*, p. 62.

137. Wright, *An Autobiography* (1943 ed.), p. 161.

138. The fact that European cubism arose in complete independence of Wright is stressed by the Dutch Neoplasticist architect J. J. P. Oud, "Der Einfluss von Frank Lloyd Wright auf die Architektur Europas," *Hollandische Architektur; Bauhausbücher 10* (Munich, 1926), pp. 80–81, reprinted from *Wendingen* (1925).

139. While Gropius sincerely denies that his work was consciously modified by the ideas of Van Doesburg, practically all art historians agree that Van Doesburg did affect the Bauhaus group. It is worth noting that the three other chief founders of the International Style, namely, Le Corbusier, Miës van der Rohe, and Oud, were also directly influenced by, or connected with, Van Doesburg. Moreover, as young men Gropius, Miës van der Rohe, and Le Corbusier had all worked for a time in the same architectural office, that of Peter Behrens.

140. See Lovejoy, "On the Discrimination of Romanticisms," *Essays in the History of*

Ideas, p. 241. One might add here, also, that cubism has usually involved a deliberate distortion of nature's forms not unlike that so often found in primitive art.

141. See especially Georges Lemaitre, *From Cubism to Surrealism in French Literature* (Cambridge, Mass., Harvard, 1941).

142. Gropius, *The New Architecture and the Bauhaus*, p. 57.

143. *Bauhaus, 1919–1928*, p. 27; and Gropius, *The New Architecture and the Bauhaus*, p. 79.

144. Gutheim, *op. cit.*, p. 260, quoting from the *Architectural Review* (August, 1939).

145. *Bauhaus, 1919–1928*, p. 23.

146. Gropius, *The New Architecture and the Bauhaus*, p. 53.

147. Wright, *Modern Architecture*, rear end paper, etc.

148. Wright, *An Autobiography* (1943 ed.), p. 561.

149. Gropius, *The New Architecture and the Bauhaus*, p. 65.

150. Wright, *An Autobiography* (1943 ed.), p. 323.

151. Frank Lloyd Wright, "Mr. Wright Talks on Broadacre City," *Taliesin*, I, No. 1 (Oct., 1940), 14.

152. *Bauhaus, 1919–1928*, pp. 7–8.

153. Sullivan, *Kindergarten Chats*, p. 124.

154. Like all varieties of pragmatism, John Dewey's peculiarly American philosophy of instrumentalism has much in common with architectural functionalism and consequently with the architectural philosophies of Sullivan and Wright. Like them it also reflects the influence of Darwinian evolution. It places a heavier emphasis on social problems, however, and in this respect, among others, has undoubtedly helped to pave the way in the United States for many of the ideas of Gropius and other architects of the International Style.

155. It is significant that the ideas for which Sullivan, Wright, and Gropius stand first began to achieve a wide audience in this country during the middle 1920's, about the same time as did Alfred North Whitehead's somewhat eclectic version of philosophical organicism. Sullivan, after long neglect, had his *Autobiography of an Idea* published in 1924 by the American Institute of Architects, which also published his *A System of Architectural Ornament According to Man's Powers* in the same year. The theories of the International Style first reached this country chiefly through Le Corbusier's *Vers une architecture* (Paris, 1923), a translation of which was first published in the United States in 1928 under the title, *Towards a New Architecture*. In 1930 Wright delivered his Princeton lectures on modern architecture, the first complete statement of his architectural philosophy, which appeared in book form the following year.

Whitehead's organicism—which has been credited by Sir William Dampier in *A History of Science* (1938), pp. 478 and 491, with playing a leading role in twentieth-century thought—was probably most clearly and popularly expressed in his Lowell lectures, *Science and the Modern World*, first published in 1925. Whitehead indicated in this book that for some time the trend in all the sciences has been toward a more or less organismic point of view, as the theoretical sciences have increasingly worked toward a group of related unifying concepts, with emphasis on enduring organisms, configuration, pattern, process, energy, and the event. One of the most thorough scientific formulations of a concept related to organicism is the Gestalt or "configuration" theory of psychology, which, although first stressed as early as 1890 by Ehrenfels, was really developed in the 1920's by Wertheimer, Koffka, and Koehler. It is worth adding here that in philosophy the nature of wholes as a fundamental feature of the world, and as always very different from the sum of their parts, was being expounded about the same time by J. C. Smuts in his *Holism and Evolution* (1926). While it is certainly true that this holistic concept can be found earlier in the history of thought, notably in ancient Greek times and in the Middle Ages, never before had it aroused so much controversy.

The point should be made, however, that the organicism of Whitehead does not exactly represent a return to the old Greek view of nature as a living thing. As R. G. Collingwood points out (in *The Idea of Nature,* p. 100), Whitehead is "not merging physics in biology as Bergson might have liked to do," but is "welcoming a view of physics which for the first time in modern history reveals a fundamental similarity, instead of an indefinite series of contrasts, between the world of matter and the world of life."

156. See J. H. Randall, Jr., *The Making of the Modern Mind* (revised ed., Boston, Houghton Mifflin, 1940), p. 492.

Acknowledgments

Fig. 3 is from H. A. Tipping, *English Houses,* Period VI, I (New York, Scribner, 1926), 105; Figs. 4, 21, and 22 from Catherine Bauer, *Modern Housing* (Boston and New York, Houghton Mifflin, 1934), pl. 8–C, p. 179, and pl. 1–A; Fig. 5 from the photograph by Hedrich-Blessing, Chicago; Fig. 6 from *A New House by Frank Lloyd Wright on Bear Run, Pa.* (New York, Museum of Modern Art, 1938), p. 4; Fig. 7 from Keystone-Underwood; Fig. 8 from the Art Institute, Chicago; Fig. 9 from H. Th. Wijdeveld and others, *The Life Work of the American Architect Frank Lloyd Wright* (Santpoort, Holland, 1925), p. 26; Figs. 10 and 18 from H.-R. Hitchcock, *In the Nature of Materials* (New York, Duell, Sloan & Pearce, 1942), figs. 355 and 79; Fig. 14 published by permission of the Smithsonian Institution; Fig. 15 from Lorado Taft, *The History of American Sculpture* (New York, Macmillan, 1930), p. 45, fig. 4; Fig. 16 from Fritz Schumacher, *Stromüngen in deutscher Baukunst seit 1800* (Leipzig, 1935), pl. 5, fig. 12; Figs. 17 and 20 from Walter Gropius, *The New Architecture and the Bauhaus* (New York, Museum of Modern Art, n.d.), pls. 2 and 7; Fig. 19 from *The International Competition for a New Administration Building for The Chicago Tribune, MCMXXII* (Chicago, The Chicago Tribune Company, 1923), pl. 197; Fig. 23 from the *Architectural Review, 86* (Nov., 1939), 192; Fig. 24 from the *Architectural Record, 77* (April, 1935), 250. Other illustrations were supplied by the Department of Art and Archaeology, Princeton University.

Figure 1
Strawberry Hill by Horace Walpole

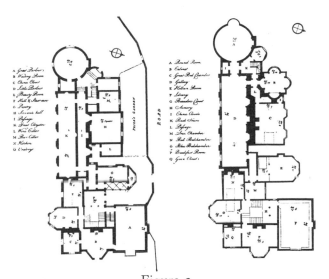

Figure 2
Strawberry Hill, plans by Horace Walpole

Figure 3
Strawberry Hill, the Holbein Chamber, by Horace Walpole

Figure 4
Welwyn Garden City, houses by Louis de Soissons

Figure 5
Falling Water, Bear Run, Penn., by Frank Lloyd Wright

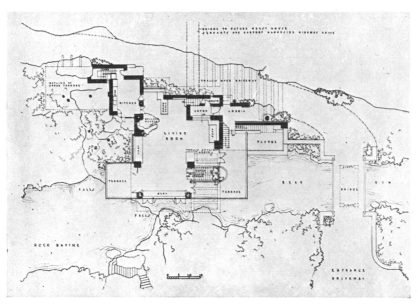

Figure 6
Falling Water, Bear Run, Penn., plan by Frank Lloyd Wright

Figure 8
Schlesinger and Mayer Building (now
Carson Pirie Scott), Chicago, by Louis
Sullivan

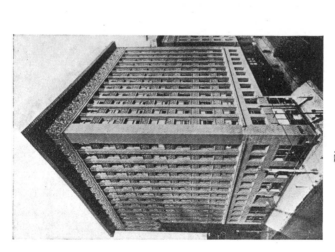

Figure 7
Wainwright Building, St. Louis,
by Louis Sullivan

Figure 9
Robie house, Chicago, by Frank Lloyd Wright

Figure 10
Taliesin West, near Phoenix, Ariz., by Frank Lloyd
Wright

Figure 11

Villa Capra, near Vicenza, by Andrea Palladio

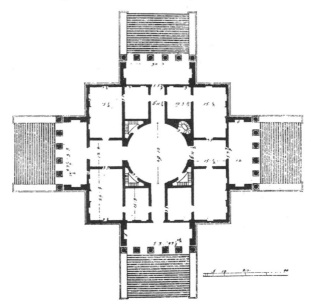

Figure 12

Villa Capra, near Vicenza, plan by Andrea
Palladio

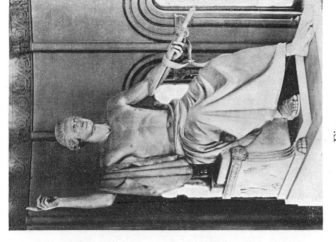

Figure 13
Chartres Cathedral

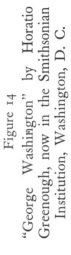

Figure 14
"George Washington" by Horatio
Greenough, now in the Smithsonian
Institution, Washington, D. C.

Figure 15
"The Rescue" by Horatio Greenough, Capitol,
Washington, D. C.

Figure 16
Design by Schinkel for a department store in Berlin

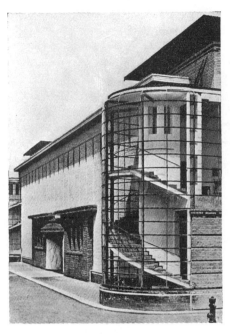

Figure 17
Administration Building, Werkbund Exposition, Cologne, by Walter Gropius and Adolf Meyer

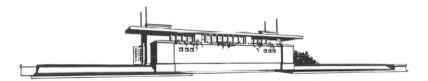

Figure 18
Project of 1902 for Yahara Boat Club, Madison, Wis., by Frank
Lloyd Wright

Figure 20

Bauhaus, Dessau, by Walter Gropius

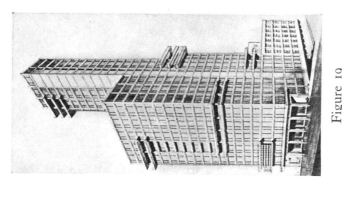

Figure 19

Project for the Chicago Tribune Tower by Walter Gropius and Adolf Meyer

Figure 21
Housing for workers, Berlin-Siemensstadt, by Walter Gropius

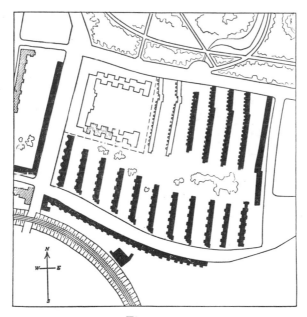

Figure 22
Berlin-Siemensstadt, plan of housing

Figure 23
Gropius house, Lincoln, Mass., by Walter Gropius and
Marcel Breuer

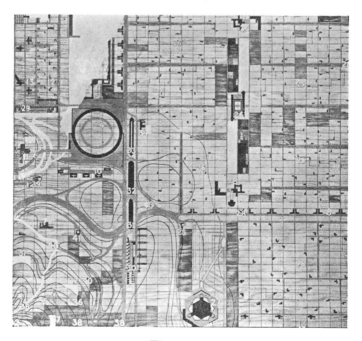

Figure 24
Detail of project for Broadacre City by Frank Lloyd
Wright

INTRODUCTION TO CHAPTER X

EVOLUTION AND MORAL THEORY IN AMERICA

IN moral theory as in many other realms of thought the first effect of the idea of evolution was to strengthen the position of those who proposed to establish a new science of man. The conflict with traditional authorities controlling the intellectual institutions was as least partially responsible for the dogmatic and indefensible opinions of the early ethical naturalists. The reductionist and deterministic ethics of these naturalists based indiscriminately upon Darwin and Lamarckian factors soon gave way to the more sophisticated thought of Dewey and the "new" naturalists, as well as to various brands of theistic ethics which, while discarding natural selection as a moral ideal, were prepared to recognize the evolution of moral ideas as manifestations of a spiritual force.

S. P.

X

EVOLUTION AND MORAL THEORY IN AMERICA

WILLIAM F. QUILLIAN, JR.

I

THE first and the most unique influence of the theory of evolution upon ethics was in the direction of a new naturalistic interpretation of the moral life. The proponents of this type of theory believed that two important contributions to moral theory were made possible by the application of the idea of evolution to man. First of all, they believed it would now be possible to give a satisfactory explanation of the origin, the development, and the value of moral sentiments, moral customs, and moral judgments. And second, ethics as a theory of value could now be placed on a solid, scientific foundation.

This school of thought first appeared in England, Darwin's *Descent of Man* (1871) and Spencer's *Data of Ethics* (1879) being early expressions of it. Both of these volumes were widely read in America, and the stir which they produced is unmistakable. Religious, philosophical, scientific, and literary journals carried article after article devoted to a discussion of the problems raised by these two men. Several books also were published. However, so far as the early development of a naturalistic theory of morality was concerned, very little that was new was added by writers in America. Probably the first important contributions in this direction were those made by John Dewey at the turn of the century; his work will be considered a little later in this chapter.

The general point of view developed by Darwin and Spencer is that the moral life can be understood by tracing it back to its roots in the impulsive and instinctive life of prehuman animals. Darwin finds the source of the moral sense of man in the social instincts; the pain of a stricken conscience is that natural feeling of dissatisfaction which follows the thwarting of any instinct, only in this case it is the permanent social instinct which has been thwarted. Spencer traces the genesis of the moral consciousness to "accumulated experiences of utility." These experiences, he writes, "organized and consolidated through all past experiences of the human race, have been producing corresponding nervous modifications, which, by continued transmission and accumulation, have become in us certain faculties of moral intuition." [1]

Similarly, Spencer derives a standard of morality from his evolutionary approach; in fact, it is here that we find one of the most distinctive features of the early forms of evolutionary ethical theory. According to Spencer, good conduct is the more highly evolved conduct and bad conduct is the relatively less evolved conduct. Since the more highly evolved conduct must be conducive to *life* in one's self, in one's offspring, and in society—else it would have disappeared in the struggle for existence—Spencer concludes that the distinctive characteristic of good conduct is that it preserves *life*. To this notion a hedonistic element is added when he states that this view rests upon the assumption that life is good or bad depending upon whether it does or does not bring a surplus of agreeable feeling. His position becomes clear when he states that "there is no escape from the admission that in calling good the conduct that subserves life, and bad the conduct which hinders or destroys it, and in so implying that life is a blessing and not a curse, we are inevitably asserting that conduct is good or bad according as its total effects are pleasurable or painful." [2] Here we see what the evolutionist means when he claims that ethics, as a theory of value, may now be treated scientifically. The real value of that conduct which we call good is that such conduct is conducive to life, that it promotes survival. This, it is claimed, is the lesson learned from evolution.

Certain American thinkers developed theories of ethics which followed closely the line of thought developed by Spencer. One of the most important of these, John Fiske, believed that his evolutionary treatment of ethics was consistent with a theistic world view; his view will be examined later when we deal with the influence of evolution upon nonnaturalistic theories of morality.

Another American follower of Spencer was Minot J. Savage, the Unitarian clergyman who preached an early version of evolutionary theism. His position was outlined in an article in the *North American Review* entitled "Natural Ethics," and given a more complete exposition by him in *The Morals of Evolution*. Savage follows Spencer both in finding life or happiness to be the standard of good conduct—a standard reached by regarding the evolutionary development of man—and also in explaining man's moral intuitions as being due to certain ways of thinking or to certain feelings which have become ingrained in man's nature through the long experience of the race. A few lines from "Natural Ethics" will show this similarity. "What is the *standard* by which actions can be measured? The experience of the world enables us to put the answer to this great question into one word: and that one word is—Life. The deepest instinct and the strongest desire of all sentient creatures—man included—is toward life. And the one effort of the world is to preserve and increase it." [3]

The evolutionary moralists thus far considered agree in recognizing the customary moral values and standards of their day; they are concerned to strengthen morality. But at least a few thinkers felt that the theory of evolution had other, more drastic consequences for morality. Outstanding among them were Friedrich W. Nietzsche and Edward Westermarck. Nietzsche contended that a recognition of the centrality of the struggle for existence in all animal life demanded a transvaluation of values by which the Christian virtues would be replaced by the virtues of physical strength and power. The distinctive feature of Westermarck's theory was his doctrine of ethical relativity.

Among American thinkers Antonio Llano similarly felt that the theory of evolution had implications for morality which were in a direction quite opposite to that taken by the usual interpretations. His ideas were set forth in an article, "Morality the Last of Dogmas," that appeared in the *Philosophical Review* in 1896. Llano restricts morality to the moral consciousness, that is, to the experience of duty or obligation. Rules of health and means of achieving happiness, he insists, are not elements of morality. Right away this distinction separates his views from those which usually bear the name of evolutionary ethics. Having thus delimited the nature of morality, Llano then maintains that morality so conceived will eventually disappear. It will disappear, he believes, as soon as man understands the illusory character of his sense of duty, when he understands that duty is simply the product of coercion by primitive chieftains who were regarded as divine. The evolution of morality, he contends, is really a devolution of morality, for morality is doomed to vanish when the view of man's life made possible by science becomes widely accepted. Llano's position involves a thoroughgoing determinism, and he insists that logical consistency involves the conclusion that responsibility is an illusion. Both moral blame and moral approbation are absurdities for, explains Llano, "No man's conduct is *his;* it is simply a manifestation of the way in which the universe exists and moves." [4] Llano does not mince his words when he explains further the implications of this determinism. He is convinced that

. . . all our moral feelings must disappear when we have become certain that human beings do not possess any personal independence; that their actions are the actions or the processes of nature; that their conduct is ruled by their organization, their organization by inheritance and environment, inheritance and environment by the eternal properties of matter and force.[5]

These conclusions, believes Llano, flow from the acceptance in a full sense of the theory of evolution.

Towards this conception, [he writes] modified and confirmed by modern science, the intellect of our age seems to be moving with irresistible force. Man has finally been included in the realm of nature; his origin and development are believed to be due to the same processes and laws which govern the formation and transformations of all other bodies and systems of bodies; his present condition, as well as his present conduct, are considered as fatal effects of his preceding conduct and states, the latter having been reached through a slow and continuous growth under the influence of physical forces.[6]

Here is naturalistic reductionism and determinism in its most extreme form. These are precisely the alleged consequences of an evolutionary naturalistic theory of morality against which non-naturalistic writers inveighed. But also they are consequences which many naturalists have been unwilling to accept; protests against such interpretations of the moral life have been frequently voiced by the so-called "newer" naturalists, an outstanding representative of whom is John Dewey.

II

Born in the year that the *Origin of Species* was published, John Dewey may almost be said to have grown up with the theory of evolution. As a student at the University of Vermont, he was impressed by the new insights gained from his studies in geology, zoology, and physiology. During this time he followed the discussions both defending and attacking evolution that were appearing in the English periodicals, the *Fortnightly,* the *Contemporary Review,* and the *Nineteenth Century.*[7]

A central note in Dewey's writings on ethics has been the use which can and should be made of the evolutionary approach in reaching solutions to human problems. The importance of the idea of evolution in his thought is indicated in a published lecture by him bearing the title, "The Influence of Darwinism on Philosophy."[8] The closing statement of this lecture suggests the direction taken by much of Dewey's thought, particularly that dealing with ethical and religious problems. "Doubtless the greatest dissolvent in contemporary thought of old questions," concludes Dewey, "the greatest precipitant of new methods, new intentions, new problems, is the one effected by the scientific revolution that found its climax in the 'Origin of Species.'"[9]

It is interesting to discover that Dewey's early treatment of the implications of evolution for ethics was quite different from the direction taken by his thinking a little later. At first he defended theological ethics against the claims of scientific ethics which were then being pressed. Although he acknowledged the contributions made by evolutionary ethics, he insisted that the divorce of morals from religion involved in this theory is untenable. Two statements from an article published in 1887 reveal this line of thought:

In spite of the vigor and ardor with which these ideas [i.e., of evolutionary ethics] are urged, some of us, at least, remain unmoved. We believe that the cause of theology and morals is one, and that whatever banishes God from the heart of things, with the same edict excludes the ideal, the ethical, from the life of man. Whatever exiles theology makes ethics an expatriate. And we believe these not from obstinacy, nor from traditional prejudice, as it seems to me, nor yet alone from a mere conviction that supernatural restraints and sanctions are needed for the practical moralizing of humanity, but we are convinced that the physical interpretation of the universe is one which necessarily shuts out those ideas and principles which are fundamental to ethics.[10]

.   .   .

It [the evolutionary theory of ethics] is painted with colors which are borrowed from the school of spiritualism, and to which it has no claim; it is filled in with the shadows of figures who live only in the realm of Will and Reason; it reflects a light which has its source in

God himself. Take away this light, abolish this realm, dismiss this school, and the picture fades out into a mere meaningless blank.[11]

Both of these comments follow precisely one line of criticism that is frequently found in discussions of Dewey's own more mature thought. The radical change which has occurred in Dewey's thinking since the publication of the article containing the above quotations may be seen by comparing these statements with the views expressed in an essay published in 1944 entitled "Antinaturalism in Extremis." [12]

An article published in 1898 in the *Monist* shows that by that time Dewey's understanding of the relationship of evolution to morality had changed considerably. In this article Dewey is criticizing the famous lecture by T. H. Huxley on "Evolution and Ethics." Huxley had contended that the "Ethical Process" which appears in man is opposed to the "Cosmic Process." As against this view, Dewey contends that the ethical process is a part of the cosmic process; therefore when human intelligence and effort intervene to restrain and control the natural impulses, they are simply making a connection between the part and the whole. Instead of seeing man as one who has turned against the very natural process which has produced him, contends Dewey, Huxley should see that ". . . man is an organ of the cosmic process in effecting its *own* progress. This progress consists essentially in making over a part of the environment by relating it more intimately to the environment as a whole; not, once more, in man setting himself against that environment." [13]

The emphasis in recent naturalistic writings upon a broader conception of nature and upon the full recognition of the uniqueness of human qualities without surrendering the view that they are end results of a completely natural process of evolution appears in this article. Man's environment is a social one, Dewey explains; consequently the meaning of "fitness for survival" will be different from what it was in a presocial setting. Selection continues to operate in the social sphere but by the success or failure of special acts rather than through the death of the individual. "If we may personify Nature," writes Dewey, "we may say that the influences of education and social approval and disapproval in modifying the behavior of the agent, mark simply the discovery on the part of Nature of a shorter and more economical form of selection than she had previously known." [14]

The interpretation of the moral life which finally emerges as one element in Dewey's developed philosophy involves the recognition of an important function performed by the knowledge of man's evolutionary development. It is the discovery of means to be used in achieving ends. All life involves a continual confronting of problems, of conditions which are unsatisfactory, and the problem of ethics is to discover the means which will bring about a more desirable situation. Dewey rejects the idea that there are certain eternal ideals or ends of moral conduct at which we should all aim. Instead of being fixed, he explains, "an end is a device of intelligence in guiding action, instrumental to freeing and harmonizing troubled and divided tendencies." [15] But such an end is impotent until it is "worked out in terms of concrete conditions available for its realization, that is in terms of 'means.' This transformation," he continues, "depends upon study of the conditions which generate or make possible the fact observed to exist already." [16] At this point the theory of evolution comes into the picture, for it is through the understanding of man's evolutionary development that we come to know what has produced those satisfactions in the past which guide us in planning for the future.

This view of evolution's contribution to the discovery of means to be employed in achieving goals is first developed by Dewey in an article that appeared in two installments in the *Philosophical Review*.[17] It is Dewey's contention that when we are dealing with physical knowledge the one sound method of investigation is that of experimentation, which, he says, is the genetic method. Obviously the experimental procedures of isolation and cumulative recombination cannot be applied to an investigation of moral ideas and practices. However, there is a genetic method that can be used for investigating these questions, namely, history. As viewed from the evolutionary viewpoint, he explains, history "is a process that reveals to us the conditions under which moral practices and ideas have originated. . . . In seeing where they came from, in what situations they arose, we see their significance." [18] Control of two kinds is the advantage gained by thus apprehending moral conduct in terms of its antecedent conditions. One gains both intellectual control, which is "the ability to interpret both obviously allied facts and divergent facts, showing the same *modus* operating under different conditions," and practical control, which is the "ability to get or to avoid an experience of a given sort when we desire";[19] or, as he explains further, "if we get knowledge of a process of generation, we get knowledge of how to proceed in getting a desired result." [20]

A more recent application of this genetic method to the question of values is found in Dewey's Gifford lectures, *The Quest for Certainty*. In a chapter called "The Construction of the Good," he explains that man's task is to determine the relations and conditions which produce results that are enjoyable and desirable and then to apply these intelligently to the materials of his individual and social life. The key to this knowledge is provided by the findings of the natural sciences. When such an application of scientific knowledge is utilized, believes Dewey, we shall produce results that are enjoyable and desirable and thus are valuable. The good is not something to be discovered; it is to be constructed.

Dewey wishes it clearly understood that, though his position is naturalistic, his approach to problems of morality is different from that followed by the late nineteenth-century evolutionary naturalists. In the first place, he opposes their reductionism, insisting that the later-evolved cannot be fully explained or understood by tracing it to its antecedents. Only from the point of view of method and control can the earlier in time be considered of greater value; not with respect to existence. In addition he criticizes their empirical method of explaining the development of moral belief by the repetition or accumulation of previous ideas or impressions. As he explains, "the empirical method holds that the belief or idea is generated by a process of repetition or cumulation; the genetic method by a process of adjustment." [21]

Nonnaturalistic thinkers agree with Dewey in the above criticisms of certain forms of evolutionary ethics. However, there is an important and sharp dividing line between the moralists of the idealist or theistic persuasions and Dewey, this difference being the latter's naturalism. While insisting that he recognizes the genuine novelty of mind, values, and morality, Dewey denies that there is need to assume any causal factor other than those operative as natural causes in order to explain the appearance of these spiritual qualities. The reception accorded the idea of evolution by these nonnaturalists is the question to which we now turn.

III

Many of the nineteenth-century American writers who discussed the new theories of evolutionary ethics were critical—critics are usually more vocal than defenders. Actually these attacks were counterattacks, for the evolutionary naturalistic treatments of morality were themselves attacks upon the strong religious character of ethics in America.

Two of the most constructive critics of evolutionary ethics were J. G. Schurman and J. T. Bixby. Schurman was professor of philosophy at Cornell University from 1886–92, and president of Cornell from 1892 until his retirement in 1920. There followed a ten-year period of service as a diplomat, first as minister to China and then as ambassador to Germany. He died in 1942. Bixby was a prominent Unitarian minister and theologian. After serving several important churches, he became professor of religious philosophy and ethnic religions in the Meadville Theological School. He died in 1921.

In *The Ethical Import of Darwinism* Schurman points out that the evolutionary view of man has made a valuable contribution to our understanding of certain aspects of man's life. However, he is strong in his insistence that a merely biological understanding of man cannot throw any light on the question of moral ends and values. Natural selection may tell us that the conduct which we judge to be morally good is useful in the struggle for existence, but it does not determine its content and meaning. "All that natural selection requires," he explains, "is that something shall be useful; *what else it may be,* what other predicates it may have, wherein its essence consists, natural selection knows not and recks not." [22] Actually, contends Schurman, the evolutionary naturalist changes the problem of ethics to suit his own purposes. His goal is to discover what kinds of action necessarily tend to produce happiness and health. Such knowledge is certainly desirable, but, insists Schurman, it is not the problem of ethics.[23]

Somewhat similar are the criticisms of Spencer advanced by Bixby in *The Ethics of Evolution*. In taking as his moral measure the external elements of conduct—the outward act and its results in happiness—Spencer, it is argued, misses the essential factors in all sound ethical systems, namely, the motive and the will. Bixby also questions the hedonism which seems ultimately to constitute Spencer's test of right conduct. Following and also going beyond the line of thought suggested in Mill's qualitative conception of hedonism, Bixby contends that happiness cannot be the ultimate test of morality because there are so many kinds of happiness and because they differ so greatly in their respective moral worth. A third objection concerns Spencer's explanation of the origin of conscience and of moral ideas by the cumulative and transmuting influence of heredity. Bixby asks why it is that there are so many experiences of utility, such as the more immediate means of gratifying the appetites, cases of prudence and economy, of industry, etc., which have been subject just as much as any others to all the accumulation and organization of which Spencer speaks, but which have not been transformed into moral intuitions.[24]

Bixby, however, was not disposed to repudiate completely either the validity of the theory of evolution or its usefulness in dealing with questions of morality. He insisted that evolution has an important role to play in the field of ethics; his only concern was that it be used logically and thoroughly and wisely. Evolution, he believed, leads us away from the a priori, abstract theories of an earlier day, and certainly we should not turn backward to these. Rather, writes Bixby, we "should go forward . . . on the pathway that the great principle of evolution has opened for us. We should carry that principle through the whole domain of ethics with the consistent fidelity which in Mr. Spencer's *Data of Ethics* is so conspicuously lacking." [25] Bixby maintains that Spencer erred in that he did not trace the unfolding of morality back to its "ultimate and eternal roots"; instead, he traces it "just far enough back to damage our respect for it." Any investigation of the foundations upon which man's moral conduct is based that goes back only to the instinctive tendencies and organized impulses of human nature may give some partial revelation of the whole plan of the cosmos, but it is always a partial revelation, the pernicious character of which is contained in the fact that it may be and is taken to be a full revelation. Rightly and fully viewed, evolution can reveal to man "the universal laws of righteousness and the eternal conditions of associated existence."

Bixby thus conceives of the entire universe in all its past history and in its future as well in terms of a cosmic organism which is moving toward the achievement of perfection. In the light of such a view of evolution the true standard of morality or the true aim of human life may be formulated, according to Bixby. It is ". . . the closest possible approximation we can achieve to such a moral and intellectual perfection as is exhibited in the Being from whom man emanates. . . . Evolution from the lower to the higher, from the carnal to the spiritual, is not merely the path of man's past pilgrimmage, but the destiny to which the future calls him." [26] Conduct, then, is to be tested by the extent to which it promotes the attainment of spiritual ends in the life of the individual and of the race; these are the ends toward which the evolution of man is moving.

There were many other critics of the newly formulated theories of evolutionary ethics, particularly of those theories founded clearly upon a reductionist type of naturalism. Some of these critics represented conservative schools of theological doctrine; they were the ones who were unable to see any truth in the evolutionary treatment of ethics. There were others who, like Schurman and Bixby, accepted the theory of evolution and believed that the evolutionary study of man's moral development could throw some light upon problems of morality; however they insisted that morality has its ground in an absolute and supremely good Being. Otto Pfleiderer dealt with this point in an article whose title was the question: "Is Morality without Religion Possible and Desirable?" His answer was in the negative. Such a morality is impossible for two reasons, he explained. In the first place, the moral sanction or the demands of moral duty cannot be found in the individual or social will or in subhuman nature; nothing less than a transcendental ground is adequate to explain this aspect of the moral experience. And in the second place, the demands of the moral law could not be realized unless the world were adapted to the purpose of realizing these ends. As he writes in summary, "The divine consciousness, therefore, must be postulated as the necessary condition of the existence of the moral law and of the possibility of its realization." [27]

IV

It is sometimes thought that the constructive application of the principles of evolution to questions of ethics has been essayed only by naturalistic philosophers and that the role of the nonnaturalistic thinker has been consistently that of a critic. Such a conclusion is understandable in the first place because the theory of evolution seemed to provide a new and incontrovertible support for a naturalistic conception of man; therefore there was immediate and unanimous acceptance of the theory by naturalistic thinkers. This conclusion is understandable also because the theory of evolution received a varied and certainly less than unanimous initial reception by persons whose thought was along theistic lines. Nevertheless, it is not correct. A full and accurate account of the reception of the theory of evolution must recognize the constructive use made of this theory by many leading nonnaturalistic thinkers. Typical of this development are the ethical theories of John Fiske, Henry Drummond, and George Harris.

John Fiske was one of the outstanding popularizers of the general philosophical implications of the theory of evolution. It is reported that while a student at Harvard in the early 1860's he defended the theory of evolution so vigorously that he came into conflict with the university authorities. Young Fiske was warned that if he should attempt to spread his opinions he would be expelled. However, he was not expelled and in 1865 he received the B.A. degree. By 1869 conditions at Harvard had changed to such an extent that Fiske was invited to lecture there in philosophy and history, and three years later he was appointed assistant librarian. A trip to England in 1873 gave him an opportunity to meet Spencer, Darwin, Huxley, and others; while in London he wrote his two volumes on *The Outlines of Cosmic Philosophy*. Resigning in 1879 his position as librarian at Harvard, he engaged very successfully in extensive lecturing and writing both in America and in England. From 1884 till his death in 1901 he was professor of American history at Washington University in St. Louis.

Fiske's especial interest in the implications of natural selection for moral theory is evident. In the *Cosmic Philosophy* he writes, "In no department of inquiry is the truth and grandeur of the Doctrine of Evolution more magnificently illustrated than in the province of Ethics." [28] Fiske's "cosmic philosophy" is patterned closely upon the principles set forth in Herbert Spencer's "synthetic philosophy." One important difference between these two philosophies is seen in their ultimate metaphysical professions. Spencer's outlook is naturalistic and reductionist, whereas Fiske's position is avowedly theistic.[29] This difference becomes clear in the interpretations given by both of them of what Spencer had called the "Unknowable." Spencer recognizes that behind the phenomenal appearance of things there must be something "through which all things exist," but he early dismisses this as being completely beyond our knowledge. In Fiske's thought, however, this Unknowable is God; it is "an Omnipresent Power that is not identifiable with Nature." [30] Fiske seeks to show that Spencer's position is not really different from his own. To this end he explains the sense in which the Deity is to be thought of as unknowable and as knowable. He writes as follows:

Deity is unknowable just in so far as it is not manifested to consciousness through the phenomenal world,—knowable just in so far as it is thus manifested; unknowable in so far as infinite and absolute,—knowable in the order of its phenomenal manifestations; knowable, in a symbolic way, as the Power which is disclosed in every throb of the mighty rhythmic life of the universe; knowable as the eternal Source of a Moral Law which is implicated with each action of our lives, and in obedience to which lies our only guaranty of the happiness which is incorruptible.[31]

This very passage, though, when compared with any passage from Spencer highlights the essential difference in world views held by these two men.

It is Fiske's contention that the theory of evolution supplies a theoretical basis for morality that is stronger and deeper than that which has ever been supplied by any other view. "For," explains Fiske,

not only does the Doctrine [of evolution] show that the principles of action which the religious instincts of men have agreed in pronouncing sacred, are involved in the very nature of life itself, regarded as a continuous adjustment; but it shows that the obligation to conform to these principles, instead of deriving its authority from the arbitrary command of a mythologic quasi-human Ruler, derives it from the innermost necessities of that process of evolution which is the perpetual revelation of Divine Power.[32]

The task which Fiske undertakes is that of explaining the presence and nature of man's moral sense or his moral intuitions. He is not satisfied with the positions reached by either the utilitarian empiricists, who explain moral intuitions as being due to the organization of experiences of pleasure and pain in the individual, or the Kantians, who consider moral intuitions to be a priori. Nevertheless he does believe that a reconciliation of these opposing views can be worked out by an evolutionary approach to the problem. The direction taken by Fiske and the closeness of his position to Spencer's are indicated when he explains that although the moral sense is important and valid, it is not to be regarded as ultimate (as the intuitionists might insist) nor as a product of the organization of experiences in the individual (as suggested by the utilitarian use of the association of ideas theory); rather, Fiske maintains that this sense has been built up by the slow organization over a long period of time of experiences of pleasure and pain. This ultimate hedonistic foundation for moral intuitions is said to be necessary, for, according to the evolutionary teaching, "races of sentient creatures could have come into existence under no other conditions."

The moral sense, then, has gradually appeared as an element in man's psychical structure, and its appearance is tied up with the coming of social evolution as distinguished from organic evolution. Prolonged infancy in human beings seems to Fiske to provide the clue which will account for this change; it is the new factor which explains the transition from instinctive gregariousness to genuine sociality. Among animals having a simple intelligence psychical actions are purely reflex and instinctive, he explains; the nervous connections being already organized at birth. But when individuals with a more complex intelligence came into existence, there arrived the phenomenon of prolonged infancy, for now the complex nervous connections were chiefly organized after birth. As the intelligence becomes more and more complex, the period of infancy during which nervous connections are being made becomes longer and longer. But a prolonged infancy is not in itself the foundation of the moral sense; it simply brings into being a set of social relationships without which the various social feelings so important to morality could not have come into existence. These social relationships first of all gave rise to parental affections, and as the period of infancy became longer these affections became more intense and more permanent. There has been a gradual expansion of these affections from the narrow family group to ever enlarging areas of human society, this expansion being due to the continued integration of communities and the resulting extension of the sense of belonging together. "Except for these circumstances," explains Fiske, "we should never have comprehended the meaning of such phrases as 'self-sacrifice' or 'devotion.' The phenomena of social life would have been omitted from the history of the world and with them the phenomena of ethics and religion." [33] But these conditions are merely the foundation for the moral life. True morality begins when, with the development of a still higher intelligence, there comes into play the deliberate pursuit of ends, these ends being those defined by the tendencies, impulses, and affections which gradually have become ingrained in man's psychical structure. This then, according to Fiske, is the highest and latest product of social evolution, namely, the conscious devotion to ends which are conducive to the happiness of society.

Another thinker of the late nineteenth century who saw in the theory of evolution certain important implications for moral theory and who believed that these results were thoroughly consistent with a theistic world view was Henry Drummond.[34] Drummond was a Scottish writer and lecturer, but he was well known in America through his books and his speaking tours, and by means of these contacts he had a pronounced influence upon the thinking of many persons, especially college students.

It was Drummond's main thesis that a full view of evolution shows that the earlier animal struggle for existence is being replaced by the struggle for the life of others. This second type of struggle, which Drummond calls "love," is not something accidental nor is it something supernatural; rather he speaks of it as "a force in Nature which was destined from the first to replace the struggle for life, and to build a nobler superstructure on the foundations which it laid." [35] Drummond espouses the antireductionist, emergent interpretation of evolution, as when he writes that

. . . to interpret the whole course of Nature by the Struggle for Life is as absurd as if one were to define the character of St. Francis by the tempers of his childhood. Worlds grow up as well as infants; their tempers change, the better nature opens out . . . The first chapter or two of the story of Evolution may be headed the Struggle for Life; but take the book as a whole and it is not a tale of battle. It is a love-story.[36]

Drummond does not believe it necessary to attempt a reconciliation of Christianity and evolution; none is necessary because the two are identical. Both are "methods of creation." Both have the same purpose, which is "to make more perfect living beings." Both work through love. "Evolution and Christianity," he maintains, "have the same Author, the same end, the same spirit." [37]

A similar approach to the relationship between evolution and ethics is suggested by George Harris, Congregational minister and educator. In 1883 he became professor of Christian theology in Andover Seminary, and after sixteen years in that position he accepted the presidency of Amherst College, serving there for thirteen years. He died in 1922.

According to Harris, there are four possible relationships that might exist between evolution and ethics, these being those of "antagonism," of "independence," of "identity," and of "harmony." [38] The relationship which Harris champions as the true and proper one is that of harmony. In this connection he seeks to show that the ethics of self-realization is harmonious with the acceptance of evolution.

The harmony between evolution and a self-realizationist or idealistic interpretation of ethics is evident at several points, believes Harris. In the first place, both have a goal or an ideal which is progressively realized. Ethics is concerned with the fullest development of the individual personality, and likewise any adequate interpretation of evolution must conceive of the whole movement as being the progressive realization of ends or ideals. The adjustment which characterizes evolutionary development, he remarks, "is as full of teleology as an egg is full of meat." [39] "The beginnings of evolution," maintains Harris, ". . . were beginnings . . . which involved ends, and which can be accounted for only as intelligent purpose realizing itself." [40]

Evolution and ethics are further said to be harmonious in that the self-regarding and also the other-regarding feelings are important elements in both. He calls attention to the evidences of social and sympathetic feelings among animals, feelings which seem clearly harmonious with man's moral conduct. Similarly, even the self-regarding, self-assertive actions of lower animals are necessary incidents of their nonmoral level of existence in which self-preservation is the one goal; indeed, he maintains, "the conditions under which the self-preservation of the individual and the species is possible must be a good, or there could be no progress. The value of the life of animals is worth more than the incident of loss." [41] The waste of animal life involved in the evolutionary process is in no sense, then, a reason for putting ethics and evolution in antagonism. The natural self-regarding and other-regarding tendencies of lower animals are carried over into man, but they have moral quality only when directed consciously to the self-realization of persons. Morality is the right direction of these animal feelings. And in any conception of the ideal good of man there must still be included both the self-regarding and the other-regarding activities. Concerning the former, about which there might seem to be some question, Harris explains that "with man, as with animals, existence is a good. . . . If it is necessary, it is right to preserve life and to have the satisfactions of life." [42]

Yet another way in which the harmony between evolution and ethics may be seen is in the optimistic expectation of progress which is found in both. Harris suggests, however, that the ethical prophet is not quite so serenely confident as the evolutionist about the moral betterment of mankind or about the inevitableness of such a prospect apart from man's conscious efforts. But both do believe in a gradual advance to a better state of society.

Undergirding the moral theories of men like Fiske, Drummond, and Harris there is the conviction that the process of evolution which leads to the development of morality is guided by a Divine Creative Power. As Harris says, "Either the variations which appeared at points of advance were new movements introduced from some source other than the universe, or all the differentiations, physical, psychical, and moral, were present potentially within the universe. In either case," he continues, "evolution, culminating in man, in rational, moral, and social man, is not a blind and purposeless, but an intelligent and purposive process." [43] It is this emphasis which primarily distinguishes this type of thinker from the evolutionary naturalistic moralists.

V

The foregoing account should show that ethical treatments of the theory of evolution have generally assumed one of two forms. They have been either reductionist or they have adopted the concept of emergent evolution.

Reductionism characterizes the ethical theories of the early Darwinians and of Spencer and his followers. It is the view which seeks to explain the moral nature of man in terms of the instinctive, impulsive actions of earlier forms of animal life. The followers of this view have also been inclined to think of evolutionary change in terms of automatic and inevitable progress. Herbert Spencer's picture of the goal of evolution as a complete state of final adaptation in which all is peace and bliss is typical of this view.[44] Associated with this interpretation has been the formulation of the standard of morality in terms of the latest in development. The best is the most evolved.

Sharply opposed to the reductionist interpretation of evolution is the theory of emergent evolution. Such an understanding of evolution has been developed by several thinkers, notably Lloyd Morgan,[45] S. Alexander,[46] J. C. Smuts,[47] and R. W. Sellars.[48] The name, emergent evolution, which was suggested by Lloyd Morgan, has become widely used because of its suggested description of the view in question. According to this conception evolution is and has been a process in which there "emerge" new qualities which cannot be explained in terms of or reduced to their antecedents. It is on this point that the antireductionist character of emergent evolution is apparent.

This doctrine of emergence is widely accepted among both naturalistic and nonnaturalistic moralists, and it has played an important role in the theories of both groups. The naturalists who adopt this theory believe that it enables them to avoid some of the criticisms made of the early evolutionary naturalists. Indeed, recent naturalistic thinkers join in these criticisms. For example, R. W. Sellars writes, "I admit the unreality of much of the naturalistic ethics which flourished immediately after the victory of Darwinism. The struggle for existence was much overdone. Too much emphasis was laid upon *fixed* instincts. Thought was elementalistic in its approach." [49] Similarly, J. B. Pratt has this to say:

Like several other theories tentatively adopted by Naturalism in its early efforts to solve its problems, this evolutionary formula for morality hardly stands the test of critical examination. A more carefully conceived and more inclusively empirical Naturalism must reject this rather hasty first generalization of many earnest and honest naturalistic thinkers. [50]

Continuing, Professor Pratt criticizes the commonly held view of these early evolutionists that evolution and progress are identical. Such a view, he contends, involves the assumption that we already possess a criterion of value which enables us to express such a judgment upon the more highly evolved. The second interpretation involves the view that the later evolved is thereby the better, but if this be followed consistently mankind would be led to approve as "better" many happenings in the lives of individuals and of nations simply because they are chronologically later. [51]

We have already seen how Dewey makes use of the idea of emergence to formulate a naturalistic theory of ethics. That which he and others of a similar trend of thought regard as the most significant development (for ethics) has been the emergence of the social level of existence for which the categories of biology are not adequate. The result has been the formulation of an ethical theory of humanistic naturalism. Man is regarded as an emergent product of the evolutionary process, and his good becomes the goal and standard of morality. The nature of this new view is clearly expressed by Sellars:

The new naturalism has added a social level to the biological level of the nineteenth century. It recognizes that man's spiritual life is largely an historical achievement. Thus it is a naturalism which apexes in social humanism. The gap between man and the dumb brute is not minimized nor maximized but understood. The modern thinker knows the part played by language and education in raising the new-born child to the level of humanity. Its capacities are played upon and drawn out. What it has taken many centuries for mankind to learn is presented to it in its perfected form. The very environment is moulded to reflect human plans and purposes into the child's mind. The family, the school, the playground, the church are the instruments of the spiritualization of the child, and all this procedure is just as natural in its way as biological evolution itself, presupposing it but not reducible to it.[52]

Emergent evolution is also the predominant interpretation found in nonnaturalistic theories of morality. Among competent scholars there is no longer any serious questioning of the evolutionary development of man. Theologians and philosophers of an idealistic or theistic trend fully accept the fact of evolution; in fact, they claim that the long panorama of evolution with its gradual emergence of ever newer and higher forms of existence supports their metaphysical position. It is their contention that man is a creature who is a product of natural evolution but who possesses emergent characteristics of mind and spirit which enable him to stand somewhat outside this natural cause-and-effect sequence and to control and direct it in some degree. As W. E. Hocking says,

Man differs from other living beings in the vim and deliberate intention of this self-shaping. All organisms do an unconscious job of self-building as they follow the destined lines of their growth to maturity; all animals further build themselves, subconsciously, as they make their way into the habits of their kind. Man alone consciously varies his pattern. He takes his biological and traditional character as an outline: on this sketch he works as an architect . . . with ideas of what he wants to be.[53]

The tremendous influence which the idea of evolution has had upon moral theory is manifest. The importance of this development becomes evident when we remember that morality is one of the deepest concerns of man, and that the theory of evolution threw an entirely new light upon the problem of man's nature. All thinkers must now take account of the long, slow process by which man's present physical and psychical condition has been reached. And yet there is no unanimity in describing exactly what are the contributions that have been made to moral theory by the application of the theory of evolution. In some cases the conclusion is that ethics can now be treated as a natural science. In others it is that a better understanding of man's natural condition has been gained but that man's uniqueness is still found in his relationship to an eternal spiritual order, in his awareness of eternal values and his conscious seeking to actualize these values in his own life and in the life of society.

It might seem that a solvent for the differences among moral philosophers might be provided by the doctrine of emergent evolution, especially since this interpretation has been so widely accepted by thinkers of divergent views. But the idea of emergence does not touch the deep metaphysical problems of ethics. It is essentially a description of a process, not an ultimate explanation of it. On the one hand, there are those who believe that the emergence of novelty can be accounted for naturalistically;[54] whereas on the other hand, there are those who believe that the appearance of new qualities and the whole process of evolution are manifestations of a Supreme, Purposive Power. Thus the lines are still sharply drawn when the important metaphysical foundations of ethics are considered.

NOTES

1. Herbert Spencer, *The Principles of Ethics* (New York, Appleton, 1898), I, 123.

2. *Ibid.*, I, 28.

3. M. J. Savage, "Natural Ethics," *North Amer. Review, 133* (Sept., 1881), 237.

4. Antonio Llano, "Morality the Last of Dogmas," *Philosophical Review,* V (July, 1896), 386.

5. *Ibid.*, p. 385.

6. *Ibid.*, p. 384.

7. For a brief biographical sketch indicating the major influences upon Dewey's thought see P. A. Schilpp, *The Philosophy of John Dewey* (Evanston, Northwestern University, 1939), pp. 3–45. As a teacher at both Chicago and Columbia and also through his multitudinous writings Dewey has come to be recognized as one of the leading American philosophers. Though now retired from active teaching, he is still engaged in writing.

8. See John Dewey, *The Influence of Darwin on Philosophy* (New York, Holt, 1910).

9. *Ibid.*, p. 19.

10. John Dewey, "Ethics and Physical Science," *Andover Review,* VII (June, 1887), 576–577.

11. *Ibid.*, p. 579.

12. The opening essay in a volume ed. by Y. H. Krikorian, *Naturalism and the Human Spirit* (New York, Columbia University Press, 1944).

13. John Dewey, "Evolution and Ethics," *Monist*, VIII (April, 1898), 325–326. Similar views have been expressed by Henry Drummond, the nineteenth-century scientist and religious leader, in *The Ascent of Man* (1894), and by Julian Huxley, the contemporary British biologist, in a recent lecture entitled "Evolutionary Ethics" (1943). Drummond will be discussed later in this chapter.

14. *Ibid.*, p. 338.

15. John Dewey, *Human Nature and Conduct* (New York, Holt, 1922), p. 231.

16. *Ibid.*, p. 234.

17. John Dewey, "The Evolutionary Method as Applied to Morality," *Philosophical Review*, XI (March and July, 1902).

18. *Ibid.*, p. 113. Cf. Dewey's discussion of the "transfer of experimental method from the technical field of physical experience to the wider field of human life" in *The Quest for Certainty* (New York, Minton, Balch, 1929), especially pp. 271 ff. "What is needed is intelligent examination of the consequences that are actually effected by inherited institutions and customs, in order that there may be intelligent consideration of the ways in which they are to be intentionally modified in behalf of generation of different consequences" (p. 273).

19. John Dewey, "The Evolutionary Method as Applied to Morality," *loc. cit.*, p. 115.

20. *Ibid.*, p. 124.

21. *Ibid.*, p. 365. A good example of the treatment being criticized by Dewey is that in Spencer's *Data of Ethics* which was mentioned earlier in this chapter.

22. J. G. Schurman, *The Ethical Import of Darwinism* (New York, Scribner, 1903), p. 134.

23. J. G. Schurman, *Kantian Ethics and the Ethics of Evolution* (London, Williams & Norgate, 1881), pp. 71–72.

24. J. T. Bixby, *The Ethics of Evolution* (Boston, Small, Maynard, 1900), p. 120.

25. *Ibid.*, p. 189.

26. *Ibid.*, p. 314.

27. Otto Pfleiderer, "Is Morality without Religion Possible and Desirable?" *Philosophical Review*, V (Sept., 1896), p. 452.

28. John Fiske, *Outlines of Cosmic Philosophy* (New York, Houghton Mifflin, 1892), II, 356.

29. Though he does not use the term, a more precise characterization of Fiske's position would be theistic naturalism. Fiske is anxious to dissociate his view from the widely prevalent "anthropomorphic theism" of his period and earlier. He explains: "The doctrine which we have expounded is, therefore, neither more nor less than Theism, in its most consistent and unqualified form. It is quite true that the word 'theism,' as ordinarily employed, connotes the ascription of an anthropomorphic personality to the Deity. But in this connotation there has been nothing like fixedness or uniformity. On the other hand the term has become less and less anthropomorphic in its connotations; from age to age, and in the sense in which it is here employed the deanthropomorphizing process is but carried one step farther." *Ibid.*, II, 424.

30. *Ibid.*, II, 428.

31. *Ibid.*, II, 470; Cf. ". . . to him whose mental habits have been nurtured by scientific studies, the principles of action prescribed by the need for harmonizing inner with outer relations are, in the truest sense, the decrees of God." *Ibid.*, II, 358.

32. *Ibid.*, II, 467–468.

33. *Ibid.*, II, 363.

34. A brief but clear sketch of Drummond's work with special reference to his attempts to show the harmony between belief in God and the Darwinian theory may be found in Walter Horton's *Theism and the Scientific Spirit* (New York, Harper, 1933), pp. 144–161.

35. Henry Drummond, *The Ascent of Man* (New York, James Pott, 1894), p. 214.

36. *Ibid.*, pp. 217–218.

37. *Ibid.*, p. 342.

38. George Harris, *Moral Evolution* (New York, Houghton Mifflin, 1896), pp. 11–29.

39. *Ibid.*, p. 160.

40. *Ibid.*, pp 163–164.

41. *Ibid.*, p. 172.

42. *Ibid.*, p. 173.

43. *Ibid.*, p. 184.

44. Dewey has characterized this view as an "insipid millennium," "Evolution and Ethics," *loc. cit.*, p. 334.

45. British zoologist, psychologist, and philosopher. From 1884 until his retirement from regular academic duties, Morgan served as professor and successively as principal and vice-chancellor in the University of Bristol. He died in 1936.

46. British philosopher, born in Sydney, Australia, in 1859. Alexander was professor of philosophy in the University of Manchester from 1893–1924. His Gifford lectures were published in 1920 under the title, *Space, Time, and Deity.* He died in 1938.

47. Statesman and philosopher who from 1939 to 1948 was prime minister of South Africa. Smuts's outstanding philosophical publication is *Holism and Evolution* (1926).

48. Prominent American philosopher of the school of "new" naturalists. Born in Canada in 1880, Sellars joined the philosophy department of the University of Michigan in 1905 and retired in 1950.

49. R. W. Sellars, *Evolutionary Naturalism* (Chicago, Open Court, 1922), p. 341.

50. J. B. Pratt, *Naturalism* (New Haven, Yale University Press, 1939), p. 152. Pratt was professor of philosophy at Williams College, where he taught from 1905 to 1944.

51. *Ibid.*, pp. 152–155.

52. R. W. Sellars, *Religion Coming of Age* (New York, Macmillan, 1928), pp. 240–241.

53. W. E. Hocking, *What Man Can Make of Man* (New York, Harper, 1942), pp. 2–3. Professor Hocking has long been one of the leaders in American philosophy. From 1914 till his retirement in 1943 he was professor of philosophy in Harvard University.

54. According to this view, there is no activity except that of "nature." But the term "nature" is ambiguous. Sometimes naturalists tend to identify "nature" with everything real. However, when such a meaning is used to deny those realities which have been customarily described as supernatural, the reasoning commits the fallacy of begging the question. For a clear discussion of this point, see Brightman, *Nature and Values* (New York, Abingdon-Cokesbury, 1945), pp. 34–38.

EVOLUTION AND THEOLOGY IN AMERICA

THE extensive modification of traditional Christian doctrines among the American Protestant churches during the nineteenth century was the result of a variety of influences of which evolution was only one, and perhaps not even the most important. Nevertheless, the evolutionary point of view succeeded in forming a rather heterogeneous group of thinkers who may be described as evolutionary theists. For these theologians, not all of whom were clergymen, the fact of evolution seemed to determine the central issues of religious thought. Representative types of evolutionary theism are analyzed in the following pages.

S. P.

EVOLUTION AND THEOLOGY IN AMERICA

STOW PERSONS

THE impact of the notion of evolution upon American theology was necessarily conditioned by the characteristics of the prevailing evangelical Protestantism in the middle of the nineteenth century. The traditional themes of sin and redemption, of grace and works, still held their central place in the Christian experience, but there were significant modifications of temper and emphasis belonging to Protestant Christianity in its mid-nineteenth-century form. These modifications were largely the result of the great conflicts of the previous two centuries between Christianity and the philosophy and spirit of the Enlightenment.

Although Christianity survived the conflict, as symbolized in America by the decline of Deism and the spread of the revivalist evangelical sects after 1800, it did so by incorporating into Christian theology much of the natural religion held by the Deists to be sufficient for the purposes of rational worship. The new astronomy and physics of Galileo and Newton had revealed a cosmos ordered by law and sustained by its own inherent properties. These discoveries were a triumph of the rational powers, which began to be exalted as man's highest powers. Thus the Deists taught that the works of God were to be apprehended through reason rather than revelation. God's role in the cosmic process was restricted to the original act of creation and to the institution of the natural laws according to which the universe was ordered. Since all men were presumed to possess the rational powers by which these truths were apprehended, no further testimony as to divine purpose seemed necessary; the Bible was relegated to the library of mythological literature; and Jesus was reduced to the status of a great moral teacher.

In the early years of the nineteenth century orthodox Protestant

Christian thinkers, both in England and in America, absorbed the Deist argument in its rationalistic aspects by harmonizing natural religion with revelation. The one was found to strengthen and confirm the other. The uniqueness of revelation could now be fully appreciated in contrast to the uniformities of the natural order; while the reasonableness of Christianity could be demonstrated by its consistency with a religion of nature. Out of this fusion of natural and revealed religion came one of the great arguments for the support of the orthodox faith. This was the doctrine of design. Just as Paley's famous watch bore its own testimony to the activity of the watchmaker, so the universe in all of its marvelous detail sang the praises of its Creator. In an age in which theories of natural law came to permeate social thought, and in which the achievements of applied science were already lending prestige to a rationalistic and materialistic view of things, the argument from design became one of the most useful and widely used defenses for Christianity. Natural religion must of course be supplemented by revealed religion, for each plumbed distinctly incommensurable dimensions. Nevertheless, natural law, as then conceived, was, like the revealed word of God, fixed, absolute, and immutable. The one was clearly apprehended by the intelligence, and the other by the study of Holy Writ. The religious thought of early nineteenth-century America shared this conception of the fixity of law with all other branches of thought.

From the first appearance of rationalistic ideas in the seventeenth century there tended to be a close alliance between rationalism, both religious and secular, and a new humanistic morality. The humanistic emphasis pointed toward a preoccupation with purely human problems, toward the sciences of man, shorn of ultimate possibilities, and restricted to the successes and failures of this world. The new humanism was also humanitarian in spirit, and it has often been asserted that the expansive and opulent environment on this side of the Atlantic fostered a humanitarian morality. The humanistic spirit was, moreover, hostile to many of the fundamental tenets of Christian orthodoxy. The Calvinist denial of free will, the teaching that only a few are elected to be saved and that no man can by his own efforts achieve salvation, the doctrine that because of the sin of Adam all men are sinful—these ideas began to seem repugnant to increasing numbers of Americans.

Yielding partially to the new spirit, early nineteenth-century Protestantism made important concessions to humanitarian humanism. In New England the Universalists insisted that all men enjoyed the promise of salvation. Similarly, the Unitarians, following William Ellery Channing, challenged the doctrine of human depravity. Nothing is to be gained, said Channing, by degrading human nature, "for in the competency of this nature to know and judge of God, all piety has its foundation." But the revolt was not confined to New England radicals. In the Middle States and in the Bible Belt the popularity of "New School," "New Divinity," and perfectionist doctrines in many denominations revealed how widely the new leaven was working. Although in many cases the concessions demanded seem infinitesimal to a nontheological age they nevertheless pointed toward a larger role for freedom and human ability in the Christian economy of salvation. The humanistic spirit was beginning to undermine the old orthodox theology by showing how some of its fundamental conceptions outraged a growing humanistic morality.[1]

A third stream of ideas consistent with the humanistic emphasis in its general import, although opposed to it when humanism and rationalism were specifically allied, was religious romanticism, or intuitionism. The intuitive or immediate awareness of religious truth in the soul of the believer has always occupied a fundamental place even in those religious systems which emphasize the duality of God and his creation. For God reveals himself in the inner consciousness of man as well as in external signs, and particularly among Protestant churches where the crisis of conversion is stressed, the blessed sense of salvation assured is a reward sought by every sinner. Among less orthodox believers the danger of depending upon the intuitive sense of religious truth at the expense of revelation, and particularly of scriptural authority, has always been present. With the spread of humanitarian and moralistic attitudes in the early nineteenth century there emerged a new religious movement which found its authority in the intuitions of the individual soul, and which was in a sense hostile both to rationalism and to revelation. This new movement was transcendental Christianity, stemming from the idealism of Kant and Schleiermacher, its chief American representative in religious circles being Theodore Parker, the Boston Unitarian.

It was the peculiar feature of transcendental Christianity for our present purposes that since it found its source of authority in the consciousness rather than in the revealed word or in the external evidences of design it had no difficulty in preserving its faith in the face of the new evolutionary theories of Darwin and his followers which were to prove so difficult for more orthodox Christians to digest. The transcendentalists were to be the first sponsors of an evolutionary religion in America, and as such we shall have to refer to them again at a later place.

I

Few comprehensive generalizations do justice to the evolutionary impact upon American religious thought because of the wide variety of beliefs and attitudes in a community that had long cherished the spirit of religious freedom. An exhaustive study would require an examination of each sect and denomination in order to determine the nature and bitterness of the conflict, which doctrines were jeopardized, how the group reacted in defense of its traditions, and what concessions if any were made to the evolutionary outlook. Such a study would yield many fruitful insights into the functioning of religious groups, although it cannot be attempted within the present limits. Here we shall confine the discussion to the major theological issues raised by the theory of evolution, and to those religious thinkers who faced the issues squarely and whose opinions consequently left their mark upon American theology.

In theology as in many other fields of thought the first major conflict over evolutionary ideas came in the wake of the Darwinian theory of natural selection.[2] This was because Darwin proposed an explanation of the method of evolutionary change that was diametrically opposed to the Christian doctrine of design. Both theories were equally mechanical in character, and one or the other must give way. The term "Darwinism" as precisely used referred to the theory of natural selection, according to which, since all individuals of a species differ from one another in minute degree, overabundant reproduction produces a struggle for existence in which those individuals possessing the more advantageous variations survive. It mattered little that Darwin confessed no knowledge of or little interest in the nature of individual variations, or that he frequently resorted to other explanations to account for particular evolutionary phenomena. The theory of natural selection remained the focus of his interest, as it has indeed remained the most celebrated of all efforts to account for the evolutionary process itself. But if evolution occurred by means of natural selection from among random and universal variations how could the process be identified with the belief in design, even if one would accept a design gradually unfolding? If natural selection were accepted it would destroy one of the strongest props of the Old Orthodoxy.

Charles Hodge, professor of theology at the Princeton Theological Seminary, and leading conservative Presbyterian theologian of his day, felt the significance of the issue keenly. He bitterly attacked Darwinism as subversive of all religion. Asa Gray, the Harvard botanist who was the most influential apologist for Darwin in the American religious community, had attempted to reconcile supernatural design with natural selection by assuring believers that the beneficent intentions of deity could be realized as effectively through natural selection as by more spectacular methods. In repudiating Gray, Hodge was supported by Darwin himself, who could find no evidence of teleology in the selective process. In fact, Hodge was able to extract several passages from the *Origin of Species* and elsewhere showing with what care Darwin had rejected design in nature. Although adaptation might have the appearance of design, it was not design, and Darwin was too careful an observer to make the identification that was all too common among his more superficial disciples. In view of the importance attached to the doctrine of design by the theology of the day it was inevitable that Hodge should seize upon this aspect of Darwin's work. Taking the naturalist at his word the theologian put natural selection to its most rigorous test by asking whether the most complex organ, the eye, could, without benefit of design, have been produced in the manner required by the theory. Satisfied that natural selection failed to meet the test Hodge consigned it to the baggage of atheism.[3]

Hodge wrote in 1874, and after that time no one undertook seriously to reconcile natural selection with design. The survival of the doctrine of design was clearly to depend upon the ability of natural selection to satisfy the critical appraisal of the generation of scientists following Darwin. Since natural selection was not the only scientific explanation of the evolutionary process theologians who clung to the doctrine of design could do so respectably while admitting the fact of evolution if they could satisfy themselves that the process occurred by means other than natural selection. This proved easier because the Neo-Darwinians, or extreme adherents of the natural selection theory, claimed few representatives among American scientists in the late nineteenth century. Presidents P. A. Chadbourne of Williams and James McCosh of Princeton both attempted to preserve the place of design in their late nineteenth-century theologies by taking advantage of the widespread criticism of Darwinism.[4] McCosh had compiled a list of twelve objections to natural selection,[5] and although he later came to believe in the fact of evolution itself he accounted for its occurrence on the basis of non-Darwinian factors. His final reconciliation of evolution with revelation was accomplished by means of an explanation of the evolutionary process that relied upon Lamarckian and Darwinian factors combined with the orthogenetic or straight-line theories of Cope and Hyatt.[6] Even in attributing a subordinate role to natural selection McCosh took unwarranted liberties with that formula, for he insisted that the Creator stacked the deck with purposeful variations and thus guided the selective process.

Nevertheless, the continuing prestige of natural selection would not in the long run permit such cavalier treatment as that accorded the theory by McCosh. The doctrine of design must undergo extensive modification if it were to retain any place in timely theological speculation. Readjustments were soon to occur on both sides that would allow an accommodation on a new basis. On the scientific side, the theoretical difficulties to which natural selection was subject were largely dissipated by the realization after 1900 of the importance of genetic mutations, which at the same time modified those accidental characteristics of Darwinism so offensive to the religious mind. McCosh himself suggested the theological compromise when he employed non-Darwinian factors to explain evolution. By abandoning the Darwinian assumption of universal random variation and by substituting for it the more spectacular saltations or mutations discovered by the geneticists the mechanical pattern of early Darwinism was avoided, and a conception of the evolutionary process was formed that promised fruitful material for theological speculation. But the equally mechanical notion of design as entertained by mid-nineteenth-century theology had also to be abandoned. Gradually a more flexible theory of adaptation came to replace the doctrine of design in theology. It became commonplace to conceive of God as immanent in the natural order, causing the emergence or unfolding of a divine plan. Such a view was consistent with the orthogenetic theories of evolution popular at the end of the century, and it could claim further support from science as soon as scientists, following the lead of Henderson,[7] began to regard adaptations as the result of an interactive process in which both organism and environment participate in each creative act.

The passing of the older doctrine of design was a necessary feature of the transition from transcendent to immanent deity. A detailed design originally conceived and imposed upon matter by the Creator was hardly consistent with the new conception of emergence. In a general sense, design in the form of faith in the ultimate cosmic purpose was by no means lost in the transition, as we shall see. In fact, under the new conditions design became identified with the pattern of successive creative acts in time, with the evolutionary process itself; consequently its significance in the new theology cut much closer to the heart of faith than it had when used as a convenient architectonic appendage to the old natural religion.

II

Before coming to the positive influences of evolutionary conceptions upon American theology it is necessary to notice another negative aspect of the problem, or more properly, to notice the failure of what might have been an expected consequence of the evolutionary movement to appear. This was the passing of rationalism from the current of theological speculation. The collapse of the argument from design led inevitably to the abandonment of natural religion in the older form in which it functioned chiefly as corroboration of the truth of revelation for the benefit of the unregenerate intelligence, or for the aesthetic delight of the elect. Under the impact of the evolutionary influence a natural theology of a radically new type might conceivably appear, since the theory of evolution itself represented a triumph of scientific rationalism. A rationalistic theology based upon the evolutionary emergence of a divine plan would clearly hold great promise for natural theology in a new form. The elaboration of such a theology was actually the life work of Francis Ellingwood Abbot, the chief significance of which, in the present context, lies in its complete failure to establish itself as one of the widely accepted results of the evolutionary movement.

Francis Abbot was a New Englander of Unitarian background who passed unaffected through the transcendentalist atmosphere of mid-century Harvard to a rationalistic "scientific theism" based explicitly upon what he conceived to be the philosophized scientific method. Thanks to the relatively liberal theological views at Harvard and at Meadville Seminary, where he studied for the Unitarian ministry during the Civil War, Abbot did not have to face the problems presented to orthodox Protestants by Darwinism. Embracing the development theory with enthusiasm he found that it provided the authentic key to the cosmic revelation of divine purpose. Abbot's was the first American theology to regard itself frankly as a product of evolutionary thought.[8]

Abbot distinguished two philosophical traditions underlying the popular theologies of the day, both of which he attacked vigorously. One was the venerable mechanical realism which, allied with dualism, formed the basis of orthodox Protestant theology with its natural religion which we have already noticed. Mechanistic realism, according to Abbot, conceived of the universe as a machine, the imperfections of which were presumably the source of evil. In its earlier forms the theory tended to distinguish between the organic and the inorganic, but being told by modern science that the distinction could no longer be clearly made, mechanistic realism sought to reduce all phenomena to mechanics. The immediate result was its failure to deal with the complexities of the organism, and consequently to cope with the facts of evolution. Apart from these more recent difficulties mechanism in its theological form had already outlived its utility. The natural theology formulated to cope with the physics of the Enlightenment had conceived of God as the great Mechanic external to his creation, the universe. This view comported logically with the notion of the machine as such, which exists only for ends external to itself, and which invariably reveals purpose on the part of its designer. This was the philosophical basis of traditional Christian supernaturalism as well as of eighteenth-century deism. We have already indicated how natural selection demolished this type of theology.[9]

The second tradition of philosophical theology was that of idealism. This was the position of New England transcendentalism which had made such inroads into Unitarianism. Abbot had no sympathy for the idealistic inability to establish a real relationship between the knowing subject and the observed phenomenon.

The unity of subject and object in the act of perception was the basic assumption of his philosophical system, and he pointed to the tremendous achievements of modern science as proof of the practical fruitfulness of his view. Abbot's criticism of idealism in its theological form as transcendental Christianity was equally fundamental. The transcendentalists maintained that religious truth was known only through the spontaneous intuition of the soul, and that reason unaided by intuition was impotent to arrive at any apprehension of the divine. Abbot maintained that consistent idealism could only result in the absurdity of pure solipsism. He required more substantial evidence of divinity than that derived from the intuitions of the individual.[10]

Abbot's theological system was based on the assumed rationality of the scientific method, properly understood. The scientific method, the study of objectively real relations, showed that the universe was intelligible, and that ultimately no part of it would elude rational analysis. The essence of intelligibility consisted of the relationships between things, and while Abbot recognized death and chaos as disorderly relations, he insisted that these existed only with reference to larger inclusive systems of orderly relations. Thus the death of cells, for instance, contributed to the life of the organism. Not only was the nature of things intelligible but intelligence itself was essentially active and creative, for its function was to elaborate new relational systems, thus indicating its teleological character.[11] Abbot's insistence on the creative function of intelligence sounded a note to be heard with increasing frequency in the philosophies of the early twentieth century.

Intelligence, wherever found, differed only in degree, but not in kind. Mind of a rudimentary sort could be discovered far down in the scale of organic forms. On the other hand, human intelligence if expanded infinitely would be adequate to comprehend the infinite All. Infinite mind must be identical in nature with the mind of man. Abbot believed that Spencer's Unknowable merely reflected the bankruptcy of a materialist philosophy. The universality of natural law was inconsistent with both the older belief in miracle or the newer belief in divine power apart from the system of nature. If nature were infinitely intelligible it followed that it must also be infinitely intelligent through and to itself. The philosophy of science that fully developed this truth would necessarily become "the supreme wisdom of Man and the self-evident word of God."[12]

The most perfect relational system known to man was the organism. The relative perfection of any particular organism was to be determined by the extent of its ability to project itself into the outer world and to subject external forces to its own ends, for this capacity was the measure of the strength of its creative understanding. The universe as an organism differed from finite organisms only in that its life was strictly immanent, since there could be nothing external to it. Its life consisted in eternally converting force into form. The facts of evolution were to Abbot the best evidence yet available of the nature of this process. It was important to note however that his conception of evolution denied the notion then popular among certain evolutionists that God first emerged into consciousness in man. For Abbot held that no more could be evolved than was already involved; the conscious could not be evolved out of the unconscious. Infinite intelligibility and intelligence must coexist as primary attributes of Being.[13]

The religious implications of his scientific philosophy placed Abbot among those who adhered to a monistic view of divine activity or emergence which orthodox Christians were quick to brand as pantheism. But Abbot insisted that only organic evolution provided a true conception of teleology. The natural organism, such as man, was found to serve both immanent and exient ends. Its immanent ends were realized in egotistic activity and in self-development, while its exient ends were expressed in the altruism, self-sacrifice, and unselfishness which contributed to the fulfillment of the universal divine life. These exient ends frequently served purposes of the cosmic organism that were of no benefit or even detrimental to the welfare of the individual. Nevertheless, the human race had always instinctively acclaimed them to be the highest manifestation of the finite spirit. It was in such moments when the ends of self were subjected to larger purposes that Abbot declared the human spirit to be identical with the divine. For the cosmic organism the exient principle logically turned in upon itself, receiving expression as the natural providence of law and love which supported every deeply religious mind. The problem of evil, which was such a difficult one within the framework of the traditional nineteenth-century conceptions of the God of love, was simply explained by scientific theism. Evil was found to be a necessary concomitant of finitude. However depressing the clash of finite interests of individuals and groups might at times appear, Abbot clung resolutely to his faith in the gradual consummation of cosmic ends through the evolution of higher forms and purer ideals. So far as man now understood these ends he could say that his God was immanent, and to the extent that they still eluded his comprehension man must acknowledge God to be transcendent.[14]

Apart from his rationalistic method there were several elements in Abbot's theology that were already becoming characteristic of evolutionary religious thought. Belief in the immanence of God was one of the chief features of the new outlook. Similarly, the conception of emergence, although Abbot did not use the term, identified evolution with progress through the actualization of cosmic purpose in the production of more complex forms and in the refinement of spiritual life. Finally the individual, now liberated from all the old theological problems of individual freedom and divine omniscience, came into his own, not as the instrument or tool of divine purpose, but as an original element of it, acting freely and creatively for the furtherance of cosmic ends. Whether he could shoulder successfully the responsibilities of his new freedom remained to be seen.

Abbot dedicated his life to the propagation of his scientific theism at both the popular and the formal levels. He was instrumental in organizing in 1867 the Free Religious Association, a liberal, nonsectarian organization devoted among other things to the scientific study of theology. The association had some influence in modifying late nineteenth-century Unitarian religious thinking, but less along the lines of Abbot's rationalism than according to tendencies to be noticed later. Largely because of his forthright attack upon Christianity in all its forms Abbot was unable to secure the university teaching position for which he was in other respects eminently qualified, and his two nonsectarian churches failed to attract sufficient followers to provide even a meager living. Many contemporaries testified to their respect for the vigor of his intellect and the singular purity of his faith, but no school of followers appeared to carry on his scientific theism. His suicide in 1903 symbolized the failure of a rationalistic theology of evolution to achieve a convincing identification of faith and reason. Although an ardent admirer of Darwin, Abbot did not deal specifically with the implications of natural selection, which he regarded as an hypothesis not to be confused with the established fact of evolution. As long, therefore, as natural selection remained a barrier to the general acceptance of evolution by religious people, a full appreciation of Abbot's work had to await a more precise understanding of the nature and role of natural selection in the evolutionary process. When this day came, Abbot's universal monistic organicism was avoided in favor of a compromise that conceived of evolution as occurring in phases or graded levels of organization.

Thus the theory of evolution, a great scientific achievement, did not produce in theology a new rationalistic current of speculation comparable to eighteenth-century natural theology. It produced rather two seemingly paradoxical tendencies. One was a renewed interest in the intuitionist type of religious thought which received its scientific impulse from the orthogenetic theories of evolution popular at the end of the century. The other tendency emphasized a historical and empirical approach to religion, derived in part at least from Herbert Spencer and from evolutionary anthropology. To the latter type of evolutionary theology we must now turn.

III

There was much in the historical approach to religious truth that was reminiscent of the old Deism. Both schools believed that natural law revealed the glory of God. Both believed that the old dogmas of supernaturalism must be destroyed. Both expected that science would yield a progressively nobler morality and truer cosmology. But the historical approach added a new and significant dimension to natural religion—that of time. Thus one type of theism was brought into accord with the secular faith in progress, and so long as belief in progress might retain its hold its prestige could easily be transferred to a religious outlook that believed the meaning of life to be exhausted in life itself, largely conceived, as ultimate religious purposes gradually worked themselves out in history. It is easy to be contemptuous of this complacent attitude. The fact remains, however, that in spite of the chaos of the twentieth century the magic of progress still casts its spell over many minds.

The indebtedness of the historical type of evolutionary theism to Herbert Spencer can be seen in its earliest American representative, Minot J. Savage. Savage was a prominent Unitarian clergyman of Boston and New York who, as an avowed disciple of Spencer, undertook to formulate a theistic version of Spencer's universal evolutionism. Savage published his *Religion of Evolu-*

tion in 1876. He embraced the theory of cosmic evolution enthusiastically, convinced that he found in it a far truer indication of God's attributes than was to be found in the traditional creeds based on the mythology of revelation. The characteristic feature of divine immanence appeared in Savage's dictum that "God is a power whose center is everywhere and his circumference nowhere."[15] Turning to the past with the aid of anthropologists and students of comparative religion it was apparent to Savage that religious beliefs themselves had grown through a process of evolution. The old anthropomorphic ideas that satisfied primitive minds had gradually been abandoned in favor of more sophisticated and enlightened creeds consistent with more exact knowledge and a more urbane outlook.

The identification of evolution with progress in every sense was a well-nigh universal characteristic of evolutionary theism.[16] The peculiar feature of the historical evolutionary school lay not so much in its belief in moral progress, however, as in its almost complete preoccupation, especially in its earlier period, with moral and social problems to the exclusion of the individual quest for salvation that had been the core of traditional Christianity. The growth of moral power, like the sense of divine power, according to Savage, was a product of the evolutionary process. Hence the issues of the moral life were between more highly evolved ideals and lower or outmoded beliefs. Sin was the supremacy of the lower; evil was maladjustment.[17]

Savage's optimism stemmed in part from the fact that he was, like his master, Spencer, a Neo-Lamarckian rather than a Darwinian. The peculiar appeal of the Lamarckian explanation of evolution for students of the social and spiritual life lay in the fact that conscious or unconscious effort by the individual to achieve more satisfying adjustments to the physical or psychical environments, was presumed to effect such adjustments in the course of time.[18] Thus Savage maintained that conscience was neither an intuition of right, as orthodox Christians would insist, nor a product of natural selection, as the Darwinian would probably argue, but a product of the awareness of social relationships impinging upon successive generations of individuals until judgments once conscious and voluntary had become instinctive. But social environments had been rapidly changing, and consciences that were the product of family and tribal conditions were ill suited to guide men in complex modern societies. Savage admitted that the conscience of modern man had far to evolve in order to react adequately in the face of modern problems. The conflict of consciences was in fact the true source of human conflicts, and while he accepted them as inevitable Savage put his faith in the future triumph of ever wider outlooks. Conscience, no matter how enlightened, should never be regarded as infallible. In fact, the supreme duty of each man was a perpetual search for truth, the implications of new truth for old notions of right being, of course, unpredictable.[19]

Savage's explanation of the origins of conscience was clearly of little practical value for a society undergoing such rapid social change as that of late nineteenth-century America. Its virtue lay rather in the fact that it avoided the static and fruitless logic of contemporary Social Darwinism. The Lamarckian belief that somatic adjustments made by several generations of individuals would eventually establish themselves as genetic changes had long been questioned and would soon be entirely abandoned. Where social and spiritual as opposed to biological problems were involved, however, the Lamarckian emphasis on the creative initiative of the individual organism provided a formula too valuable to be abandoned until the study of social evolution could produce a substitute capable of doing justice to spiritual ideals and to the power of the conscious intellect. Classical Darwinism in its early guise as Social Darwinism was notoriously unable to contribute in any direct way to the understanding of social evolution, and it remained a major task for such thinkers as Dewey, James, and Baldwin to do justice to the peculiar problems of the social life of man within the larger framework of organic evolution.

The optimism usually attributed to theists of the historical school was actually tempered in their own minds by a realization of what joyous compensations of orthodoxy they had voluntarily abandoned. Religious faith or experience apart from the dictates of intellect they had consciously renounced. Faith must be strained through the fine mesh of reason, and the product thus derived was frequently but slender diet. Furthermore, that immediate sense of sanctification which was the most precious gift of the older faith had no place in the new outlook. For historical theists the quest for spiritual truth was an endless process in which the individual participated but could not possibly experience in its fullness. Since truth was eternal and unfathomable there was a sense in which life became a quest for the unobtainable. Savage believed that man must abandon the firmly planted spiritual home of his fathers and live as it were in a tent, always ready to break camp and set off on "a forward march towards something which is higher and grander and broader in the way of truth." [20] This was a reaffirmation in humanistic terms of the seventeenth-century seeker spirit. Its value was, however, limited, as William James later observed, to persons of a "tough-minded" temperament for whom the stimulus of traditional religious experience was unnecessary.

In its earlier phase the historical school of evolutionary thought was permeated with the rationalist temper. Savage and several other representative figures were members of the Free Religious Association, which, as we have said, had been formed to foster religious values compatible with the scientific spirit. The scientific spirit, however, is not only rationalistic, but also empirical in its approach to its materials. It was not surprising, therefore, that from the beginning the historical theists should display a much more comprehensive interest in the phenomena of the religious life than was characteristic of orthodox religious circles. If he rejected supernatural revelation and was yet unable to formulate a satisfying basis for faith by the processes of reason the historical theist could always rest his faith in God and in moral values on the fact that these were universal attributes of men to be found in all human societies. Anthropology and the study of comparative religion showed an almost invariable acceptance of fundamentally similar ideas of God, of immortality, and of the moral law. It was easy to accept these beliefs as natural or inherent in the human mind. It could almost be said that man was a worshiping animal.

The empirical approach to religious phenomena was much more comprehensive than the rationalist approach. Rationalism had been hostile or unsympathetic to Christianity, but empiricism was prepared to take the elements of religious experience as it found them, whether Christian or otherwise, and examine their fruits on their own merits. By the end of the century it was clear that the rationalist task had been a negative one, namely, to clear away the rubbish of the old religious formulas in order that a fresh appraisal might discover what perennial truths it had concealed. It was the function of the empiricist phase of the historical movement to review traditional religious values from a point of view at once more objective and sympathetic in order to discover which elements of faith might remain valid in the light of common human experience. It was the empiricist criterion of general human experience, that which recommended itself to the common sense of men as conditioned by the values and outlook of the day concerned, which justifies us in classifying the empirical approach to religion as within the historical school.

Such an empirical reappraisal of religious values was implicitly the task of Protestant modernism at the beginning of the twentieth century. It was explicitly that of William James, whose *Varieties of Religious Experience* (1902) revealed much that was characteristic of the temper of modernism. James the psychologist, who had learned from Agassiz how to classify specimens of organic life, turned to those aspects of religious experience traditionally acknowledged by believers to comprise the core of the religious life and dissected each type of experience in order to discover both its dynamics and its fruits as revealed in tangible form to the disinterested observer.

Taking the fundamental element of personal religious experience, the actual contact of the individual with what he conceived to be the divine, James proposed to assay its nature and effects in the light of human experience in the widest sense. He found in the phenomena of conviction of sin and consequent weakness, conversion, sense of salvation, and the various attributes of the saintly or redeemed character the true materials for the study of religious experience. As indubitable facts of life these things lay within the common observation of all men even though they might elude rationalistic analysis. The evidence showed that for many people the religious experience embodied a vivid sense of immediate contact with a higher power, and that as a result of these contacts the believer was transformed in character and liberated from the fears or weaknesses that had obstructed him. An empirical approach to religion could clearly lead the investigator much closer to the substance of traditional faith than the earlier historical theists had believed possible.[21]

In dealing with religion as experience or fact, rather than as belief or theology, James was obliged to differentiate between them in a way that challenged the importance traditionally attributed to theological speculation. He found that personal religious experience had its root in the mystical state of consciousness, a state in which the subliminal or unconscious life of the individual momentarily emerged into consciousness. This state resembled sensation rather than conceptual thought, and while it thus re-

mained essentially incommunicable James was able to conclude
from careful case study that the religious experience was usually
optimistic and that it conveyed a feeling of union with a larger
power. Since the religious experience had no intellectual content of
its own, the overt expression given by the individual to his experience was necessarily drawn from his own stock of ideas and
conditioned by the climate of his time. Thus James held explicitly
that theological speculation was inferior to mysticism as a means of
approaching religious truth since the former was merely a way of
expressing the latter. His problem, therefore, was to separate religious doctrine or belief from the fact of religious experience as
such, and to show how experience was primary and doctrine derivative; yet at the same time to indicate how doctrine necessarily
formulated and made articulate the real experience, on occasion
even opening up the path to experience.[22] The primacy of feeling
over belief implicit in the psychological approach to religious phenomena with its consequent neglect of theology was to become one
of the chief characteristics of Protestant modernism.

As psychologist James isolated and verified the importance of
the facts of religious experience. As philosophical empiricist he
undertook to interpret their meaning. The fruits of religion appeared in the saintly life, in the acts and attitudes of those transformed by the energies released in the mystical state. But the
chronicle of sainthood showed extravagant as well as admirable
virtues, the distinction being made according to the criteria of common sense and knowledge of human affairs which remained for
James the last court of appeal. After sorting the valuable attributes
from the insignificant it still remained that the empirical standard
of value accorded to such religious attributes as charity and asceticism a "towering place in history." In reducing religion to its
lowest and hence universal terms as a type of human experience
James was appealing to history much as his predecessors of the historical school had done. But whereas they had found the common
factor in certain great religious conceptions, such as God or immortality, James found it in a recurrent problem—the sense of helpless-
ness and sin—with its solution: salvation through surrender and
union with a larger power not of ourselves. In thus shifting the
criteria of religious truth from doctrine to experience James identified himself with the functionalist tradition which received such
an impetus from Darwinism.[23]

This is not the place to discuss James's invidious distinction between belief and experience, whereby the former served only to rationalize or give expression to the latter. We may accept his finding that while religious feeling and conduct were almost universally the same the world over, thought about these things varied widely. He nevertheless concluded that while ideals or "overbeliefs" were not essential to religious experience, such ideals frequently served both to open the road to direct mystical contact with the divine and to define the contact in terms that recommended themselves to the wisdom of the race.[24] A hostile critic might charge that James the functionalist had reduced religion to a source of fuel for getting work done, not to mention its "cash value." Nevertheless, his vigorous attack on the rationalist or intellectualist approach to religious problems, whether in the form of scholasticism, natural theology, or scientific theism, had the effect of recalling the attention of liberal Christians from problems of morality and fixing it again upon the traditional core of the Christian experience. By insisting upon the real work accomplished upon the individual through the process of conversion James was also assisting at the fusion of the historical with the romantic or intuitive school of evolutionary religious thought, since the latter likewise emphasized the transforming power of direct religious experience.

IV

The roots of romantic evolutionism were planted more firmly in the pre-Darwinian period than were those of the historical school. At the beginning of the nineteenth century the Kantian tradition of philosophical idealism held that certain fundamental ideas were apprehended directly or intuitively because of the very structure of the human mind, rather than through reason or through sense impressions. In religious terms, the soul was held to be directly aware by intuition of the existence of God and of its relation to Him. Therefore the romantic school had a sympathetic feeling for the value of mystical experience, and its early American representatives, Emerson in particular, prized the mystical state highly.

Formal religious faith based on an intuitive sense of God's being was introduced to America by Antinomians and Quakers of the seventeenth century and revived by transcendental Unitarians in the 1820's. These Unitarians revolted against the combination of revealed and natural religion which characterized the orthodox

Lockean Unitarianism of the time. For the transcendentalists the source of ultimate religious authority was to be found internally in the intuitions of the soul, and not externally in the Bible or in supernatural revelation. Consequently, these transcendentalists were not disturbed by the more obvious implications of evolution for the external supports of traditional Christian supernaturalism. All of them accepted the theory of evolution gladly, being the first American religious thinkers to do so. Most of them were Unitarian clergymen who refused to follow the example of Emerson and George Ripley in leaving the ministry. Their chief spokesman before the Civil War was Theodore Parker, who called the intuitive sense of religious truth "absolute religion," [25] in contradistinction to the Christian or any other historical religion which might or might not conform to the absolute intuitions of the soul.

It was a distinguishing mark of the romantic evolutionary school that intuitive feeling should take precedence over external authority and even over reason. These thinkers were also monistic with respect to the processes of nature, for although romantics might refer to God as the Oversoul, they nevertheless believed that communion between man and the Oversoul was established through an intimate adjustment with nature, the three elements merging into one in moments of religious rapture. The romantic attitude promoted singular flexibility in the interpretation of nature, and with the concentration upon the study of natural processes which came with the stimulus of Darwinism the romantic tradition was calculated to produce a school of evolutionary thought which may be called romantic naturalism.

The major issue confronting evolutionary thought at the end of the nineteenth century was the controversy between adherents of the Neo-Darwinian and the Neo-Lamarckian explanations of the mechanics of evolutionary change. While the controversy raged more sharply in Europe than in the United States, thinkers everywhere who proposed to deal with evolutionary problems in fruitful fashion had necessarily to wait upon its outcome. We have already found how inhospitable natural selection was to traditional religious conceptions. On the other hand, the special application of Lamarckism made by the historical theists to social and spiritual problems lacked convincing verification. Unless radically new factors were to appear, therefore, the situation seemed to require some kind of compromise. The issue was not one which confronted theology alone. In many other fields of speculative thought as well as in the practical problems of social democracy much depended upon an understanding of the character of the evolutionary process. One of the first and most suggestive solutions for religious thought was offered by the distinguished geologist and naturalist, Joseph Le Conte.

Le Conte was a Southerner of New England ancestry who inherited from his parents a combination of stern piety and a deep interest in nature. Although a student of Agassiz, he became an ardent evolutionist, and apart from his professional work devoted much thought to a consideration of the implications of evolution for other fields of thought, particularly religion. Before reading Darwin or Spencer Le Conte had come to believe in evolution as a general process of nature. He described it as a process of differentiation, by which organic nature as a whole, although not in all of its aspects, underwent progressive development. An important feature of Le Conte's conception of evolution was what he called the law of cyclical movement. According to this law evolutionary progress was supposed to have occurred in a series of cyclical waves, apparently identified with successive geological epochs, each cycle being characterized by a dominant or distinguishing type of life which displayed its own peculiar mode of evolutionary development. The present was, needless to say, the age of man.[26]

Le Conte distinguished six factors by which evolution occurred. The first appearance of each factor depended upon the degree of development displayed by organic forms at that particular stage of the evolutionary process. Thus the first and for a long time the only factors in operation were the two originally isolated by Lamarck, namely, pressure of environment upon the organism, and the use and disuse of parts. Evolution brought about by the operation of these two factors alone was necessarily very slow, but no other factor could come to bear until sexual reproduction first appeared in the scale of being. With the relatively wide variation among the individuals of sexually reproduced species, however, the Darwinian factor of natural selection came into play, which greatly accelerated the rate of evolutionary development. At the same time the fourth factor, physiological selection, commenced to operate by preventing the swamping of varieties through crossbreeding. The fifth factor, sexual selection, operating through competition for mates occurring in the later stages of sexual reproducing organisms, presupposed at least a rudimentary psychical development. Finally, with the appearance of man, the sixth and most recent factor, the rational factor, came into play. This factor was defined as "conscious, voluntary cooperation of the thing evolving—the spirit of man—in the work of its own evolution." [27]

Inasmuch as the pursuit of ideals provided the dynamics of rational evolution, Le Conte was willing to concede that the new factor was in effect another kind of evolution. Reason subordinates the factors and processes of nature, thus liberating man from the necessary evolution of the organic world into the self-determined evolution of the spiritual world. It was the greatest change that had ever occurred in the history of evolution, since it enormously accelerated the rate of change and altered the evolutionary factors from compulsive forces of brute nature to the attractive power of conscious ideals. Thus the particular factor which dominated and characterized each cycle of the evolutionary process was in turn submerged but not obliterated by a new and more efficient factor. The significance of Le Conte's theory was twofold. By relegating the dominance of the natural selection factor to the prehuman period it indicated the irrelevance of the contemporary concern with the problems of Social Darwinism. The theory also introduced to America the notion of stages or levels of organization, each level being characterized by properties peculiar to itself and hence requiring a unique technique for analysis. This idea proved to be of inestimable service in liberating many branches of social thought from the generalized uniformities of reductionism, and from the principles of Darwinian biology.

Le Conte took particular pains to distinguish the fundamental differences between organic and human evolution as determined by the rational factor. "The fittest" in organic nature were those most in harmony with the physical environment, whereas in human society the fittest were conceded to be those most in harmony with the ideal. These latter might not in fact survive, especially in the earlier phase of society when organic factors still exercised powerful influence. The power of ideals nevertheless distinguished human society from all others, and would ultimately reign supreme. In organic nature the weak should perish in order to strengthen the species, whereas in human society the weak should be protected in order to refine the moral nature and virtues. Under natural selection bodily structure changed to conform to the environment through adaptation. The rational factor, on the other hand, enabled man so to modify the environment for his own purposes that changes in bodily structure became unnecessary. Thus for man evolution involved modification of spirit rather than modification of form. Furthermore, up to the rational stage the evolutionary process was irreversible; no organism that had followed a different path from that of man's prehuman ancestors could ever attain rational powers. In the human stage, however, this was largely untrue since man now possessed the power to rectify his mistakes. This observation suggested the final distinction between organic and human evolution. Reason, the highest evolutionary factor, now completely controlled and transformed the lower factors, including natural selection, which became what might be called rational selection. Used but slightly thus far, chiefly in the breeding of lower animals and plants, the possibilities of rational selection, or eugenics, as Galton called it, suggested to what an extent man might control his own development if he chose to do so.[28]

The sharpness of Le Conte's contrasts between organic and human evolution seemed to suggest the oppositions of the Hegelian dialectic. It is perhaps of some significance that during his many years of teaching at the University of California after the Civil War Le Conte was intimately acquainted with the Hegelian G. H. Howison, to whom he acknowledged great intellectual indebtedness. He also read Kant, Fichte, and Hegel, although he confessed that "the technology of philosophy" repelled him.[29] In any event, Le Conte's conception of the successive stages of the evolutionary process, each dominated by a peculiar type of factor, culminating in the self-conscious control of evolution by the ideal, was similar to the Hegelian interpretation of evolution. The theory of cultural stages was familiar to sociology at least since the time of Comte, and while Le Conte made no attempt to extend the method to the interpretation of human history he at least suggested that history might be best understood in the light of the perennial conflict between instinctive evolutionary drives and what he called artistic or empirical behavior based upon conscious purpose.[30] Nothing in his writing, however, even faintly suggested the Marxist application of Hegelianism.

Turning to the theological implications of evolution Le Conte conceded that nothing less than a fundamental reconstruction of Christian theology was necessary. Although he considered the reconciliation of science and religion to be one of his most important tasks, the religion that seemed ultimately compatible with his interpretation of evolution bore only the faintest resemblance to the evangelical faith of his boyhood. It was now clear that God worked only through the process of law, and that evolution was his mode of creation. The question of the relationship between divine and natural forces was not to be settled after the fashion of the Deist compromise, since Darwin had destroyed it by awarding creation itself to nature. The solution was to reject both the independent existence of matter and the real efficient agency of natural forces and to return to the older idea of direct divine agency. God was conceived as immanent spirit, real efficient force, and the only real independent existence. Le Conte held his view to differ from ordinary idealism in that the external world was not the objectified mental state of the observer, but was the objectified mode of the mind of God, and was real enough so far as man was concerned.[31]

Le Conte was able to salvage several of the fundamental doctrines of theism by means of the theory now known as emergence or integrative levels. He seems to have been the first American to have made any significant use of this theory. Force and matter were found to exist in nature on several distinct planes or levels: elements, chemical compounds, vegetable life, animal life, rational life, and, if one would concede the point, immortal life. On each level the nature of the integrative principles and the characteristic phenomena and forces were appropriate to that level. The transition of energy from one stage to another occurred instantaneously, as when the combination of hydrogen and oxygen under proper circumstances produced water. It was to be observed that the properties of the new material on the higher level were unique. The successive appearance of these levels was consistent with the evolution of the world. Moreover, the emergence of each successive level coincided with the progressive individuation of force and matter, the forces of nature being merely different forms of divine energy.

The culmination of the evolutionary process of individuation occurred with the emergence of the spirit of man as a separate and self-conscious entity. Freed from matter and therefore capable of independent existence, the soul must be immortal. Still attached in this life to nature through its corporeal habitation, the soul achieves its final permanent level of liberation from the ascending stages of force and matter upon the death of the body. At the final level the soul is merged in the absolute.[32]

If God operated in nature through physical laws it seemed reasonable to Le Conte to assume that he operated in the soul of man by means of divine law, or revelation. From the natural point of view this might seem like sheer mysticism until one recalled that the characteristics of each level of integration appeared incomprehensible from the perspective of those below it. Le Conte's conception of the direct intuitive sense of the soul's relationship with God differed from the usual romantic theism only in his interpretation of the nature and role of revelation. Revelation was vouchsafed to all men, he believed, but with differing degrees of purity, and was commonly called conscience. It had received perfect overt expression only in the figure of Jesus. The content and quality of revelation must necessarily differ among men because in passing through finite minds it was conditioned by the outward circumstances and inward character of the individual. Only through reason and experience could the content of revelation be refined of its imperfections.[33] Thus Le Conte's conception of the nature of the religious impulse resembled that of James in so far as both held that the original inspiration was either void of content or dependent upon conscious elaboration.

Several lines of thought suggested to Le Conte the tenability of the traditional faith in the personality of God. Our own self-conscious personality lurking securely behind the futile probing of brain physiology seemed analogous to the personality of a deity whose immanent attributes had already been discerned in the evolutionary process. By a similar analogous inference the notion of causation which arose originally from our sense of originating external acts in response to the will suggested an infinite creative will behind the phenomena of nature. Finally, the finite effects of nature as determined by successive acts indicated the activity of a finite will, a will which nevertheless was capable of determining the endless evolution of the cosmos.[34]

In their effort to isolate the essentials of religion as such the historical theists had attempted to view Christianity with the same objectivity and with as little emotional sympathy as they would have felt for any non-Christian faith. In so doing they reduced Christ to the role of a moral teacher and ignored the miraculous and mediatorial place assigned to him by traditional Christianity. The romantic theists were, however, as a class much more than mere moralists. For them Christ was a warm and appealing figure, not because of the decisive functions assigned to him in the Christian drama of salvation, but because of the very exaltation of the highest human qualities exemplified in his life and teachings.

It was in the romantic spirit that Le Conte looked to Christ as the fulfillment of the evolutionary process. Just as organic evolution reached its goal in man, so human evolution reached its fulfillment in Christ, the ideal man who was also the perfect image of God. It will be recalled that each level of evolutionary development, according to Le Conte, responded to its own form of dynamic. Organic evolution proceeded by necessary law, including the law of natural selection. Human evolution on the other hand occurred through voluntary cooperation of the human spirit with its own evolution. Hence Le Conte assumed that the culmination of organic evolution in the appearance of human rational powers, though apparent enough in retrospect, could not have been foreseen before the end of the series, while the ideals determining the direction of human evolution must necessarily appear as soon as men were capable of shaping ideals. The most compulsive ideal in terms of character and spiritual energy that had yet appeared was embodied in the figure of Christ. Although all men possessed the divine spirit in embryo, this spirit blossomed in its fullness in Christ. Just as animals reached conscious relations with God in man, so man reached union with God in Christ. It was through Christ, then, that the path of evolution pointed.[35]

The significance for religious thought of Le Conte's treatment of evolution as a series of integrated levels lay in the liberation of the level of human evolution from the mechanical factors which had dominated the evolutionary process at lower stages. Physical evolution now appeared to be at an end, and vistas of intellectual and spiritual refinement attained in the pursuit of ever nobler ideas opened before the imagination. Naïve as these assumptions were soon to appear, the premise on which they were based would have aided the twentieth century in avoiding much agony had it been more widely accepted. For the premise asserted that the peculiar or distinguishing features of life at each level of the evolutionary process must be understood only in their own terms, and that the most comprehensive understanding of the prevailing forms of organization must be sought in those forms themselves. Biologists and paleontologists had succeeded in thus laying bare the characteristic dynamics of lower life forms. It remained for humanists and theologians to do the same for mankind.

In a sense, therefore, the romantic theists seemed to bring the evolutionary inquisition of religion to full cycle by returning religious problems to the very hands of theologians from which they had originally been taken. Familiar as the surroundings may have seemed, however, the meeting place was not the same. Many concessions had been made by Protestant Christianity in order to effect the reunion. This became clear when religious thinkers following up the suggestions of Le Conte and other post-Darwinians undertook to formulate a considered statement of romantic theism.

One of the best representatives of this group was the Congregationalist clergyman, Francis Howe Johnson, who published his *God in Evolution; A Pragmatic Study of Theology* in 1911. In acknowledging his indebtedness to James and Dewey Johnson recalled the familiar insistence of pragmatism upon novelty and the open universe. At the end of the nineteenth century the convergence of several lines of thought in the theory of evolution seemed to him to suggest the immanence of a new religious synthesis. Science appeared to be abandoning the rigidly mechanical outlook of Darwinism in favor of a more plastic and psychological interpretation of evolution. Pragmatism was its philosophical counterpart, reconciling liberty and authority, and harmonizing religion with science. In religion, finally, there was a growing tendency to think of God not as external, but as a living, in-dwelling spirit. Protestant theology had already come to accept human experience as constituting a revelation not inferior to the original supernatural revelation, but it had still to abandon its dependence upon miracle and place its faith fully in the actualities of religious and moral development. The theology of evolution must be built upon these foundations.

Johnson's review of the scientific theories of evolution was less satisfactory than that of Le Conte. Instead of employing the theory of integrative levels he adopted the vitalist position on the assumption that the operation of psychic factors alone accounted for evolutionary development. The mechanical theory of evolution suggested that the universe was analogous to the machine, whereas all of the relevant facts indicated rather the analogy of personality, which accounted both for mechanics and mind, uniformity and growth, causation and freedom.[36]

In religious terms this interpretation of evolution meant that God and the creature cooperated in the process of creation. Divine immanence was confirmed as the vital theological doctrine of the new faith. But it also fixed the limits of God's creative power within the processes of nature, compelling the abandonment of the notions of divine omnipotence which had characterized the old supernaturalism.

His work gives the impression of one Who moves slowly, tentatively, as it were, feeling his way, to some dimly foreseen end by the use of instrumentalities not thoroughly mastered; the process is apparently characterized by many setbacks, by unfulfilled promises, roads that seem to have been built a certain way and abandoned. Although, viewed as a whole, the process is seen to be a grand ever-expanding movement upward on the scale of being, there is also an immense amount of destruction and incidental waste; there is much conflict and much suffering on the part of creatures so constituted as to be capable of great happiness. In short, the God of evolution appears to be one Who, like ourselves, is beset with limitations over which he triumphs by the use of infinitely varied appliances and adjustments.[37]

Apart from the fact that man could scarcely conceive of God save in terms of personality the limitations of power involved in that conception provided a key for the solution of several of the perennial problems of religion. While the whole course of evolution showed God's power to triumph over obstacles, the very fact of the obstacles made it clear that both God and man faced the same problems of freedom and necessity. If then God also worked with man's methods, his values and evils must be man's. Through man's highest ideals the future course of evolution must lie. The problem of evil was similarly illuminated by the notion of a "struggling God." It justified a moral interpretation of the struggle for existence. In producing a state of consciousness in man evolution had also necessarily introduced a sense of joy in triumph over obstacles, and of pain at failure. Good and evil were but two sides of the same activity; and without effort on the part of the creature there would be no occasion for growth or the refinement of faculty. Under these circumstances there was no need to wonder at failure and misfortune, for the failure of the individual was a necessary condition of the progress of the whole. By observing nature one should come to expect, in the language of genetics, that most social mutations would be lethal.[38]

While he did not explicitly use the theory of integrative levels introduced by Le Conte, Johnson's argument seemed to imply it. He noted that the course of evolution was marked by a succession

of new factors, each releasing a new kind of energy which dominated its epoch by a series of modifications establishing organic
forms more complex than any to be found in previous epochs.
Thus the nervous system of man dominates the present, and from
it the future of evolution will emerge. But because the activity of
the nervous system does not register itself in physical heredity it
was clear that future evolution would be social rather than physical.

At the human level of evolution the intellectual activity and
spiritual insight of the individual provide the variations or mutations by which the evolutionary process is advanced. Lest this
seemed to be a purely human function Johnson reminded his
readers that a new idea remained the greatest of mysteries, in
which brain cells, like genes, seemed to recombine in unique combinations. In these moments, he believed, we sense an intelligence
not our own that combines with ours and assists us. To state the
evolutionary mandate in religious terms: "Work out your own salvation. It is God that worketh in you." Salvation implied not
merely the rescue of a soul in the traditional sense, but also the
rescue of the evolutionary process from misdirection or premature
ending. Nor was the mandate consistent merely with the struggle
for existence. It also liberated the self-realizing and idealizing
faculties which accounted for the wealth and variety of human
life as opposed to the brute struggle of animals.[39]

If salvation was to be conceived as self-realization in the advancement of the cosmic process there could be no social utopia in
which many expected the process to culminate. Herbert Spencer
had been one of the first to elaborate the analogy between society
and the organism. According to the theory of the organic analogy
the differentiation of social functions was comparable to the
specialization of function among the cells of an organism. The
primitive human society with but rudimentary division of labor
was analogous to the lowest orders of multicellular organisms
where each cell performed most if not all of the functions of the
life process. The future of the social organism was thus held to
lie along the path of increased interdependence and specialization
of activity. The implications of such a theory for democratic individualism were obvious.

Johnson took considerable pains to deflate the organic analogy.
Apart from the fact that it proposed to upset the delicate balance
between egoistic and altruistic values, it ignored the creative role

of the individual in the evolutionary process. While the advancement of civilization might superficially seem to depend upon
specialization of function, spiritual development clearly implied
the elaboration and cultivation of diversified talents both in the
society and in the individual. The end of social evolution could not
lie in the comfort, happiness, or freedom from friction of the members of society. Such conditions could only mean the stultification
of evolution. The function of society was rather to educate its
members in order that each might be enabled to realize to the full
his highest potentialities. Each individual must forever face the
tension between the mandates of self-development and self-sacrifice. Between the limits of this great dialectic the process of evolution must work its way.[40]

V

We have selected the work of the foregoing religious thinkers
to illustrate the characteristic modifications of American Protestant
Christianity wherever the implications of evolutionary ideas were
squarely faced by men who did not feel obliged to fit those implications into the older structure of theological dogma. The results
displayed a considerable variety of doctrine and temper, but certain broad generalizations can be made.

The most striking feature of evolutionary theology was its abandonment of the old literal anthropomorphic dualism in favor of
a belief in the immanence of God and of the emergence of the
divine plan in the natural order. Although there was a certain
tendency on logical grounds to conceive of God in terms of personality the real spirit of the movement was rather away from personality as inconsistent with a deity so closely identified with the
cosmic process. Here was perhaps the source of the great veneration expressed by liberal Protestants at the end of the nineteenth
century for the person of Jesus. He supplied the element of personal leadership and inspiration that had formerly been sought in
the Father. While few went so far as F. H. Johnson in insisting
upon the limitations of God's power it did seem to be true that
evolutionary theists no longer had access to the simple faith in the
guiding hand that stretched forth to aid the sinner. The evidence
assembled by William James made it quite clear that the sense of
the immediacy of God's presence was actually experienced by
many people, but it was also clear that the contact was confined to

the realm of feeling and that its character was not essentially different from that of other types of emotional stimulus.

A second major characteristic of evolutionary theism was its abandonment of the Bible not only as the authentic record of revelation, but even as a primary textbook of religious truth, apart from its importance as the source of knowledge of the life of Jesus. Much as they might venerate the Scriptures as proof of man's instinctive religious feeling evolutionists were uncomfortably conscious of the crude and childlike context in which this feeling was expressed. The sources of religious truth were now to be discovered empirically in the universal experience of the race. In so far as religious truth deserved credence it did so, as with James, because it transformed the character through the release of energy. Even here, however, it was indissolubly associated with concrete ideas or values not given in the inspiration as such, but which were the product of the individual's own thought and experience.

The fusion of human and divine elements in the content of religious experience pointed to the third aspect of the movement, namely, its emphasis upon this world as the center of being. While for many evolutionists the belief in the emergence of the divine spirit justified their faith in immortality, it was nevertheless a faith guaranteed by a cosmic process in which spirit and matter were two sides of the same whole. Certainly evolution did not foster the other-worldly type of faith. If man was to work out his own salvation he must do it in terms of this world, and the focus of his interest must necessarily be ethical.

Finally, then, the monistic and ethical orientation of evolutionary theism required the abandonment of the old Christian economy of salvation. George F. Wright had pointed to the analogy between natural selection and the Calvinist struggle for salvation, in which but few are chosen. But the evolutionary theists generally abandoned this Calvinist-Malthusianism in favor of a more charitable universalist economy of abundance which promised room at God's banquet table for all who would work for the privilege.

NOTES

1. J. Haroutunian, *Piety Versus Moralism; the Passing of the New England Theology* (New York, Holt, 1932); S. E. Mead, *Nathaniel William Taylor, 1786–1858, a Connecticut Liberal* (University of Chicago Press, 1942); B. B. Warfield, *Studies in Perfectionism* (New York, Oxford University Press, 1931), II, 3–333.

2. The pre-Darwinian evolution implicit in the uniformitarian geology of Lyell and his school, for instance, caused no such crisis. See Conrad Wright, "The Religion of Geology," *New England Quarterly,* XIV (June, 1941), 335–358.

3. Charles Hodge, *What Is Darwinism?* (New York, Scribner, Armstrong, 1874), pp. 174–175, 52–64, 68–69, 176–177.

4. P. A. Chadbourne, "Design in Nature," *Princeton Review,* I (March, 1878), 272–303; James McCosh, *The Religious Aspect of Evolution* (enlarged ed. New York, Scribner, 1890), pp. 58–68.

5. J. McCosh, *The Development Hypothesis: Is It Sufficient?* (New York, Carter, 1876), pp. 13–22.

6. McCosh, *Religious Aspect of Evolution,* pp. 28–68.

7. L. J. Henderson, *The Fitness of the Environment* (New York, Macmillan, 1913).

8. For a brief systematic expression of his theology see Francis E. Abbot, *Scientific Theism* (2d ed. Boston, Little, Brown, 1886). Abbot's essential principles were crystallized many years earlier, however. See, for example, his article, "Philosophical Biology," *North Amer. Review, 107* (Oct., 1868), 377–422; also papers in the *Index,* III (April 13, 1872), 113–115, and *passim.*

9. Abbot, *Scientific Theism,* pp. 180–190.

10. *Ibid.,* pp. 168–180.

11. *Ibid.,* pp. 119–143

12. *Ibid.,* pp. 147–157.

13. *Ibid.,* pp. 163–167.

14. *Ibid.,* pp. 192–213.

15. M. J. Savage, *The Religion of Evolution* (Boston, Lockwood, Brooks, 1876), p. 55.

16. It is true that George F. Wright, Congregationalist theologian and geologist of Oberlin, insisted that Darwinism was not a theory of progressive development, and that in this as in several other senses it was analogous to the Calvinist interpretation of human experience. See G. F. Wright, "Some Analogies between Calvinism and Darwinism," *Bibliotheca Sacra,* XXXVII (Jan., 1880), pp. 48–76. But Wright's observations were less significant as a dissent from the generalization just made than as a contribution to the understanding of the moral implications of natural selection, a subject that few Americans had dealt with in serious fashion.

17. Savage, *op. cit.,* pp. 86–87, 100.

18. See the discussion of this point, with particular reference to religious beliefs, by the leading American Neo-Lamarckian of the late nineteenth century, E. D. Cope, "Foundations of Theism," *Monist,* III (July, 1893), 623–639.

19. Savage, *op. cit.,* pp. 112–129.

20. *Ibid.,* p. 12.

21. William James, *The Varieties of Religious Experience* (Modern Library ed. New York, Random House, n.d.), pp. 31–32, 72–73, 159, 322–324.

22. *Ibid.,* pp. 370, 396–423.

23. *Ibid.,* pp. 333–368, 498.

24. *Ibid.,* pp. 426, 494, 504–505.

25. C. H. Faust, "The Background of Unitarian Opposition to Transcendentalism," *Modern Philology,* XXXV (1937–38), 297–324.

26. Joseph Le Conte, *Evolution. Its Nature, Its Evidences, and Its Relation to Religious Thought* (2d ed. New York, Appleton, 1891), pp. 16–27.

27. *Ibid.,* pp. 79–80.

28. *Ibid.,* pp. 88–92.

29. *The Autobiography of Joseph Le Conte,* ed. by W. D. Armes (New York, Appleton, 1903), pp. 261, 287.

30. J. Le Conte, "The Theory of Evolution and Social Progress," *Monist,* V (July, 1895), 481–500.

31. Le Conte, *Evolution,* pp. 298–302.

32. *Ibid.*, pp. 313–329.
33. *Ibid.*, pp. 331–334.
34. *Ibid.*, pp. 341–345.
35. *Ibid.*, pp. 360–364.
36. F. H. Johnson, *God in Evolution; A Pragmatic Study of Theology* (New York, Longmans, Green, 1911), pp. 60–83.
37. *Ibid.*, p. 87.
38. *Ibid.*, pp. 87–120.
39. *Ibid.*, pp. 154–189.
40. *Ibid.*, pp. 190–232.

INDEX